Joseph Priestley

Joseph Priestley
From a portrait by Rembrandt Peale

JOSEPH PRIESTLEY

*Selections from His
Writings*

Edited by

I R A V. B R O W N

1962

*The Pennsylvania State University
Press*

University Park, Pennsylvania

PREFACE

"Yours is one of the few lives precious to mankind, and for the continuance of which every thinking man is solicitous." The subject of this tribute was Joseph Priestley, the author was Thomas Jefferson, and the time was 1801. Scientist, educator, religious scholar, and political liberal, Priestley, like Jefferson, embodied many admirable qualities of the eighteenth-century Enlightenment. Like Jefferson, he was outstanding for the variety of his interests.

Priestley has won fame as a chemist, largely because he is usually given the credit for the discovery of oxygen. However, teaching, the ministry, and writing absorbed most of his time and energy. His experiments in chemistry were only an avocation. Born near Leeds, England, in 1733, he died at Northumberland, Pennsylvania, threescore and ten years later, in 1804. He lived richly in the world of ideas, and his multifarious publications, which fill about forty volumes, afford an encyclopedic view of the intellectual currents of the eighteenth century. Among the numerous subjects on which he wrote were education, history, biography, grammar, oratory, political theory, electricity, optics, chemistry, philosophy, theology, and church history.

Priestley's scientific experiments were important, of course. So were his contributions to the development of Unitarianism. He also deserves notice as an historian — as a pioneer, indeed, in the history of ideas. He approached almost every field of learning from the historical viewpoint. Of even more significance is his earnest advocacy of untrammeled freedom of inquiry. Whether the field was science, religion, or politics, Priestley was convinced, like his friend Jefferson, that truth could prevail only in a free market of ideas. The courage with which he tackled controversial issues is rare and estimable. He was not a gifted stylist. "My object was not to acquire the character of a fine writer," he declared, "but of a useful one." Nevertheless, the sincerity and candor of his expression lend a special charm to his writings.

Most of Priestley's books appeared in several different editions. Shortly after his death his theological and miscellaneous works, as well as his autobiography, were edited and published in twenty-five volumes by John T. Rutt, a wealthy English Unitarian. For practical reasons the texts for this anthology have been taken as far as possible from Rutt's monumental collection. There has never been an inclusive edition of his scientific treatises. All of Priestley's works have long been out of print.

The object of the present volume is to make available a representative sampling of his writings in a more convenient form and thus, it is hoped, to make them more widely known. Short introductions have been included to set each of the selections in its context. Subheadings (in italics) have been added in the first two chapters. Half-inch lines have been used to indicate extensive omissions within particular selections. Capitalization, italics, spelling, and, to some extent, punctuation have been modernized in the interests of greater readability. The footnotes serve two purposes. One is to identify important persons and terms mentioned in the text which may not be familiar to the reader. The other is to supply bibliographical references for those who may wish to pursue further various aspects of Priestley's life and thought.

Of the available biographies, T. E. Thorpe, *Joseph Priestley* (London, 1906), is especially useful on the scientific work, and Anne Holt, *A Life of Joseph Priestley* (London, 1931), is best on the religious writings. Also worth consulting are the articles on Priestley by the Reverend Alexander Gordon and Sir Philip J. Hartog in the *Dictionary of National Biography*, edited by Leslie Stephen and Sidney Lee (63 volumes, London, 1885-1901), Volume XLVI, pages 357-376.

Grateful acknowledgement is made for the assistance of Mrs. Elizabeth C. Rochow in research, Frances Reinwand in photostating, Mrs. Ilene Glenn in typing, and Mrs. Barbara M. Altman in proofreading. Special thanks are due Ralph

W. McComb, Librarian, and other members of the staff of The Pennsylvania State University Library (which has an unusually good collection of Priestley materials). The Central Fund for Research of the University supplied financial aid. Helen M. Brown lent the patient ear of a loyal wife and provided indispensable encouragement and help throughout the preparation of this book.

Ira V. Brown

University Park, Pa.
November 18, 1961

CONTENTS

I
The Memoirs

Perhaps the most interesting and revealing introduction to Priestley's varied life is his autobiography, the bulk of which was completed in 1787, while he was pastor of a Unitarian congregation at Birmingham, England, and before the famous riots of 1791 destroyed his house and his laboratory. He subsequently added a continuation that takes the story to 1795, describing briefly his persecution in England and his removal to Pennsylvania. At his own request these reminiscences were not published until after his death. His son Joseph completed the narrative for the last years of Priestley's life, and the Memoirs *were first printed at Northumberland, Pennsylvania, in 1806. There were several later editions.*[1]

[1] Text taken from *The Theological and Miscellaneous Works of Joseph Priestley,* ed. by John T. Rutt (25 vols., London, 1817-1832), Vol. I (in 2 parts), *passim.*

Memoirs of the Rev. Dr. Joseph Priestley
to the Year 1795, Written by Himself

Having thought it right to leave behind me some account of my friends and benefactors, it is in a manner necessary that I also give some account of myself; and as the like has been done by many persons, and for reasons which posterity has approved, I make no further apology for following their example. If my writings in general have been useful to my contemporaries, I hope that this account of myself will not be without its use to those who may come after me, and especially in promoting virtue and piety, which, I hope I may say, it has been my care to practice myself, as it has been my business to inculcate them upon others.

My father, Jonas Priestley, was the youngest son of Joseph Priestley, a maker and dresser of woolen cloth. His first wife, my mother, was the only child of Joseph Swift, a farmer at Shafton, a village about six miles southeast of Wakefield. By this wife he had six children, four sons and two daughters. I, the oldest, was born on the thirteenth of March, old style, 1733, at Fieldhead, about six miles southwest of Leeds, in Yorkshire. My mother dying in 1739, my father married again in 1745, and by his second wife had three daughters.

My mother having children so fast, I was very soon committed to the care of her father, and with him I continued with little interruption till my mother's death.

It is but little that I can recollect of my mother. I remember, however, that she was careful to teach me the Assembly's Catechism,[2] and to give me the best instructions

---

[2] Adopted by the Westminster Assembly in 1647, this creed was "a classic of Calvinism." See John T. McNeill, *The History and Character of Calvinism* (New York, 1954), p. 325. Priestley's religious pilgrimage was to take him a long way from his starting point.

the little time that I was at home. Once in particular, when I was playing with a pin, she asked me where I got it; and on telling her that I found it at my uncle's, who lived very near to my father, and where I had been playing with my cousins, she made me carry it back again; no doubt to impress my mind, as it could not fail to do, with a clear idea of the distinction of property, and of the importance of attending to it. She died in the hard winter of 1739, not long after being delivered of my youngest brother, and having dreamed a little before her death that she was in a delightful place, which she particularly described, and imagined to be heaven, the last words which she spoke, as my aunt informed me, were, "Let me go to that fine place."

On the death of my mother I was taken home, my brothers taking my place, and was sent to school in the neighborhood. But being without a mother, and my father encumbered with a large family, a sister of my father's, in the year 1742, relieved him of all care of me by taking me entirely to herself and considering me as her child, having none of her own. From this time she was truly a parent to me, till her death in 1764.

My aunt was married to a Mr. Keighley, a man who had distinguished himself for his zeal for religion and for his public spirit. He was also a man of considerable property, and dying soon after I went to them, left the greatest part of his fortune to my aunt for life, and much of it at her disposal after her death.

By this truly pious and excellent woman, who knew no other use of wealth, or of talents of any kind, than to do good, and who never spared herself for this purpose, I was sent to several schools in the neighborhood, especially to a large free school under the care of a clergyman, Mr. Hague, under whom, at the age of twelve or thirteen, I first began to make any progress in the Latin tongue, and acquired the elements of Greek. But about the same time that I began to learn Greek at this public school, I learned Hebrew on holidays of the Dissenting minister of the place, Mr. Kirkby; and upon the removal of Mr. Hague from the free school, Mr. Kirkby opening a school of his own, I was wholly under his care. With this instruction, I had acquired a pretty good knowledge of the learned languages at the age of sixteen; but from this time, Mr. Kirkby's increasing infirmities obliged him to relinquish his school, and beginning to be of a weakly consumptive habit, so that it was not thought advisable to send me to any other place of education, I was left to conduct my studies as well as I could till I went to the academy at Daventry, in the year 1752.

From the time I discovered any fondness for books, my aunt entertained hopes of my being a minister, and I readily entered into her views. But my ill health obliged me to turn my thoughts another way and, with a view to trade, I learned the modern languages, French, Italian, and High Dutch, without a master; and in the first and last of them I translated and wrote letters for an uncle of mine, who was a merchant, and who intended to put me into a counting-house in Lisbon. A house was actually engaged to receive me there, and everything was nearly ready for my under-taking the voyage; but getting better health, my former destination for the ministry was resumed, and I was sent to Daventry, to study under Mr. Ashworth, afterwards Dr. Ashworth.

RELIGIOUS INSTRUCTION

Looking back, as I often do, upon this period of my life, I see the greatest reason to be thankful to God for the pious care of my parents and friends, in giving me religious in-struction. My mother was a woman of exemplary piety, and my father also had a strong sense of religion, praying with his family morning and evening, and carefully teaching his children and servants the Assembly's Catechism, which was all the system of which he had any knowledge. In the latter part of his life he became very fond of Mr. Whitefield's writings, and other works of a similar kind, having been brought up in the principles of Calvinism, and adopting them, but without ever giving much attention to matters of speculation, and entertaining no bigoted aversion to those who differed from him on the subject.

The same was the case with my excellent aunt; she was truly Calvinistic in principle, but was far from confining salvation to those who thought as she did on religious subjects. Being left in good circumstances, her home was the resort of all the Dissenting ministers in the neighborhood, without distinction; and those who were the most obnoxious on account of their heresy were almost as welcome to her, if she thought them honest and good men (which she was not unwilling to do), as any others.

The most heretical ministers in the neighborhood were Mr. Graham, of Halifax; and Mr. Walker, of Leeds; but they were frequently my aunt's guests. With the former of these my intimacy grew with my years, but chiefly after I became a preacher. We kept up a correspondence to the last, thinking alike on most subjects. To him I dedicated my *Disquisitions on Matter and Spirit;* and when he died, he left me his manuscripts, his Polyglot Bible, and two hundred pounds. Besides being a rational Christian, he was an excellent classical scholar, and wrote Latin with great facility and elegance. He frequently wrote to me in that language.

Thus I was brought up with sentiments of piety, but without bigotry; and having, from my earliest years, given much attention to the subject of religion, I was as much confirmed as I well could be in the principles of Calvinism, all the books that came in my way having that tendency.

The weakness of my constitution, which often led me to think that I should not be long-lived, contributed to give my mind a still more serious turn; and having read many books of experiences, and, in consequence, believing that a new birth, produced by the immediate agency of the spirit of God, was necessary to salvation, and not being able to satisfy myself that I had experienced anything of the kind, I felt occasionally such distress of mind as it is not in my power to describe, and which I still look back upon with horror. Notwithstanding I had nothing very material to reproach myself with, I often concluded that God had forsaken me, and that mine was like the case of Francis Spira, to whom, as he imagined, repentance and salvation were denied. In that state of mind I remember reading the account of "the man in an iron cage," in the *Pilgrim's Progress*, with the greatest perturbation.

I imagine that even these conflicts of mind were not without their use, as they led me to think habitually of God and a future state. And though my feelings were then, no doubt, too full of terror, what remained of them was a deep reverence for divine things, and in time a pleasing satisfaction which can never be effaced, and, I hope, was strengthened as I have advanced in life, and acquired more rational notions of religion. The remembrance, however, of what I sometimes felt in that state of ignorance and darkness gives me a peculiar sense of the value of rational principles of religion, and of which I can give but an imperfect description to others.

As truth, we cannot doubt, must have an advantage over error, we may conclude that the want of these peculiar feelings is compensated by something of greater value, which arises to others from always having seen things in a just and pleasing light, from having always considered the Supreme Being as the kind parent of all his offspring. This, however, not having been my case, I cannot be so good a judge of the effects of it. At all events, we ought always to inculcate just views of things, assuring ourselves that proper feelings and right conduct will be the consequence of them.

In the latter part of the interval between my leaving the grammar school and going to the academy, which was something more than two years, I attended two days in the week upon Mr. Haggerstone, a Dissenting minister in the neighborhood, who had been educated under Mr. Maclaurin. Of him I learned geometry, algebra, and various branches of mathematics, theoretical and practical. And at the same time I read, but with little assistance from him, Gravesande's *Elements of Natural Philosophy*, Watts's *Logic*, Locke's *Essay on the Human Understanding*, etc., and made such a proficiency in other branches of learning that when I was admitted at the academy (which was on Coward's foundation), I was excused all the studies of the first year, and a great part of those of the second.

In the same interval I spent the latter part of every week with Mr. Thomas, a Baptist minister, now of Bristol, but then of Gildersome, a village about four miles from Leeds, who had had no learned education. Him I instructed in Hebrew, and by that means made myself a considerable proficient in that language. At the same time I learned Chaldee and Syriac, and just began to read Arabic. Upon the whole, going to the academy later than is usual, and being thereby better furnished, I was qualified to appear there with greater advantage.

Before I went from home I was very desirous of being admitted a communicant in the congregation which I had always attended, and the old minister, as well as my aunt, was as desirous of it as myself; but the elders of the church, who had the government of it, refused me, because, when they interrogated me on the subject of the sin of Adam, I appeared not to be quite orthodox, not thinking that all the human race (supposing them not to have any sin of their own) were liable to the wrath of God, and "the pains of hell forever," on account of that sin only; for such was the question that was put to me. Some time before, having then no doubt of the truth of the doctrine, I well remember being much distressed that I could not feel a proper repentance for the sin of Adam; taking it for granted that, without this, it could not be forgiven me. Mr. Haggerstone, above-mentioned, was a little more liberal than the members of the congregation in which I was brought up, being what is called a Baxterian;[3] and his general conversation had a liberal turn, and such as tended to undermine my prejudices. But what contributed to open my eyes still more was the conversation of a Mr. Walker, from Ashton-under-Line, who preached as a candidate when our old minister was superannuated. He was an avowed Baxterian, and being rejected on that account, his opinions were much canvassed, and he being a guest at the house of my aunt, we soon became very intimate, and I thought I saw much of reason in his sentiments. Thinking farther on these subjects, I was, before I went to the academy, an Arminian;[4] but had by no means rejected the doctrine of the Trinity, or that of atonement.

Though, after I saw reason to change my opinions, I found myself incommoded by the rigor of the congregation with which I was connected, I shall always acknowledge with great gratitude that I owe much to it. The business of religion was effectually attended to in it. We were all catechized in public till we were grown up, servants as well as others. The minister always expounded the Scriptures with as much regularity as he preached, and there was hardly a day in the week in which there was not some meeting of one or other part of the congregation. On one evening there was a meeting of the young men for conversation and prayer. This I constantly attended, praying extempore with others when called upon.

[3] Richard Baxter (1615-1691) was a liberal Calvinist theologian noted for his independence of mind and catholicity of spirit. His followers were called, often in reproach, "Baxterians." See James Hastings, ed., *Encyclopedia of Religion and Ethics* (13 vols., Edinburgh & New York, 1908-1926), II, 438-441.

[4] Arminius (1560-1609) was a Dutch theologian whose followers taught, in opposition to Calvin, that the possibility of salvation is open to all mankind and that men may freely choose to receive it. See Hastings, ed., *Encyclopedia*, I, 807-816.

At my aunt's there was a monthly meeting of women, who acquitted themselves in prayer as well as any of the men belonging to the congregation. Being at first a child in the family, I was permitted to attend their meetings, and growing up insensibly, heard them after I was capable of judging. My aunt, after the death of her husband, prayed every morning and evening in her family, until I was about seventeen, when that duty devolved upon me.

The Lord's day was kept with peculiar strictness. No victuals were dressed on that day in any family. No member of it was permitted to walk out for recreation, but the whole of the day was spent at the public meeting, or at home in reading, meditation, and prayer, in the family or the closet.

It was my custom at that time to recollect as much as I could of the sermons I heard, and to commit it to writing. This practice I began very early, and continued it until I was able from the heads of a discourse to supply the rest myself. For, not troubling myself to commit to memory much of the amplification, and writing at home almost as much as I had heard, I insensibly acquired a habit of composing with great readiness; and from this practice I believe I have derived great advantage through life; composition seldom employing so much time as would be necessary to write in longhand anything I have published.

By these means, not being disgusted with these strict forms of religion, as many persons of better health and spirits probably might have been (and on which account I am far from recommending the same strictness to others), I acquired in early life a serious turn of mind. Among other things, I had at this time a great aversion to plays and romances, so that I never read any works of this kind, except *Robinson Crusoe,* until I went to the academy. I well remember seeing my brother Timothy reading a book of knight-errantry, and with great indignation I snatched it out of his hands, and threw it away. This brother, afterwards, when he had for some time followed my father's business (which was that of a cloth dresser), became, if possible, more serious than I had been; and, after an imperfect education, took up the profession of a minister among the Independents, in which he now continues.

While I was at the grammar school, I learned "Mr. Annet's short-hand," and thinking I could suggest some improvements in it, I wrote to the author, and this was the beginning of a correspondence which lasted for several years. He was, as I ever perceived, an unbeliever in Christianity, and a Necessarian. On this subject, several letters, written with care on both sides, passed between us, and these Mr. Annet often pressed me to give him leave to publish, but I constantly refused. I had undertaken the defense of philosophical liberty, and the correspondence was closed without my being convinced of the fallacy of my arguments, though upon studying the subject regularly, in the course of my academical education afterwards, I became a confirmed Necessarian,[5] and I have through life derived, as I imagine, the greatest advantage from my full persuasion of the truth of that doctrine.

My aunt, and all my relations, being strict Calvinists, it was their intention to send me to the academy at Mile-End, then under the care of Dr. Conder. But, being at that time an Arminian, I resolutely opposed it, especially upon finding that if I went thither, besides giving an experience, I must subscribe my assent to ten printed articles of the strictest Calvinistic faith, and repeat it every six months. My opposition, however, would probably have been to no purpose, and I must have adopted some other mode of life, if Mr. Kirkby (above-mentioned) had not interposed, and strongly recommended the academy of Dr. Doddridge, on

[5] Priestley's doctrine of "Necessarianism" should be distinguished both from Calvinist predestination and from atheistic fatalism. To him it meant essentially that the universe was governed by divine law rather than by arbitrary caprice. It implied "a chain of causes and effects, established by infinite wisdom, and terminating in the greatest good of the whole universe." See below, pp. 273-277, the selections from his *Doctrine of Philosophical Necessity Illustrated* (1777).

the idea that I should have a better chance of being made a scholar. He had received a good education himself, was a good classical scholar, and had no opinion of the mode of education among the very orthodox Dissenters, and being fond of me, he was desirous of my having every advantage that could be procured for me. My good aunt, not being a bigoted Calvinist, entered into his views, and Dr. Doddridge being dead, I was sent to Daventry, and was the first pupil that entered there. My stepmother also, who was a woman of good sense, as well as of religion, had a high opinion of Dr. Doddridge, having been some time housekeeper in his family. She had always recommended his academy, but died before I went thither.[6]

DAVENTRY ACADEMY

Three years, viz. from September 1752 to 1755, I spent at Daventry, with that peculiar satisfaction with which young persons of generous minds usually go through a course of liberal study, in the society of others engaged in the same pursuits, and free from the cares and anxieties which seldom fail to lay hold on them when they come out into the world.

In my time, the academy was in a state peculiarly favorable to the serious pursuit of truth, as the students were about equally divided upon every question of much importance, such as liberty and necessity, the sleep of the soul, and all the articles of theological orthodoxy and heresy; in consequence of which, all these topics were the subject of continual discussion. Our tutors also were of different opinions; Dr. Ashworth taking the orthodox side

[6] Oxford and Cambridge were closed to Dissenters at this time. On the importance of the academies in eighteenth-century England see H. McLachlan, *English Education under the Test Acts: Being the History of the Nonconformist Academies, 1662-1820* (Manchester, 1931) and J. W. Ashley Smith, *The Birth of Modern Education: The Contribution of the Dissenting Academies, 1660-1800* (London, 1954).

of every question, and Mr. Clark, the sub-tutor, that of heresy, though always with the greatest modesty.[7]

Both of our tutors being young, at least as tutors, and some of the senior students excelling more than they could pretend to do in several branches of study, they indulged us in the greatest freedoms, so that our lectures had often the air of friendly conversations on the subjects to which they related. We were permitted to ask whatever questions, and to make whatever remarks we pleased; and we did it with the greatest, but without any offensive, freedom. The general plan of our studies, which may be seen in Dr. Doddridge's published lectures, was exceedingly favorable to free inquiry, as we were referred to authors on both sides of every question, and were even required to give an account of them. It was also expected that we should abridge the most important of them for our future use. The public library contained all the books to which we were referred.

It was a reference to Dr. Hartley's *Observations on Man,*[8] in the course of our lectures, that first brought me acquainted with that performance, which immediately engaged my closest attention, and produced the greatest, and in my opinion the most favorable effect on my general turn of thinking through life. It established me in the belief of the doctrine of Necessity, which I first learned from Collins;[9] it greatly improved that disposition to piety which I

[7] Caleb Ashworth (1722-1775) and Samuel Clark (1728-1769) had both studied under Philip Doddridge (1702-1751) at the Northampton Academy. See McLachlan, *English Education,* pp. 143-164.

[8] David Hartley (1705-1757) was a physician, philosopher, and pioneer in the study of psychology, whose *Observations on Man* (1749) attempted to explain all mental phenomena on physical grounds. His was "an attempt to exhibit man as a microcosm, a world ruled by law and by the laws of the universe outside him." See George S. Brett, *A History of Psychology* (3 vols., London and New York, 1912-1921), II, 278-285, esp. p. 283.

[9] Anthony Collins (1676-1729), the deist, wrote *A Philosophical Enquiry concerning Human Liberty* (1715) which Priestley interpreted in terms of "Necessarianism."

brought to the academy, and freed it from the rigor with which it had been tinctured. Indeed, I do not know whether the consideration of Dr. Hartley's theory contributes more to enlighten the mind, or improve the heart; it affects both in so supereminent a degree.

In this situation, I saw reason to embrace what is generally called the heterodox side of almost every question. But notwithstanding this, and though Dr. Ashworth was earnestly desirous to make me as orthodox as possible, yet, as my behavior was unexceptionable, and as I generally took his part in some little things by which he often drew upon himself the ill will of many of the students, I was upon the whole a favorite with him. I kept up more or less of a correspondence with Dr. Ashworth till the time of his death, though much more so with Mr. Clark. This continued till the very week of his melancholy death, by a fall from his horse, at Birmingham, where he was minister.

Notwithstanding the great freedom of our speculations and debates, the extreme of heresy among us was Arianism;[10] and all of us, I believe, left the academy with a belief, more or less qualified, of the doctrine of atonement.

Warm friendships never fail to be contracted at places of liberal education; and when they are well chosen, are of singular use. Such was mine with Mr. Alexander, of Birmingham.[11] We were in the same class, and during the first year occupied the same room. By engagements between ourselves we rose early, and dispatched many articles of business every day. One of them, which continued all

[10] Arianism modified the orthodox view of the Trinity by holding that Christ was a created being not co-eternal with God but pre-existing before appearing in the flesh. The more radical Socinianism, to which Priestley later subscribed, maintained that the Saviour was a mere man. See James H. Colligan, *The Arian Movement in England* (Manchester, 1913), and Roland N. Stromberg, *Religious Liberalism in Eighteenth-Century England* (London, 1954).

[11] John Alexander (1736-1765) like Priestley became a minister and a scholar. See Leslie Stephen and Sidney Lee, eds., *Dictionary of National Biography* (63 vols., London, 1885-1901), I, 273.

the time we were at the academy, was to read every day ten folio pages in some Greek author, and generally a Greek play in the course of the week besides. By this means we became very well acquainted with that language, and with the most valuable authors in it. This exercise we continued long after we left the academy, communicating to each other by letter an account of what we read. My life becoming more occupied than his, he continued his application to Greek longer than I did, so that before his death he was, I imagine, one of the best Greek scholars in this or any other country. My attention was always more drawn to mathematical and philosophical[12] studies than his was.

These voluntary engagements were the more necessary in the course of our academical studies, as there was then no provision made for teaching the learned languages. We had even no compositions or orations in Latin. Our course of lectures was also defective in containing no lectures on the Scriptures, or on ecclesiastical history, and by the students in general (and Mr. Alexander and myself were no exceptions) commentators in general and ecclesiastical history also were held in contempt. On leaving the academy, he went to study under his uncle, Dr. Benson, and with him learned to value the critical study of the Scriptures so much that at length he almost confined his attention to them.

My other particular friends among my fellow students were Mr. Henry Holland, of my own class, Messrs. Whitehead, Smithson, Rotherham, and Scholefield, in that above me, and Mr. Tayler in that below me. With all these I kept up more or less of a correspondence, and our friendship was terminated only by the death of those who are now dead, viz. the three first named of these six, and I hope it will subsist to the same period with those who now survive.

All the while I was at the academy, I never lost sight of the great object of my studies, which was the duties of a

---

[12] The word "philosophical," which occurs frequently in Priestley's writings, should generally be understood as meaning "scientific."

Christian minister, and there it was that I laid the general plan which I have executed since. Particularly, I there composed the first copy of my *Institutes of Natural and Revealed Religion*, Mr. Clark, to whom I communicated my scheme, carefully perusing every section of it, and talking over the subject of it with me.

But I was much discouraged even then with the impediment in my speech, which I inherited from my family, and which still attends me. Sometimes I absolutely stammered, and my anxiety about it was the cause of much distress to me. However, like St. Paul's "thorn in the flesh," I hope it has not been without its use. Without some such check as this, I might have been disputatious in company, or might have been seduced by the love of popular applause as a preacher; whereas my conversation and my delivery in the pulpit having nothing in them that was generally striking, I hope I have been more attentive to qualifications of a superior kind.

It is not, I believe, usual for young persons in Dissenting academies to think much of their future situations in life. Indeed, we are happily precluded from that by the impossibility of succeeding in any application for particular places. We often, indeed, amused ourselves with the idea of our dispersion in all parts of the kingdom, after living so happily together; and used to propose plans of meeting at certain times, and smile at the different appearance we should probably make after being ten or twenty years settled in the world. But nothing of this kind was ever seriously resolved upon by us. For my own part, I can truly say I had very little ambition, except to distinguish myself by my application to the studies proper to my profession; and I cheerfully listened to the first proposal that my tutor made to me, in consequence of an application made to him to provide a minister for the people of Needham Market, in Suffolk, though it was very remote from my friends in Yorkshire, and a very inconsiderable place.

FIRST PASTORATE: NEEDHAM MARKET

When I went to preach at Needham as a candidate, I found a small congregation, about a hundred people, under a Mr. Meadows, who was superannuated. They had been without a minister the preceding year on account of the smallness of the salary; but there being some respectable and agreeable families among them, I flattered myself that I should be useful and happy in the place, and therefore accepted the unanimous invitation to be assistant to Mr. Meadows, with a view to succeed him when he died. He was a man of some fortune.

This congregation had been used to receive assistance from both the Presbyterian and Independent funds; but upon my telling them that I did not choose to have anything to do with the Independents, and asking them whether they were able to make up the salary they promised me (which was forty pounds per annum) without any aid from the latter fund, they assured me they could. I soon, however, found that they deceived themselves; for the most that I ever received from them was in the proportion of about thirty pounds per annum, when the expense of my board exceeded twenty pounds.

Notwithstanding this, everything else for the first half year appeared very promising, and I was happy in the success of my schemes for promoting the interest of religion in the place. I catechized the children, though there were not many, using Dr. Watts's Catechism;[13] and I opened my lectures on the theory of religion from the *Institutes* which I had composed at the academy, admitting all persons to attend them, without distinction of sex or age; but in this I soon found that I had acted imprudently. A minister in that neighborhood had been obliged to leave his place on account of Arianism; and though nothing had been said

[13] Isaac Watts (1674-1748), the famous hymn writer, was the author of a popular catechism. See Stephen and Lee, eds., *Dictionary of National Biography*, LX, 68.

to me on the subject, and from the people so readily consenting to give up the Independent fund, I thought they could not have much bigotry among them, I found that when I came to treat of the Unity of God, merely as an article of religion, several of my audience were attentive to nothing but the soundness of my faith in the doctrine of the Trinity.

Also, though I had made it a rule to myself to introduce nothing that could lead to controversy into the pulpit, yet making no secret of my real opinions in conversation, it was soon found that I was an Arian. From the time of this discovery my hearers fell off apace, especially as the old minister took a decided part against me. The principal families, however, still continued with me; but notwithstanding this, my salary fell far short of thirty pounds per annum; and if it had not been for Dr. Benson and Dr. Kippis, especially the former, procuring me now and then an extraordinary five pounds from different charities, I do not believe that I could have subsisted. I shall always remember their kindness to me, at a time when I stood in so much need of it.

When I was in this situation, a neighboring minister, whose intimate friend had conformed to the Church of England, talked to me on that subject. He himself, I perceived, had no great objection to it; but rejecting the proposal, as a thing that I could not think of, he never mentioned it to me any more.

To these difficulties, arising from the sentiments of my congregation, was added that of the failure of all remittances from my aunt, owing in part to the ill offices of my orthodox relations, but chiefly to her being exhausted by her liberality to others, and thinking that when I was settled in the world, I ought to be no longer burdensome to her. Together with me, she had brought up a niece, who was almost her only companion, and being deformed, could not have subsisted without the greatest part, at least, of all she had to bequeath. In consequence of these circumstances, though my aunt had always assured me that, if I chose to be a minister, she would leave me independent of the profession, I was satisfied she was not able to perform her promise, and freely consented to her leaving all she had to my cousin; I had only a silver tankard as a token of her remembrance. She had spared no expense in my education, and that was doing more for me than giving me an estate.

But what contributed greatly to my distress was the impediment in my speech, which had increased so much as to make preaching very painful, and took from me all chance of recommending myself to any better place. In this state, hearing of the proposal of one Mr. Angier, to cure all defects of speech, I prevailed upon my aunt to enable me to pay his price, which was twenty guineas; and this was the first occasion of my visiting London. Accordingly, I attended him about a month, taking an oath not to reveal his method, and I received some temporary benefit; but soon relapsed again, and spoke worse than ever. When I went to London, it was in company with Mr. Smithson, who was settled at Harleston, in Norfolk. By him I was introduced to Dr. Kippis, and Dr. Benson, and by the latter to Dr. Price, but not at that time.

At Needham I felt the effect of a low despised situation, together with that arising from the want of popular talents. There were several vacancies in congregations in that neighborhood, where my sentiments would have been no objection to me, but I was never thought of. Even my next neighbor, whose sentiments were as free as my own, and known to be so, declined making exchanges with me, which, when I left that part of the country, he acknowledged was not owing to any dislike his people had to me as heretical, but for other reasons, the more genteel part of his hearers always absenting themselves when they heard I was to preach for him. But visiting that country some years afterwards, when I had raised myself to some degree of notice in the world, and being invited to preach in that very pulpit, the same people crowded to hear me, though my elocution was not much improved, and they professed to admire one of the same discourses they had formerly despised.

Notwithstanding these unfavorable circumstances, I was far from being unhappy at Needham. I was boarded in a family from which I received much satisfaction; I firmly believed that a wise Providence was disposing everything for the best, and I applied with great assiduity to my studies, which were classical, mathematical, and theological. These required but few books. As to experimental philosophy, I had always cultivated an acquaintance with it, but I had not the means of prosecuting it.

With respect to miscellaneous reading, I was pretty well supplied by means of a library belonging to Mr. S. Alexander, a Quaker, to which I had the freest access. Here it was that I was first acquainted with any person of that persuasion; and I must acknowledge my obligation to many of them in every future stage of my life. I have met with the noblest instances of liberality of sentiment, and the truest generosity, among them.

THEOLOGICAL STUDIES

My studies, however, were chiefly theological. Having left the academy, as I have observed, with a qualified belief of the doctrine of atonement, such as is found in Mr. Tomkin's book, entitled *Jesus Christ the Mediator,* I was desirous of getting some more definite ideas on the subject, and with that view set myself to peruse the whole of the Old and New Testament, and to collect from them all the texts that appeared to me to have any relation to the subject. This I therefore did with the greatest care, arranging them under a great variety of heads. At the same time I did not fail to note such general considerations as occurred to me while I was thus employed. The consequence of this was what I had no apprehension of when I began to work, viz. a full persuasion that the doctrine of atonement, even in its most qualified sense, had no countenance either from Scripture or reason. Satisfied of this, I proceeded to digest my observations into a regular treatise, which a friend of mine, without mentioning my name, submitted to the perusal of Dr. Fleming and Dr. Lardner. In consequence of this, I was urged by them to publish the greater part of what I had written. But being then about to leave Needham, I desired them to do whatever they thought proper with respect to it, and they published about half of my piece, under the title of the *Doctrine of Remission*, etc.

This circumstance introduced me to the acquaintance of Dr. Lardner,[14] whom I always called upon when I visited London. The last time I saw him, which was little more than a year before his death, having by letter requested him to give me some assistance with respect to the history I then prepared to write of the corruptions of Christianity, and especially that article of it, he took down a large bundle of pamphlets, and turning them over, at length showing me my own, said, "This contains my sentiments on the subject." He had then forgotten that I wrote it, and on my remarking it, he shook his head, and said that his memory began to fail him, and that he had taken me for another person. He was then at the advanced age of eighty-three. This anecdote is trifling in itself, but it relates to a great and good man.

I have observed that Dr. Lardner only wished to publish a part of the treatise which my friend put into his hand. The other part of it contained remarks on the reasoning of the Apostle Paul, which he could not by any means approve. They were, therefore, omitted in this publication. But the attention which I gave to the writings of this apostle at the

[14] Nathaniel Lardner (1684-1768) was counted "the most learned theologian" among the eighteenth-century English Independents. His *Letter on the Logos* (1759), which asserted that "there is one God, even the Father, and that Jesus Christ is a man with a reasonable soul and a human body," was influential in converting Priestley to Socinianism. See Earl M. Wilbur, *A History of Unitarianism in Transylvania, England, and America* (Cambridge, Mass., 1952), pp. 264-265.

time that I examined them, in order to collect passages relating to the doctrine of atonement, satisfied me that his reasoning was in many places far from being conclusive; and in a separate work I examined every passage in which his reasoning appeared to me to be defective, or his conclusions ill supported, and I thought them to be pretty numerous.

At that time I had not read any commentary on the Scriptures, except that of Mr. Henry, when I was young. However, seeing so much reason to be dissatisfied with the Apostle Paul as a reasoner, I read Dr. Taylor's *Paraphrase on the Romans;* but it gave me no sort of satisfaction; and his general *Key to the Apostolic Writings,* still less. I therefore at that time wrote some remarks on it, which were a long time after published in the *Theological Repository.*

As I found that Dr. Lardner did not at all relish any of my observations on the imperfections of the sacred writers, I did not put this treatise into his hands; but I showed it to some of my younger friends, and also to Dr. Kippis; and he advised me to publish it under the character of an unbeliever, in order to draw the more attention to it. This I did not choose, having always had a great aversion to assume any character that was not my own, even so much as disputing for the sake of discovering truth. I cannot even say that I was quite reconciled to the idea of writing to a fictitious person, as in my *Letters to a Philosophical Unbeliever,* though nothing can be more innocent, or sometimes more proper, our Saviour's parables implying a much greater departure from strict truth than those letters do. I therefore wrote the book with great freedom, indeed, but as a Christian, and an admirer of the Apostle Paul, as I always was in other respects.

When I was at Nantwich, I sent this treatise to the press; but when nine sheets were printed off, Dr. Kippis dissuaded me from proceeding, or from publishing anything of the kind, until I should be more known, and my character

better established. I therefore desisted; but when I opened
the *Theological Repository*, I inserted in that work everything that was of much consequence in the other, in order
to its being submitted to the examination of learned Christians. Accordingly these communications were particularly
animadverted upon by Mr. Willet, of Newcastle, under the
signature of W. W. But I cannot say that his remarks gave
me much satisfaction.

When I was at Needham, I likewise drew up a treatise
on the doctrine of divine influence, having collected a number of texts for that purpose, and arranged them under
proper heads, as I had done those relating to the doctrine
of atonement. But I published nothing relating to it until
I made use of some of the observations in my sermon on
that subject, delivered at an ordination, and published
many years afterwards.

While I was in this retired situation, I had, in consequence
of much pains and thought, become persuaded of the falsity
of the doctrine of atonement, of the inspiration of the
authors of the books of Scripture as writers, and of all idea
of supernatural influence, except for the purpose of miracles.
But I was still an Arian, having never turned my attention
to the Socinian doctrine, and contenting myself with seeing
the absurdity of the Trinitarian system.

Another task that I imposed on myself, and in part executed at Needham, was an accurate comparison of the
Hebrew text of the Hagiographa and the Prophets with the
version of the Septuagint, noting all the variations, etc.
This I had about half finished before I left that place; and
I never resumed it, except to do that occasionally for particular passages, which I then began, though with many
disadvantages, with a design to go through the whole. I
had no polyglot Bible, and could have little help from the
labors of others.

The most learned of my acquaintance in this situation
was Mr. Scott, of Ipswich, who was well versed in the
Oriental languages, especially the Arabic. But though he

was far from being Calvinistical, he gave me no encouragement in the very free inquiries which I then entered upon. Being excluded from all communication with the more orthodox ministers in that part of the country, all my acquaintance among the Dissenting ministers, besides Mr. Scott, were Mr. Tailor, of Stowmarket; Mr. Dickinson, of Diss; and Mr. Smithson, of Harleston; and it is rather remarkable that we all left that country in the course of the same year; Mr. Tailor removing to Carter Lane, in London, Mr. Dickinson to Sheffield, and Mr. Smithson to Nottingham.

But I was very happy in a great degree of intimacy with Mr. Chauvet, the rector of Stowmarket. He was descended of French parents; and, I think, was not born in England. While he lived, we were never long without seeing each other. But he was subject to great unevenness of spirits, sometimes the most cheerful man living, and at other times most deplorably low. In one of these fits he at length put an end to his life. I heard afterwards that he had at one time been confined for insanity and had even made the same attempt some time before.

Like most other young men of a liberal education, I had conceived a great aversion to the business of a schoolmaster, and had often said that I would have recourse to anything else for a maintenance in preference to it. But having no other resource, I was at length compelled by necessity to make some attempt in that way; and for this purpose I printed and distributed proposals, but without any effect. Not that I was thought to be unqualified for this employment, but because I was not orthodox. I had proposed to teach the classics, mathematics, etc. for half-a-guinea per quarter, and to board the pupils in the house with myself for twelve guineas per annum.

Finding this scheme not to answer, I proposed to give lectures to grown persons, in such branches of science as I could conveniently procure the means of doing; and I began with reading about twelve lectures on the use of the globes, at half-a-guinea. I had one course of ten hearers, which did something more than pay for my globes; and I should have proceeded in this way, adding to my apparatus as I should have been able to afford it, if I had not left that place, which was in the following manner.

My situation being well known to my friends, Mr. Gill, a distant relation by my mother, who had taken much notice of me before I went to the academy, and had often lent me books, procured me an invitation to preach as a candidate at Sheffield, on the resignation of Mr. Wadsworth. Accordingly I did preach as a candidate, but though my opinions were no objection to me there, I was not approved. But Mr. Haynes, the other minister, perceiving that I had no chance at Sheffield, told me that he could recommend me to a congregation at Nantwich, in Cheshire, where he himself had been settled; and as it was a great distance from Needham, he would endeavor to procure me an invitation to preach there for a year certain. This he did, and I, gladly accepting of it, removed from Needham, going thence to London by sea, to save expense. This was in 1758, after having been at Needham just three years.

AT NANTWICH

At Nantwich I found a good-natured, friendly people, with whom I lived three years very happily; and in this situation I heard nothing of those controversies which had been the topics of almost every conversation in Suffolk; and the consequence was that I gave little attention to them myself. Indeed it was hardly in my power to do it, on account of my engagement with a school, which I was soon able to establish, and to which I gave almost all my attention; and in this employment, contrary to my expectations, I found the greatest satisfaction, notwithstanding the confinement and labor attending it.

My school generally consisted of about thirty boys, and I had a separate room for about half-a-dozen young ladies. Thus I was employed from seven in the morning until four in the afternoon, without any interval except one hour for dinner; and I never gave a holiday on any consideration, the red letter days, as they are called, excepted. Immediately after this employment in my own school rooms, I went to teach in the family of Mr. Tomkinson, an eminent attorney, and a man of large fortune, whose recommendation was of the greatest service to me; and here I continued until seven in the evening. I had, therefore, but little leisure for reading, or for improving myself in any way, except what necessarily arose from my employment.

Being engaged in the business of a schoolmaster, I made it my study to regulate it in the best manner, and I think I may say with truth, that in no school was more business done, or with more satisfaction, either to the master or the scholars, than in this of mine. Many of my scholars are probably living, and I am confident that they will say that this is no vain boast.

At Needham I was barely able, with the greatest economy, to keep out of debt (though this I always made a point of doing at all events), but at Nantwich my school soon enabled me to purchase a few books, and some philosophical instruments, as a small air pump, an electrical machine, etc. These I taught my scholars in the highest class to keep in order, and make use of; and by entertaining their parents and friends with experiments, in which the scholars were generally the operators, and sometimes the lecturers too, I considerably extended the reputation of my school; though I had no other object originally than gratifying my own taste. I had no leisure, however, to make any original experiments until many years after this time.

As there were few children in the congregation (which did not consist of more than sixty persons, and a great proportion of them traveling Scotchmen), there was no scope for exertion with respect to my duty as a minister. I therefore contented myself with giving the people what assistance I could at their own houses, where there were young persons; and I added very few sermons to those which I had composed at Needham, where I never failed to make at least one every week.

Being boarded with Mr. Eddowes, a very sociable and sensible man, and at the same time the person of the greatest property in the congregation, and who was fond of music, I was induced to learn to play a little on the English flute, as the easiest instrument; and though I was never a proficient in it, my playing contributed more or less to my amusement many years of my life. I would recommend the knowledge and practice of music to all studious persons; and it will be better for them, if like myself, they should have no very fine ear, or exquisite taste; as by this means they will be more easily pleased, and be less apt to be offended when the performances they hear are but indifferent.

At Nantwich I had hardly any literary acquaintance besides Mr. Brereton, a clergyman in the neighborhood, who had a taste for astronomy, philosophy, and literature in general. I often slept at his house, in a room to which he gave my name. But his conduct afterwards was unworthy of his profession.

Of Dissenting ministers, I saw most of Mr. Keay, of Whitchurch; and Dr. Harwood, who lived and had a school at Congleton, preaching alternately at Leek and Wheelock, the latter place about ten miles from Nantwich. Being both of us schoolmasters, and having in some respect the same pursuits, we made exchanges for the sake of spending a Sunday evening together every six weeks in the summer time. He was a good classical scholar, and a very entertaining companion.

In my congregation there was (out of the house in which I was boarded) hardly more than one family in which I could spend a leisure hour with much satisfaction, and that

was Mr. James Caldwall's, a Scotchman. Indeed several of
the traveling Scotchmen who frequented the place, but
made no long stay at any time, were men of very good
sense; and, what I thought extraordinary, not one of them
was at all Calvinistical.

My engagements in teaching allowed me but little time
for composing anything while I was at Nantwich. There,
however, I recomposed my *Observations on the Character
and Reasoning of the Apostle Paul,* as mentioned before.
For the use of my school, I then wrote an *English Grammar,*
on a new plan, leaving out all such technical terms as were
borrowed from other languages, and had no corresponding
modifications in ours, as the future tense, etc.; and to this I
afterwards subjoined *Observations for the Use of Proficients
in the Language,* from the notes which I collected at Warrington, where, being tutor in the languages and belles-
lettres, I gave particular attention to the English language,
and intended to have composed a large treatise on the
structure and present state of it. But dropping the scheme
in another situation, I lately gave such parts of my collection
as I had made no use of to Mr. Herbert Croft, of Oxford, on
his communicating to me his design of compiling a dictionary and grammar of our language.

The academy at Warrington was instituted when I was at
Needham, and Mr. Clark, knowing the attention that I had
given to the learned languages when I was at Daventry,
had then joined with Dr. Benson and Dr. Taylor in recommending me as tutor in the languages. But Mr. (afterwards
Dr.) Aikin, whose qualifications were superior to mine, was
justly preferred to me. However, on the death of Dr. Taylor,
and the advancement of Mr. Aikin to be tutor in divinity, I
was invited to succeed him. This I accepted, though my
school promised to be more gainful to me. But my employment at Warrington would be more liberal and less painful.
It was also a means of extending my connections. But, as I
told the persons who brought me the invitation, viz. Mr.
Seddon and Mr. Holland, of Bolton, I should have preferred

the office of teaching the mathematics and natural philosophy, for which I had at that time a great predilection.

TEACHING AT WARRINGTON

My removal to Warrington was in September, 1761, after a residence of just three years at Nantwich. In this new situation I continued six years, and in the second year I married a daughter of Mr. Isaac Wilkinson, an ironmaster, near Wrexham, in Wales, with whose family I had become acquainted in consequence of having the youngest son, William, at my school at Nantwich. This proved a very suitable and happy connection, my wife being a woman of an excellent understanding, much improved by reading, of great fortitude and strength of mind, and of a temper in the highest degree affectionate and generous; feeling strongly for others and little for herself. Also, greatly excelling in everything relating to household affairs, she entirely relieved me of all concern of that kind, which allowed me to give all my time to the prosecution of my studies, and the other duties of my station. And though, in consequence of her father becoming impoverished, and wholly dependent on his children, in the later part of his life, I had little fortune with her, I unexpectedly found a great resource in her two brothers, who had become wealthy, especially the elder of them. At Warrington I had a daughter, Sarah, who was afterwards married to Mr. William Finch, of Heath Forge, near Dudley.

Though at the time of my removal to Warrington I had no particular fondness for the studies relating to my profession then, I applied to them with great assiduity; and besides composing courses of lectures on the theory of language, and on oratory and criticism, on which my predecessor had lectured, I introduced lectures on history and general policy, on the laws and constitution of England, and on the history of England. This I did in consequence of observing that, though most of our pupils were young men designed for situations in civil and active life, every article in the plan of their education was adapted to the learned professions.

In order to recommend such studies as I introduced, I composed an *Essay on a Course of Liberal Education for Civil and Active Life,* with syllabuses of my three new courses of lectures; and Dr. Brown having just then published a plan of education, in which he recommended it to be undertaken by the state, I added some remarks on his treatise, showing how inimical it was to liberty and the natural rights of parents. This leading me to consider the subject of civil and political liberty, I published my thoughts on it, in an *Essay on Government,* which in a second edition I much enlarged, including in it what I wrote in answer to Dr. Balguy on church authority, as well as my animadversions on Dr. Brown.

My *Lectures on the Theory of Language and Universal Grammar* were printed for the use of the students, but they were not published. Those on *Oratory and Criticism* I published when I was with Lord Shelburne; and those on *History and General Policy* are now printed, and about to be published.

Finding no public exercises at Warrington, I introduced them there, so that afterwards every Saturday the tutors, all the students, and often strangers, were assembled to hear English and Latin compositions, and sometimes to hear the delivery of speeches, and the exhibition of scenes in plays. It was my province to teach elocution, and also logic and Hebrew. The first of these I retained; but after a year or two I exchanged the two last articles with Dr. Aikin for the civil law, and one year I gave a course of lectures in anatomy.

With a view to lead the students to a facility in writing English, I encouraged them to write in verse. This I did not with any design to make them poets, but to give them a greater facility in writing prose, and this method I would recommend to all tutors. I was myself far from having any pretension to the character of a poet; but in the early part of my life I was a great versifier, and this, I believe, as well as my custom of writing after preachers, mentioned before, contributed to the ease with which I always wrote prose. Mrs. Barbauld has told me that it was the perusal of some verses of mine that first induced her to write anything in verse, so that this country is in some measure indebted to me for one of the best poets it can boast of. Several of her first poems were written when she was in my house, on occasions that occurred while she was there.

It was while I was at Warrington that I published my *Chart of Biography*, though I had begun to construct it at Nantwich. Lord Willoughby, of Parham, who lived in Lancashire, being pleased with the idea of it, I, with his consent, inscribed it to him; but he died before the publication of it. The *Chart of History*, corresponding to it, I drew up some time after at Leeds.

ELECTRICITY

I was in this situation, when, going to London, and being introduced to Dr. Price, Mr. Canton, Dr. Watson (the physician), and Dr. [Benjamin] Franklin, I was led to attend to the subject of experimental philosophy more than I had done before; and having composed all the lectures I had occasion to deliver, and finding myself at liberty for any undertaking, I mentioned to Dr. Franklin an idea that had occurred to me of writing the history of discoveries in electricity, which had been his favorite study. This I told him might be a useful work, and that I would willingly undertake it, provided I could be furnished with the books necessary for the purpose. This he readily undertook, and my other friends assisting him in it, I set about the work, without having the least idea of doing anything more than writing a distinct and methodical account of all that had been done by others. Having, however, a pretty good machine, I was led, in the course of my writing the history, to endeavor to ascertain several facts which were disputed; and this led me by degrees into a large field of original experiments, in which I spared no expense that I could possibly furnish.

These experiments employed a great proportion of my leisure time; and yet before the complete expiration of the year, in which I gave the plan of my work to Dr. Franklin, I sent him a copy of it in print. In the same year five hours of every day were employed in lectures, public or private, and one two-months' vacation I spent chiefly at Bristol, on a visit to my father-in-law.

This I do not mention as a subject of boasting, for many persons have done more in the same time, but as an answer to those who have objected to some of my later writings, as hasty performances; for none of my publications were better received than this *History of Electricity,* which was the most hasty of them all. However, whether my publications have taken up more or less time, I am confident that more would not have contributed to their perfection in any essential particular; and about anything farther I have never been very solicitous. My object was not to acquire the character of a fine writer, but of a useful one. I can also truly say that gain was never the chief object of any of my publications. Several of them were written with the prospect of certain loss.

During the course of my electrical experiments in this year, I kept up a constant correspondence with Dr. Franklin, and the rest of my philosophical friends in London; and my letters circulated among them all, as also every part of my *History* as it was transcribed. This correspondence would have made a considerable volume, and it took up much time; but it was of great use with respect to the accuracy of my experiments and the perfection of my work.

After the publication of my *Chart of Biography,* Dr.

Percival, of Manchester, then a student at Edinburgh, procured me the title of Doctor of Laws from that university; and not long after, my new experiments in electricity were the means of introducing me into the Royal Society, with the recommendation of Dr. Franklin, Dr. Watson, Mr. Canton, and Dr. Price.

In the whole time of my being at Warrington, I was singularly happy in the society of my fellow tutors, and of Mr. Seddon, the minister of the place. We drank tea together every Saturday, and our conversation was equally instructive and pleasing. I often thought it not a little extraordinary that four persons who had no previous knowledge of each other should have been brought to unite in conducting such a scheme as this, and all be zealous Necessarians, as we were. We were likewise all Arians, and the only subject of much consequence on which we differed was respecting the doctrine of atonement, concerning which Dr. Aikin held some obscure notions. Accordingly, this was frequently the topic of our friendly conversations. The only Socinian in the neighborhood was Mr. Seddon, of Manchester; and we all wondered at him. But then we never entered into any particular examination of the subject.

Receiving some of the pupils into my own house, I was by this means led to form some valuable friendships, but especially with Mr. Samuel Vaughan, a friendship which has continued hitherto, has in a manner connected our families, and will, I doubt not, continue through life. The two eldest of his sons were boarded with me.

The tutors having sufficient society among themselves, we had not much acquaintance out of the academy. Sometimes, however, I made an excursion to the towns in the neighborhood. At Liverpool I was always received by Mr. Bentley, afterwards partner with Mr. Wedgwood, a man of excellent taste, improved understanding, and a good disposition, but an unbeliever in Christianity, which was therefore often the subject of our conversation. He was then a widower, and we generally, and contrary to my usual custom, sat up late.

At Manchester I was always the guest of Mr. Potter, whose son Thomas was boarded with me. He was one of the worthiest men that ever lived. At Chowbent I was much acquainted with Mr. Mort, a man equally distinguished by his cheerfulness and liberality of sentiment.

Of the ministers in the neighborhood I recollect with much satisfaction the interviews I had with Mr. Godwin, of Gatecre; Mr. Holland, of Bolton; and Dr. Enfield, of Liverpool, afterwards tutor at Warrington.

Though all the tutors in my time lived in the most perfect harmony, though we all exerted ourselves to the utmost, and there was no complaint of want of discipline, the academy did not flourish. There had been an unhappy difference between Dr. Taylor and the trustees, in consequence of which all his friends, who were numerous, were our enemies; and too many of the subscribers being probably weary of the subscription, were willing to lay hold of any pretense for dropping it, and of justifying their conduct afterwards.

It is possible that in time we might have overcome the prejudices we labored under; but there being no prospect of things being any better, and my wife having very bad health, on her account chiefly I wished for a removal, though nothing could be more agreeable to me at the time than the whole of my employment, and all the laborious part of it was over. The terms also on which we took boarders, viz. fifteen pounds per annum, and my salary being only one hundred pounds per annum, with a house, it was not possible, even living with the greatest frugality, to make any provision for a family. I was there six years, most laboriously employed, for nothing more than a bare subsistence. I therefore listened to an invitation to take the charge of the congregation of Mill-Hill Chapel, at Leeds, where I was pretty well known, and thither I removed in September, 1767.

Though while I was at Warrington it was no part of my duty to preach, I had from choice continued the practice; and wishing to keep up the character of a Dissenting minister, I chose to be ordained while I was there; and though I was far from having conquered my tendency to stammer, and probably never shall be able to do it effectually, I had, by taking much pains, improved my pronunciation, some time before I left Nantwich, where, for the first two years, this impediment had increased so much that I once informed the people that I must give up the business of preaching, and confine myself to my school. However, by making a practice of reading very loud and very slow every day, I at length succeeded in getting, in some measure, the better of this defect, but I am still obliged occasionally to have recourse to the same expedient.

PASTOR AT LEEDS

At Leeds I continued six years very happy with a liberal, friendly, and harmonious congregation, to whom my services (of which I was not sparing) were very acceptable. Here I had no unreasonable prejudices to contend with, so that I had full scope for every kind of exertion; and I can truly say that I always considered the office of a Christian minister as the most honorable of any upon earth, and in the studies proper to it I always took the greatest pleasure.

In this situation I naturally resumed my application to speculative theology, which had occupied me at Needham, and which had been interrupted by the business of teaching at Nantwich and Warrington. By reading with care Dr. Lardner's *Letter on the Logos,* I became what is called a Socinian, soon after my settlement at Leeds; and after giving the closest attention to the subject, I have seen more and more reason to be satisfied with that opinion to this day, and likewise to be more impressed with the idea of its importance.

On reading Mr. Mann's *Dissertation on the Times of the Birth and Death of Christ,* I was convinced that he was right in his opinion of our Saviour's ministry having con-

tinued little more than one year, and on this plan I drew
out a *Harmony of the Gospels,* the outline of which I first
published in the *Theological Repository,* and afterwards
separately and at large, both in Greek and English, with
notes, and an occasional paraphrase. In the same work I
published my "Essay on the Doctrine of Atonement," improved from the tract published by Dr. Lardner, and also
my animadversions on the reasoning of the Apostle Paul.

The plan of this *Repository* occurred to me on seeing
some notes that Mr. Turner, of Wakefield, had drawn up on
several passages of Scripture, which I was concerned to
think should be lost. He very much approved of my proposal of an occasional publication, for the purpose of
preserving such original observations as could otherwise
probably never see the light. Of this work I published three
volumes while I was at Leeds, and he never failed to give
me an article for every number of which they were composed.

Giving particular attention to the duties of my office, I
wrote several tracts for the use of my congregation, as two
Catechisms, an *Address to Masters of Families* on the subject of family prayer, a *Discourse on the Lord's Supper,* and
on *Church Discipline,* and *Institutes of Natural and Revealed Religion.* Here I formed three classes of cate-
chumens, and took great pleasure in instructing them in the
principles of religion. In this respect I hope my example has
been of use in other congregations.

The first of my controversial treatises was written here
in reply to some angry remarks on my *Discourse on the
Lord's Supper* by Mr. Venn, a clergyman in the neighborhood. I also wrote *Remarks on Dr. Balguy's Sermon on
Church Authority,* and on some paragraphs in Judge Black-
stone's *Commentaries on the Laws of England,* relating to
the Dissenters. To the two former no reply was made; but
to the last the Judge replied in a small pamphlet; on which
I addressed a letter to him in the *St. James's Chronicle.*
This controversy led me to print another pamphlet, en-

titled *A View of the Principles and Conduct of the Protestant Dissenters, with Respect to the Civil and Ecclesiastical Constitution of England.* With the encouragement of Dr. Price and Dr. Kippis, I also wrote an *Address to Protestant Dissenters as Such, by a Dissenter,* but without my name. Several of these pamphlets having been animadverted upon by an anonymous acquaintance, who thought I had laid too much stress on the principles of the Dissenters, I wrote a defense of my conduct in *Letters* addressed to him.

The Methodists being very numerous in Leeds, and many of the lower sort of my own hearers listening to them, I wrote *An Appeal to the Serious and Candid Professors of Christianity, An Illustration of Certain Passages of Scripture,* and republished the *Trial of Elwall,* all in the cheapest manner possible. Those small tracts had a great effect in establishing my hearers in liberal principles of religion, and in a short time had a far more extensive influence than I could have imagined. By this time [1787] more than thirty thousand copies of the *Appeal* have been dispersed.

Besides these theoretical and controversial pieces, I wrote, while I was at Leeds, my *Essay on the First Principles of Government,* mentioned before, my *English Grammar* enlarged, *Familiar Introduction to the Study of Electricity,* a *Treatise on Perspective,* and my *Chart of History,* and also some anonymous pieces, in favor of civil liberty, during the persecution of Mr. Wilkes, the principal of which was an *Address to Dissenters on the Subject of the Difference with America,* which I wrote at the request of Dr. Franklin and Dr. Fothergill.

CHEMISTRY

But nothing of a nature foreign to the duties of my profession engaged my attention while I was at Leeds so much as the prosecution of my experiments relating to electricity, and especially the doctrine of air. The last I was led into in consequence of inhabiting a house adjoining to a public brewery, where I at first amused myself with making experiments on the fixed air which I found ready-made in the process of fermentation. When I removed from that house I was under the necessity of making the fixed air for myself; and one experiment leading to another, as I have distinctly and faithfully noted in my various publications on the subject, I by degrees contrived a convenient apparatus for the purpose, but of the cheapest kind.

When I began these experiments, I knew very little of chemistry, and had in a manner no idea on the subject before I attended a course of chemical lectures, delivered in the academy at Warrington, by Dr. Turner, of Liverpool. But I have often thought that upon the whole this circumstance was no disadvantage to me; as in this situation I was led to devise an apparatus, and processes of my own, adapted to my peculiar views. Whereas, if I had been previously accustomed to the usual chemical processes, I should not have so easily thought of any other; and without new modes of operation I should hardly have discovered anything materially new.

My first publication on the subject of air was in 1772. It was a small pamphlet on the method of impregnating water with fixed air; which being immediately translated into French, excited a great degree of attention to the subject, and this was much increased by the publication of my first paper of experiments, in a large article of the *Philosophical Transactions,* the year following, for which I received the gold medal of the Society. My method of impregnating water with fixed air was considered at a meeting of the College of Physicians, before whom I made the experiments, and by them it was recommended to the Lords of the Admiralty (by whom they had been summoned for the purpose) as likely to be of use in the sea scurvy.

The only person in Leeds who gave much attention to my experiments was Mr. Hey, a surgeon. He was a zealous Methodist, and wrote answers to some of my theological tracts; but we always conversed with the greatest freedom on philosophical subjects, without mentioning anything relating to theology. When I left Leeds, he begged of me the earthen trough in which I had made all my experiments on air while I was there. It was such a one as is there commonly used for washing linen.

Having succeeded so well in the *History of Electricity,* I was induced to undertake the history of all the branches of experimental philosophy; and at Leeds I gave out proposals for that purpose, and published the *History of Discoveries Relating to Vision, Light, and Colors.* This work, also, I believe I executed to general satisfaction, and being an undertaking of great expense, I was under the necessity of publishing it by subscription. The sale, however, was not such as to encourage me to proceed with a work of so much labor and expense; so that after purchasing a great number of books, to enable me to finish my undertaking, I was obliged to abandon it, and to apply wholly to original experiments.

In writing the *History of Discoveries Relating to Vision,* I was much assisted by Mr. Michell, the discoverer of the method of making artificial magnets. Living at Thornhill, not very far from Leeds, I frequently visited him, and was very happy in his society, as I also was in that of Mr. Smeaton, who lived still nearer to me. He made me a present of his excellent air pump, which I constantly use to this day. Having strongly recommended his construction of this instrument, it is now generally used; whereas before that, hardly any had been made during the twenty years which had elapsed after the account that he had given of it in the *Philosophical Transactions.*

I was also instrumental in reviving the use of large electrical machines and batteries in electricity, the generality of electrical machines being little more than playthings at the time that I began my experiments. The first very large electrical machine was made by Mr. Nairne, in consequence of a request made to me by the Grand Duke of Tuscany, to get him the best machine that we could make in England. This, and another that he made for Mr. Vaughan, were constituted on a plan of my own. But afterwards Mr. Nairne made large machines on a more simple and improved construction; and in consideration of the service which I had rendered him, he made me a present of a pretty large machine of the same kind.

The review of my *History of Electricity* by Mr. Bewley, who was acquainted with Mr. Michell, was the means of opening a correspondence between us, which was the source of much satisfaction to me as long as he lived. I instantly communicated to him an account of every new experiment that I made, and in return was favored with his remarks upon them. All that he published of his own were articles in the "Appendices" to my volumes on air, all of which are ingenious and valuable. Always publishing in this manner, he used to call himself my "satellite." There was a vein of pleasant wit and humor in all his correspondence, which added greatly to the value of it. His letters to me would have made several volumes, and mine to him still more. When he found himself dangerously ill, he made a point of paying me a visit before he died; and he made a journey from Norfolk to Birmingham, accompanied by Mrs. Bewley, for that purpose; and after spending about a week with me, he went to his friend Dr. Burney, and at his house he died.

While I was at Leeds, a proposal was made to me to accompany Captain Cook in his second voyage to the South Seas. As the terms were very advantageous, I consented to it, and the heads of my congregation had agreed to keep an assistant to supply my place during my absence. But Mr. Banks informed me that I was objected to by some clergymen in the Board of Longitude, who had the direction of this business, on account of my religious principles; and presently after I heard that Dr. Forster, a person far better qualified for the purpose, had got the appointment. As I had barely acquiesced in the proposal, this was no disappointment to me, and I was much better employed at home, even with respect to my philosophical pursuits. My knowledge of natural history was not sufficient for the undertaking; but at that time I should, by application, have been able to supply my deficiency, though now I am sensible I could not do it.

At Leeds I was particularly happy in my intercourse with Mr. Turner, of Wakefield, and occasionally with Mr. Graham, of Halifax, and Mr. Cappe, of York. And here it was that, in consequence of a visit, which, in company with Mr. Turner, I made to the Archdeacon Blackburne, at Richmond (with whom I had kept up a correspondence from the time that his son was under my care at Warrington) I first met with Mr. Lindsey,[15] then of Catterick, and a correspondence and intimacy commenced, which has been the source of more real satisfaction to me than any other circumstance in my whole life. He soon discovered to me that he was uneasy in his situation, and had thoughts of quitting it. At first I was not forward to encourage him in it, but rather advised him to make what alteration he thought proper in the offices of the church, and leave it to his superiors to dismiss him if they chose. But his better judgment, and greater fortitude, led him to give up all connection with the Established Church of his own accord.

This took place about the time of my leaving Leeds, and it was not until long after this that I was apprised of all the difficulties he had to struggle with before he could accomplish his purpose. But the opposition made to it by his nearest friends, and those who might have been expected to approve of the step that he took, and to have endeavored to make it easy to him, was one of the greatest. Notwithstanding this he left Catterick, where he had lived in affluence, idolized by his parish, and went to London without

---

[15] Theophilus Lindsey (1723-1808) resigned from the Church of England in 1774 to organize in London the first English congregation avowedly Unitarian — the Essex Street Chapel. He was Priestley's closest friend and most valued correspondent. See Wilbur, *Unitarianism*, pp. 280-292.

any certain prospect, where he lived in two rooms on a ground floor, until by the assistance of his friends he was able to pay for the use of the upper apartments, which the state of his health rendered necessary. In this humble situation have I passed some of the most pleasing hours of my life when, in consequence of living with Lord Shelburne, I spent my winters in London.

On this occasion it was that my intimacy with Mr. Lindsey was much improved, and an entire concurrence in everything that we thought to be for the interest of Christianity gave fresh warmth to our friendship. To his society I owe much of my zeal for the doctrine of the Divine Unity, for which he made so great sacrifices, and in the defense of which he so much distinguished himself, so as to occasion a new era in the history of religion in this country.

As we became more intimate, confiding in his better taste and judgment, and also in that of Mrs. Lindsey, a woman of the same spirit and views, and in all respects a helpmeet for him, I never chose to publish anything of moment relating to theology without consulting him; and hardly ever ventured to insert anything that they disapproved, being sensible that my disposition led to precipitancy, to which their coolness was a seasonable check.

At Leeds began my intercourse with Mr. Lee, of Lincoln's Inn.[16] He was a native of the place, and exactly one week older than myself. At that time he was particularly connected with the congregation and, before he was married, spent his vacations with us. His friendship was a source of much greater satisfaction and advantage to me after I came to reside in London, and especially at the time of my leaving Lord Shelburne, when my prospects wore rather a cloudy aspect.

When I visited London, during my residence at Leeds,

[16] John Lee (1733-1793) was a prominent lawyer and politician, who held several legal posts with the English government and served in Parliament for some years. See Stephen and Lee, eds., *Dictionary of National Biography*, XXXII, 361.

commenced my particular friendship for Dr. Price,[17] to whom I had been introduced several years before, by Dr. Benson; our first interview having been at Mr. Brownsword's, at Newington, where they were members of a small literary society, in which they read various compositions. At that time Dr. Benson read a paper which afterwards made a section in his *Life of Christ.* For the most amiable simplicity of character, equalled only by that of Mr. Lindsey, a truly Christian spirit, disinterested patriotism, and true candor, no man, in my opinion, ever exceeded Dr. Price. His candor will appear the more extraordinary, considering his warm attachments to the theological sentiments which he embraced in very early life. I shall ever reflect upon our friendship as a circumstance highly honorable, as it was a source of peculiar satisfaction to me.

I had two sons born to me at Leeds, Joseph and William, and though I was very happy there, I was tempted to leave it, after continuing there six years, to go into the family of the Earl of Shelburne, now the Marquis of Lansdowne;[18] he stipulating to give me two hundred and fifty pounds per annum, a house to live in, and a certainty for life in case of his death, or of my separation from him; whereas at Leeds my salary was only one hundred guineas per annum and a house, which was not quite sufficient for the subsistence of my family, without a possibility of making a provision for them after my death.

[17] Richard Price (1723-1791) was a Welsh minister, mathematician, and philosopher whose career paralleled Priestley's to a considerable extent. Though Price and Priestley differed slightly on metaphysics and theology, they are both distinguished as religious and political liberals. See Roland Thomas, *Richard Price, Philosopher and Apostle of Liberty* (London, 1924), and Carl B. Cone, *Torchbearer of Freedom: The Influence of Richard Price on Eighteenth Century Thought* (Lexington, Ky., 1952).

[18] Sir William Petty, first Marquis of Lansdowne, better known as Lord Shelburne (1737-1805), served in English cabinets both before and after the American Revolution. He is famous as a friend of the American cause. See Stephen and Lee, eds., *Dictionary of National Biography*, XLV, 119-127.

WITH LORD SHELBURNE

I had been recommended to Lord Shelburne, by Dr. Price, as a person qualified to be a literary companion to him. In this situation, my family being at Calne, in Wiltshire, near to his lordship's seat at Bowood, I continued seven years, spending the summer with my family, and a great part of the winter in his lordship's house in London. My office was nominally that of librarian, but I had little employment as such, besides arranging his books, taking a catalogue of them, and of his manuscripts, which were numerous, and making an index to his collection of private papers. In fact, I was with him as a friend, and the second year made with him the tour of Flanders, Holland, and Germany, as far as Strasburgh; and after spending a month at Paris, returned to England. This was in the year 1774.

This little excursion made me more sensible than I should otherwise have been of the benefit of foreign travel, even without the advantage of much conversation with foreigners. The very sight of new countries, new buildings, new customs, etc., and the very hearing of an unintelligible new language gives new ideas and tends to enlarge the mind. To me this little time was extremely pleasing, especially as I saw everything to the greatest advantage, and without any anxiety or trouble, and had an opportunity of seeing and conversing with every person of eminence, wherever we came; the political characters by his lordship's connections, and the literary ones by my own.[19] I was soon, however, tired of Paris, and chose to spend my evenings at the hotel, in company with a few literary friends. Fortunately for me, Mr. Magellan, being at Paris at the same time, spent most of the evenings with me; and, as I chose to return before his lordship, he accompanied me to London, and made the journey very pleasing to me; he being used to the country,

[19] It was at this time that Lavoisier learned of Priestley's discovery of "dephlogisticated air," which Lavoisier was later to label "oxygen."

the language, and the manners of it, which I was not. He had seen much of the world, and his conversation during our journey was particularly interesting to me. Indeed, in London, both before and after this time, I always found him very friendly, especially in everything that related to my philosophical pursuits.

As I was sufficiently apprised of the fact, I did not wonder, as I otherwise should have done, to find all the philosophical persons to whom I was introduced at Paris unbelievers in Christianity and even professed atheists. As I chose on all occasions to appear as a Christian, I was told by some of them that I was the only person they had ever met with, of whose understanding they had any opinion, who professed to believe Christianity. But on interrogating them on the subject, I soon found that they had given no proper attention to it, and did not really know what Christianity was. This was also the case with a great part of the company that I saw at Lord Shelburne's. But I hope that my always avowing myself to be a Christian, and holding myself ready on all occasions to defend the genuine principles of it, was not without its use. Having conversed so much with unbelievers, at home and abroad, I thought I should be able to combat their prejudices with some advantage, and with this view I wrote, while I was with Lord Shelburne, the first part of my *Letters to a Philosophical Unbeliever,* in proof of the doctrines of a God and a Providence, and to this I have added, during my residence at Birmingham, a second part, in defense of the evidences of Christianity. The first part being replied to by a person who called himself Mr. Hammon, I wrote a reply to his piece, which has hitherto remained unanswered. I am happy to find that this work of mine has done some good, and I hope that in due time it will do more. I can truly say that the greatest satisfaction I receive from the success of my philosophical pursuits arises from the weight it may give to my attempts to defend Christianity, and to free it from those corruptions which prevent its reception with philosophical and thinking persons, whose influence with the vulgar and the unthinking is very great.

With Lord Shelburne I saw a great variety of characters; but of our neighbors in Wiltshire the person I had the most frequent opportunity of seeing was Dr. Frampton, a clergyman, whose history may serve as a lesson to many. No man, perhaps, was ever better qualified to please in a convivial hour, or had greater talents for conversation and repartee; in consequence of which, though there were several things very disgusting about him, his society was much courted, and many promises of preferment were made to him. To these, notwithstanding his knowledge of the world and of high life, he gave too much credit; so that he spared no expense to gratify his taste and appetite, until he was universally involved in debt; and though his friends made some efforts to relieve him, he was confined a year in the county prison, at a time when his bodily infirmities required the greatest indulgences; and he obtained his release but a short time before his death, on condition of his living on a scanty allowance, the income of his livings (amounting to more than four hundred pounds per annum) being in the hands of his creditors. Such was the end of a man who kept the table in a roar.

Dr. Frampton being a high churchman, he could not at first conceal his aversion to me, and endeavored to do me some ill offices. But being a man of letters, and despising the clergy in his neighborhood, he became at last much attached to me; and in his distress was satisfied, I believe, that I was was one of his most sincere friends. With some great defects, he had some considerable virtues and uncommon abilities, which appeared more particularly in extempore speaking. He always preached without notes, and when, on some occasions, he composed his sermons, he could, if he chose to do it, repeat the whole verbatim. He frequently extemporized in verse, in a great variety of measures.

In Lord Shelburne's family was Lady Arabella Denny,

who is well known by her extensive charities. She is (for she is still living) a woman of good understanding and great piety. She had the care of his lordship's two sons, until they came under the care of Mr. Jervis, who was their tutor during my continuance in the family. His lordship's younger son, who died suddenly, had made astonishing attainments both in knowledge and piety, while very young, far beyond anything that I had an opportunity of observing in my life.

When I went to his lordship, I had materials for one volume of *Experiments and Observations on Different Kinds of Air,* which I soon after published, and inscribed to him; and before I left him, I published three volumes more, and had materials for a fourth, which I published immediately on my settling in Birmingham. He encouraged me in the prosecution of my philosophical inquiries, and allowed me forty pounds per annum for expenses of that kind, and was pleased to see me make experiments to entertain his guests, and especially foreigners.

Notwithstanding the attention that I gave to philosophy in this situation, I did not discontinue my other studies, especially in theology and metaphysics. Here I wrote my *Miscellaneous Observations Relating to Education,* and published my *Lectures on Oratory and Criticism,* which I dedicated to Lord Fitzmaurice, Lord Shelburne's eldest son. Here also I published the third and last part of my *Institutes of Natural and Revealed Religion;* and having in the preface attacked the principles of Dr. Reid, Dr. Beattie, and Dr. Oswald, with respect to their doctrine of common sense, which they made to supersede all rational inquiry into the subject of religion, I was led to consider their system in a separate work, which, though written in a manner I do not entirely approve, has, I hope, upon the whole, been of service to the cause of free inquiry and truth.

In the preface I had expressed my belief of the doctrine of philosophical necessity, but without any design to pursue the subject, and also my great admiration of Dr. Hartley's theory of the human mind, as indeed I had taken many opportunities of doing before. This led me to publish that part of his *Observations on Man*, which related to the doctrine of association of ideas, detached from the doctrine of vibrations, prefixing "Three Dissertations," explanatory of his general system. In one of these I expressed some doubt of the immateriality of the sentient principle in man; and the outcry that was made on what I casually expressed on that subject can hardly be imagined. In all the newspapers, and most of the periodical publications, I was represented as an unbeliever in revelation, and no better than an atheist.

This led me to give the closest attention to the subject, and the consequence was the firmest persuasion that man is wholly material, and that our only prospect of immortality is from the Christian doctrine of a resurrection. I therefore digested my thoughts on the subject, and published my *Disquisitions Relating to Matter and Spirit*. Also, the subjects of Socinianism and necessity being nearly connected with the doctrine of the materiality of man, I advanced several considerations from the state of opinions in ancient times in favor of the former; and in a separate volume, discussed more at large what related to the latter, dedicating the first volume of this work to Mr. Graham, and the second to Dr. Jebb.

It being probable that this publication would be unpopular, and might be a means of bringing odium on my patron, several attempts were made by his friends, though none by himself, to dissuade me from persisting in it. But being, as I thought, engaged in the cause of important truth, I proceeded without regard to any consequences, assuring them that this publication should not be injurious to his lordship.

In order, however, to proceed with the greatest caution in a business of such moment, I desired some of my learned friends, and especially Dr. Price, to peruse the work before it was published; and the remarks that he made upon it led to a free and friendly discussion of the several subjects of it, which we afterwards published jointly; and it remains a proof of the possibility of discussing subjects mutually considered as of the greatest importance, with the most perfect good temper, and without the least diminution of friendship. This work I dedicated to our common friend Mr. Lee.

In this situation I published my *Harmony of the Gospels*, on the idea of the public ministry of Jesus having continued little more than one year, a scheme which I first proposed in the *Theological Repository;* and the Bishop of Waterford having, in his *Harmony*, published a defense of the common hypothesis, viz. that of its having been three years, I addressed a letter to him on the subject, and to this he made a reply in a separate work. The controversy proceeded to several publications on both sides, in the most amicable manner, and the last *Postscript* was published jointly by us both. Though my side of the question was without any advocates that I know of, and had only been adopted by Mr. Mann, who seemed to have had no followers, there are few persons, I believe, who have attended to our discussion of the subject, who are not satisfied that I have sufficiently proved what I had advanced. This controversy was not finished until after my removal to Birmingham.

Reflecting on the time that I spent with Lord Shelburne, being as a guest in the family, I can truly say that I was not at all fascinated with that mode of life. Instead of looking back upon it with regret, one of the greatest subjects of my present thankfulness is the change of that situation for the one in which I am now placed; and yet I was far from being unhappy there, much less so than those who are born to such a state, and pass all their lives in it. These are generally unhappy from the want of necessary employment; on which account chiefly there appears to be much more happiness in the middle classes of life, who are above the fear of want, and yet have a sufficient motive for a constant exertion of their faculties, and who have always some other object besides amusement.

I used to make no scruple of maintaining that there is not only most virtue, and most happiness, but even most true politeness, in the middle classes of life. For in proportion as men pass more of their time in the society of their equals, they get a better established habit of governing their tempers; they attend more to the feelings of others, and are more disposed to accommodate themselves to them. On the other hand, the passions of persons in higher life, having been less controlled, are more apt to be inflamed; the idea of their rank and superiority to others seldom quits them; and though they are in the habit of concealing their feelings, and disguising their passions, it is not always so well done but that persons of ordinary discernment may perceive what they inwardly suffer. On this account they are really entitled to compassion, it being the almost unavoidable consequence of their education and mode of life. But when the mind is not hurt in such a situation, when a person born to affluence can lose sight of himself, and truly feel and act for others, the character is so god-like, as shows that this inequality of condition is not without its use. Like the general discipline of life, it is for the present lost on the great mass, but on a few it produces what no other state of things could do.

The greatest part of the time that I spent with Lord Shelburne I passed with much satisfaction, his lordship always behaving to me with uniform politeness, and his guests with respect; but about two years before I left him I perceived evident marks of dissatisfaction, though I never understood the cause of it; and until that time he had been even lavish on all occasions in expressing his satisfaction in my society to our common friends. When I left him, I asked him whether he had any fault to find with my conduct, and he said, "None."

At length, however, he intimated to Dr. Price that he wished to give me an establishment in Ireland, where he had large property. This gave me an opportunity of acquainting him that if he chose to dissolve the connection, it should be on the terms expressed in the writings which we mutually signed when it was formed, in consequence of which I should be entitled to an annuity of a hundred and fifty pounds, and then I would provide for myself, and to this he readily acceded. He told Dr. Price that he wished our separation to be amicable, and I assured him that nothing should be wanting on my part to make it truly so. Accordingly, I expected that he would receive my visits when I should be occasionally in London, but he declined them.

However, when I had been some years settled at Birmingham, he sent an especial messenger, and common friend, to engage me again in his service, having, as that friend assured me, a deep sense of the loss of Lord Ashburton (Mr. Dunning) by death, and of Colonel Barré, by his becoming almost blind, and his want of some able and faithful friend, such as he had experienced in me, with other expressions more flattering than those. I did not choose, however, on any consideration, to leave the very eligible situation in which I now am, but expressed my readiness to do him any service in my power. His lordship's enemies have insinuated that he was not punctual in the payment of my annuity; but the contrary is true. Hitherto nothing could have been more punctual, and I have no reason to suppose that it will ever be otherwise.

At Calne I had another son born to me, whom, at Lord Shelburne's request, I called Henry.

It was at the time of my leaving Lord Shelburne that I found the great value of Mr. and Mrs. Lindsey's friendship, in such a manner as I certainly had no expectation of when our acquaintance commenced, especially by their introducing me to the notice of Mrs. Rayner, one of his hearers and most zealous friends.

Nothwithstanding my allowance from Lord Shelburne was larger than that which I had at Leeds, yet my family growing up, and my expenses, on this and other accounts, increasing more than in proportion, I was barely able to support my removal. But my situation being intimated to Mrs. Rayner, besides smaller sums with which she occasionally assisted me, she gave me a hundred guineas to defray the expense of my removal, and deposited with Mrs. Lindsey, which she soon after gave up to me, four hundred guineas, and to this day has never failed giving me, every year, marks of her friendship. Hers is, indeed, I seriously think, one of the first Christian characters that I was ever acquainted with, having a cultivated, comprehensive mind, equal to any subject of theology or metaphysics, intrepid in the cause of truth, and most rationally pious.

Spending so much of my time in London was the means of increasing my intimacy with both Mr. Lindsey and Mr. Lee, our common friend; who, amidst the bustle of politics, always preserved his attachment to theology, and the cause of truth. The Sunday I always spent with Mr. Lindsey, attending the service of his chapel, and sometimes officiating for him; and with him and Mrs. Lindsey I generally spent the evening of that day at Mr. Lee's, who then admitted no other company, and seldom have I enjoyed society with more relish.

FRIENDSHIP WITH FRANKLIN

My winter's residence in London was the means of improving my acquaintance with Dr. Franklin.[20] I was seldom many days without seeing him, and being members of the same club, we constantly returned together. The difference with America breaking out at this time, our conversation was chiefly of a political nature, and I can bear witness that he was so far from promoting, as was generally supposed, that he took every method in his power to prevent a rupture between the two countries. He urged so much the doctrine of forbearance, that for some time he was unpopular with the Americans on that account, as too much a friend to Great Britain. His advice to them was to bear everything for the present, as they were sure in time to

[20] Benjamin Franklin (1706-1790) was Pennsylvania's "colonial agent" in England at this time.

outgrow all their grievances, as it could not be in the power of the mother country to oppress them long.

He dreaded the war, and often said that if the difference should come to an open rupture, it would be a war of ten years, and he should not live to see the end of it. In reality the war lasted nearly eight years, but he did live to see the happy termination of it. That the issue would be favorable to America, he never doubted. The English, he used to say, may take all our great towns, but that will not give them possession of the country. The last day that he spent in England, having given out that he should leave London the day before, we passed together, without any other company; and much of the time was employed in reading American newspapers, especially accounts of the reception which the Boston Port Bill met with in America, and as he read the addresses to the inhabitants of Boston, from the places in the neighborhood, the tears trickled down his cheeks.

It is much to be lamented that a man of Dr. Franklin's general good character and great influence should have been an unbeliever in Christianity, and also have done so much as he did to make others unbelievers. To me, however, he acknowledged that he had not given so much attention as he ought to have done to the evidences of Christianity, and desired me to recommend to him a few treatises on the subject, such as I thought most deserving of his notice, but not of great length, promising to read them, and give me his sentiments on them. Accordingly, I recommended to him Hartley's evidences of Christianity in his *Observations on Man,* and what I had then written on the subject in my *Institutes of Natural and Revealed Religion;* but the American war breaking out soon after, I do not believe that he ever found himself sufficiently at leisure for the discussion. I have kept up a correspondence with him occasionally ever since; and three of his letters to me were, with his consent, published in his miscellaneous works, in quarto. The first of them, written immediately on his landing in America, is very striking.

About three years before the dissolution of my connection with Lord Shelburne, Dr. Fothergill,[21] with whom I had always lived on terms of much intimacy, having observed, as he said, that many of my experiments had not been carried to their proper extent on account of the expense that would have attended them, proposed to me a subscription from himself and some of his friends, to supply me with whatever sums I should want for that purpose, and named a hundred pounds per annum. This large subscription I declined, lest the discovery of it (by the use that I should, of course, make of it) should give umbrage to Lord Shelburne; but I consented to accept of forty pounds per annum, which from that time he regularly paid me from the contribution of himself, Sir Theodore Jansen, Mr. Constable, and Sir George Savile.

On my leaving Lord Shelburne, which was attended with the loss of one half of my income, Dr. Fothergill proposed an enlargement of my allowance for my experiments, and likewise for my maintenance, without being under the necessity of giving my time to pupils, which I must otherwise have done. And, considering the generosity with which this voluntary offer was made by persons who could well afford it, and who thought me qualified to serve the interests of science, I thought it right to accept of it; and I preferred it to any pension from the court, offers of which were more than once made by persons who thought they could have procured one for me.

HIS PATRONS

As it was my wish to do what might be in my power to show my gratitude to my friends and benefactors that suggested the idea of writing these memoirs, I shall subjoin a list of their names. Some of the subscriptions were made

[21] John Fothergill (1712-1780) was a prominent physician and botanist. See Stephen and Lee, eds., *Dictionary of National Biography*, XX, 66-68.

with a view to defray the expense of my experiments only; but the greater part of the subscribers were persons who were equally friends to my theological studies.

The persons who made me this regular annual allowance were: Dr. Watson and his son, Mr. Wedgwood, Mr. Moseley, Mr. Samuel Salte, Mr. Jeffries, Mr. Radcliffe, Mr. Remington, Mr. Strutt of Derby, Mr. Shore, Mr. Reynolds of Paxton, Messrs. Galton, father and son, and the Rev. Mr. Simpson.

Besides the persons whose names appear in this list, as regular subscribers, there were other persons who, without choosing to be known as such, contributed no less to my support, and some considerably more.

My chief benefactress was Mrs. Rayner, and next to her Dr. Heberden, equally distinguished for his love of religious truth, and his zeal to promote science. Such also is the character of Mr. Tayleur, of Shrewsbury, who has, at different times, remitted me considerable sums, chiefly to defray the expenses incurred by my theological inquiries and publications.

Mr. Parker, of Fleet Street, very generously supplied me with every instrument that I wanted in glass, particularly a capital burning lens, sixteen inches in diameter. All his benefactions in this way would have amounted to a considerable sum. Mr. Wedgwood[22] also, besides his annual benefaction, supplied me with everything that I wanted made of pottery, such as retorts, tubes, etc., which the account of my experiments will show to have been of great use to me.

On my removal to Birmingham commenced my intimacy with Mr. William Russell,[23] whose public spirit and zeal in

22 Josiah Wedgwood (1730-1795), the famous potter, was of great assistance to Priestley in his chemical experiments. For a selection of their letters, see Henry C. Bolton, ed., *Scientific Correspondence of Joseph Priestley* (New York, 1892).

23 William Russell (1740-1818) was engaged in a prosperous export trade from Birmingham and Sheffield to various parts of Europe and

every good cause can hardly be exceeded. My obligations to him were various and constant, so as not to be estimated by sums of money. At his proposal, I doubt not, some of the heads of the congregation made me a present of two hundred pounds to assist me in my theological publications.

Mr. Lee showed himself particularly my friend, at the time that I left Lord Shelburne, assisting me in the difficulties with which I was then pressed, and continuing to befriend me afterwards by seasonable benefactions. By him it was hinted to me during the administration of Lord Rockingham, with whom he had great influence, that I might have a pension from the government to assist in defraying the expense of my experiments. Another hint of the same kind was given me in the beginning of Mr. Pitt's administration, by a bishop, in whose power it was to have procured it from him. But in both cases I declined the overture, wishing to preserve myself independent of everything connected with the court, and preferring the assistance of generous and opulent individuals, lovers of science, and also lovers of liberty. Without assistance I could not have carried on my experiments except on a very small scale, and under great disadvantages.

Mr. Galton, before I had any opportunity of being personally acquainted with him, had, on the death of Dr. Fothergill, taken up his subscription. His son did the same, and the friendship of the latter has added much to the happiness of my situation here [Birmingham]. Seldom, if ever, have I known two persons of such cultivated minds, pleasing manners, and liberal dispositions, as he and Mrs. Galton. The latter had the greatest attachment imaginable to my wife.

America. Like Priestley, he sympathized with the French Revolution, and his home was burned in the famous Birmingham riots of 1791 which also destroyed Priestley's house and laboratory. He subsequently spent some years in France and the United States. See S. H. Jeyes, *The Russells of Birmingham in the French Revolution and in America, 1791-1814* (London, 1911).

Mr. Salte was zealous in promoting the subscriptions to my experiments, and moreover proposed to take one of my sons as an apprentice, without any fee. But my brother-in-law making the same offer, I gave it the preference. Mr. Wedgwood, who has distinguished himself by his application to philosophical pursuits, as well as by his great success in the improvements of his manufactory, was very zealous to serve me, and urged me to accept of a much larger allowance than I chose.

The favors that I received from my two brothers-in-law deserve my most grateful acknowledgments. They acted the part of kind and generous relations, especially at the time when I most wanted assistance. It was in consequence of Mr. John Wilkinson's proposal, who wished to have us nearer to him, that, being undetermined where to settle, I fixed upon Birmingham, where he soon provided a house for me.

My apology for accepting of these large benefactions is, that besides the great expense of my philosophical and even my theological studies, and the education of three sons and a daughter, the reputation I had, justly or unjustly, acquired, brought on me a train of expenses not easy to describe, to avoid, or to estimate; so that without so much as keeping a horse (which the kindness of Mr. Russell made unnecessary), the expense of housekeeping, etc., was more than double the amount of any regular income that I had.

AT BIRMINGHAM

I consider my settlement at Birmingham as the happiest event in my life, being highly favorable to every object I had in view, philosophical or theological. In the former respect I had the convenience of good workmen of every kind, and the society of persons eminent for their knowledge of chemistry, particularly Mr. Watt, Mr. Keir, and Dr. Withering. These, with Mr. Boulton, and Dr. Darwin (who soon left us, by removing from Lichfield to Derby), Mr. Galton, and afterwards Mr. Johnson, of Kenilworth, and myself, dined together every month, calling ourselves the Lunar Society, because the time of our meeting was near the full moon.[24]

With respect to theology, I had the society of Mr. Hawkes, Mr. Blyth, and Mr. Scholefield, and his assistant, Mr. Coates, and, while he lived, Mr. Palmer, before of Macclesfield. We met and drank tea together every fortnight. At this meeting we read all the papers that were sent for the *Theological Repository,* which I revived some time after my coming hither, and in general our conversation was of the same cast as that with my fellow tutors at Warrington.

Within a quarter of a year of my coming to reside at Birmingham, Mr. Hawkes resigned, and I had a unanimous invitation to succeed him as colleague with Mr. Blyth, a man of a truly Christian temper. The congregation we serve is the most liberal, I believe, of any in England; and to this freedom the unwearied labors of Mr. Bourn had eminently contributed.

With this congregation I greatly improved my plan of catechizing and lecturing, and my classes have been well attended. I have also introduced the custom of expounding the Scriptures as I read them, which I had never done before, but which I would earnestly recommend to all ministers. My time being much taken up with my philosophical and other studies, I agreed with the congregation to leave the business of baptizing and visiting the sick to Mr. Blyth,

[24] James Watt (1736-1819) and Matthew Boulton (1728-1809) had formed a partnership for the manufacture of steam engines at Birmingham in 1775. Erasmus Darwin (1731-1802), grandfather of Charles, was a distinguished physician, botanist, and poet. On the Lunar Society see two valuable articles by Robert E. Schofield: "Membership of the Lunar Society of Birmingham," *Annals of Science,* XII (June, 1956), 118-136; and "The Industrial Orientation of the Lunar Society of Birmingham," *Isis,* XLVIII (December, 1957), 408-415.

and to confine my services to the Sundays. I have been minister here between seven and eight years, without any interruption of my happiness; and for this I am sensible I am in a great measure indebted to the friendship of Mr. Russell.

Here I have never long intermitted my philosophical pursuits, and I have published two volumes of experiments, besides communications to the Royal Society.

In theology I have completed my friendly controversy with the Bishop of Waterford on the duration of Christ's ministry. I have published a variety of single sermons, which, with the addition of a few others, I have lately collected and published in one volume, and I am now engaged in a controversy of great extent, and which promises to be of considerable consequence, relating to the person of Christ.

This was occasioned by my *History of the Corruptions of Christianity,* which I composed and published presently after my settlement at Birmingham, the first section of which being rudely attacked in the *Monthly Review,* then by Dr. Horsley, and afterwards by Mr. Howes, and other particular opponents, I undertook to collect from the original writers the state of opinions on the subject in the age succeeding that of the apostles, and I have published the result of my investigation in my *History of Early Opinions Concerning Jesus Christ,* in four volumes octavo. This work has brought me more antagonists, and I now write a pamphlet annually in defense of the Unitarian doctrine against all my opponents.

My only Arian antagonist is Dr. Price, with whom the discussion of the question has proceeded with perfect amity. But no Arian has as yet appeared upon the ground to which I wish to confine the controversy, viz. the state of opinions in the primitive times, as one means of collecting what was the doctrine of the apostles, and the true sense of Scripture on the subject.

Some years ago I resumed the *Theological Repository,* in

which I first advanced my objections to the doctrine of the miraculous conception of Jesus, and his natural fallibility and peccability. These opinions gave at first great alarm, even to my best friends; but that is now in a great measure subsided. For want of sufficient sale I shall be obliged to discontinue this *Repository* for some time.

At present, I thank God, I can say that my prospects are better than they have ever been before, and my own health, and that of my wife, better established, and my hopes as to the dispositions and future settlement of my children satisfactory.

I shall now close this account of myself with some observations of a general nature, but chiefly on account of those circumstances for which I have more particular reason to be thankful to that good Being who has brought me hitherto, and to whom I trust I habitually ascribe whatever my partial friends think the world indebted to me for.

HIS HEALTH AND DISPOSITION

Not to enlarge again on what has been mentioned already, on the fundamental blessings of a religious and liberal education, I have particular reason to be thankful for a happy temperament of body and mind, both derived from my parents. My father, grandmother, and several branches of the family, were remarkably healthy and long-lived; and though my constitution has been far from robust, and was much injured by a consumptive tendency, or rather an ulcer in my lungs, the consequence of improper conduct of myself when I was at school (being often violently heated with exercise, and as often imprudently chilled by bathing, etc.), from which with great difficulty I recovered, it has been excellently adapted to that studious life which has fallen to my lot.

I have never been subject to headaches, or any other complaints that are peculiarly unfavorable to study. I have never found myself less disposed or less qualified for mental exertions of any kind at one time of the day more than another; but all seasons have been equal to me, early or late, before dinner or after, etc.; and so far have I been from suffering by my application to study (which, however, has never been so close or intense as some have imagined) that I have found my health improving from the age of eighteen to the present time; and never have I found myself more free from any disorder than at present; I must, however, except a short time preceding and following my leaving Lord Shelburne, when I labored under a bilious complaint, in which I was troubled with gallstones, which sometimes gave me exquisite pain; but by confining myself to a vegetable diet I perfectly recovered, and have now been so long free from the disorder, that I am under no apprehension of its return.

It has been a singular happiness to me, and a proof, I believe, of a radically good constitution, that I have always slept well, and have awaked with my faculties perfectly vigorous, without any disposition to drowsiness. Also, whenever I have been fatigued with any kind of exertion, I could at any time sit down and sleep; and whatever cause of anxiety I may have had, I have almost always lost sight of it when I have got to bed, and I have generally fallen asleep as soon as I have been warm.

I even think it an advantage to me, and am truly thankful for it, that my health received the check that it did when I was young, since a muscular habit from high health and strong spirits are not, I think, in general accompanied with that sensibility of mind which is both favorable to piety and to speculative pursuits.

To a fundamentally good constitution of body, and the Being who gave it me, I owe an even cheerfulness of temper, which has had but few interruptions. This I inherit from my father, who had uniformly better spirits than any man that I ever knew, and by this means was as happy towards the close of life, when reduced to poverty, and dependent upon others, as in his best days, and who, I am confident, would not have been unhappy, as I have frequently heard him say, in a workhouse.

Though my readers will easily suppose that, in the course of a life so full of vicissitude as mine has been, many things must have occurred to mortify and discompose me, nothing has ever depressed my mind beyond a very short period. My spirits have never failed to recover their natural level; and I have frequently observed, and at first with some surprise, that the most perfect satisfaction I have ever felt has been a day or two after an event that afflicted me the most, and without any change having taken place in the state of things. Having found this to be the case after many of my troubles, the persuasion that it would be so after a new cause of uneasiness has never failed to lessen the effect of its first impression, and, together with my firm belief of the doctrine of necessity (and consequently that of everything being ordered for the best), has contributed to that degree of composure which I have enjoyed through life, so that I have always considered myself as one of the happiest of men.

When I was a young author (though I did not publish anything until I was about thirty), strictures on my writings gave me some disturbance, though I believe even then less than they do most others; but after some time, things of that kind hardly affected me at all, and on this account I may be said to have been well formed for public controversy. But what has always made me easy in any controversy in which I have been engaged has been my fixed resolution frankly to acknowledge any mistake that I might perceive I had fallen into. That I have never been in the least backward to do this in matters of philosophy can never be denied.

HIS MENTAL HABITS

As I have not failed to attend to the phenomena of my own mind, as well as to those of other parts of nature, I have not been insensible of some great defects, as well as some advantages, attending its constitution; having, from an early period, been subject to a most humbling failure of recollection, so that I have sometimes lost all ideas of both persons and things that I have been conversant with. I have so completely forgotten what I have myself published, that in reading my own writings, what I find in them often appears perfectly new to me, and I have more than once made experiments, the results of which had been published by me.

I shall particularly mention one fact of this kind, as it alarmed me much at the time, as a symptom of all my mental powers totally failing me, until I was relieved by the recollection of things of a similar nature having happened to me before. When I was composing the "Dissertations" which are prefixed to my *Harmony of the Gospels,* I had to ascertain something which had been the subject of much discussion relating to the Jewish Passover (I have now forgotten what it was), and for that purpose had to consult and compare several writers. This I accordingly did, and digested the result in a compass of a few paragraphs, which I wrote in shorthand; but having mislaid the paper, and my attention having been drawn off to other things, in the space of a fortnight I did the same thing over again, and should never have discovered that I had done it twice, if, after the second paper was transcribed for the press, I had not accidentally found the former, which I viewed with a degree of terror.

Apprised of this defect, I never fail to note down, as soon as possible, everything that I wish not to forget. The same failing has led me to devise, and to have recourse to, a variety of mechanical expedients to secure and arrange my thoughts, which have been of the greatest use to me in the composition of large and complex works; and what has excited the wonder of some of my readers would only have made them smile if they had seen me at work. But by simple and mechanical methods one man shall do that in a month which shall cost another, of equal ability, whole years to execute. This methodical arrangement of a large work is greatly facilitated by mechanical methods, and nothing contributes more to the perspicuity of a large work than a good arrangement of its parts.

What I have known with respect to myself has tended much to lessen both my admiration and my contempt of others. Could we have entered into the mind of Sir Isaac Newton, and have traced all the steps by which he produced his great works, we might see nothing very extraordinary in the process. And great powers with respect to some things are generally attended with great defects in others; and these may not appear in a man's writings. For this reason it seldom happens but that our admiration of philosophers and writers is lessened by a personal knowledge of them.

As great excellencies are often balanced by great, though not apparent, defects, so great and apparent defects are often accompanied by great, though not apparent, excellencies. Thus my defect in point of recollection, which may be owing to a want of sufficient coherence in the association of ideas formerly impressed, may arise from a mental constitution more favorable to new associations; so that what I have lost with respect to memory, may have been compensated by what is called invention, or new and original combinations of ideas. This is a subject that deserves attention, as well as everything else that relates to the affections of the mind.

Though I have often composed much in a little time, it by no means follows that I could have done much in a given time. For whenever I have done much business in a short time, it has always been with the idea of having time more than sufficient to do it in; so that I have always felt myself at ease, and I could have done nothing, as many can, if I had been hurried.

Knowing the necessity of this state of my mind to the dispatch of business, I have never put off anything to the last moment; and instead of doing that on the morrow which ought to be done today, I have often blamed myself for doing today what had better have been put off until tomorrow; precipitancy being more my fault than procrastination.

It has been a great advantage to me that I have never been under the necessity of retiring from company in order to compose anything. Being fond of domestic life, I got a habit of writing on any subject by the parlor fire, with my wife and children about me, and occasionally talking to them, without experiencing any inconvenience from such interruption. Nothing but reading, or speaking without interruption, has been any obstruction to me. For I could not help attending (as some can) when others spoke in my hearing. These are useful habits, which studious persons in general might acquire if they would; and many persons greatly distress themselves, and others, by the idea that they can do nothing except in perfect solitude or silence.

Another great subject of my thankfulness to a good Providence is my perfect freedom from any embarrassment in my circumstances, so that, without any anxiety on the subject, my supplies have always been equal to my wants; and now that my expenses are increased to a degree that I had no conception of some years ago, I am a richer man than I was, and without laying myself out for the purpose. What is more, this indifference about an increase of fortune has been the means of attaining it. When I began my experiments, I expended on them all the money I could possibly raise, carried on by my ardor in philosophical investigations, and entirely regardless of consequences, except so far as never to contract any debt; and if this had been without success, my imprudence would have been manifest. But having succeeded, I was in time more than indemnified for all that I had expended.

My theological studies, especially those which made it necessary for me to consult the Christian fathers, etc., have also been expensive to me. But I have found my theological friends even more liberal than my philosophical ones, and all beyond my expectations.

In reflecting on my past life, I have often thought of two sayings of Jacob. When he had lost one of his sons, and thought of other things that were afflictions to him, he said, "All these things are against me," at the same time that they were in reality making for him. So the impediment in my speech, and the difficulties of my situation at Needham, I now see as much cause to be thankful for, as for the most brilliant scenes in my life.

I have also applied to myself what Jacob said on his return from Padan Aram, "With my staff I went over this Jordan, and now I am become two bands"; when I consider how little I carried with me to Needham and Nantwich, how much more I had to carry to Warrington, how much more still to Leeds, how much more than that to Calne, and then to Birmingham.

Yet, frequently as I have changed my situation, and always for the better, I can truly say that I never wished for any change on my own account. I should have been contented even at Needham, if I could have been unmolested, and had bare necessaries. This freedom from anxiety was remarkable in my father, and therefore is in a manner hereditary to me, but it has been much increased by reflection; having frequently observed, especially with respect to Christian ministers, how often it has contributed to embitter their lives, without being of any use to them. Some attention to the improvement of a man's circumstances is, no doubt, right, because no man can tell what occasion he may have for money, especially if he have children, and therefore I do not recommend my example to others. But I am thankful to that good Providence which always took more care of me than ever I took of myself.

Hitherto I have had great reason to be thankful with respect to my children, as they have a prospect of enjoying a good share of health, and a sufficient capacity for performing the duties of their stations. They have also good dispositions, and, as much as could be expected at their age, a sense of religion. But as I hope they will live to see this work, I say the less on this subject, and I hope they will consider what I say in their favor as an incitement to exert themselves to act a Christian and useful part in life; that the care that I and their mother have taken of their instruction may not be lost upon them, and that they may secure a happy meeting with us in a better world.

I esteem it a singular happiness to have lived in an age and country in which I have been at full liberty both to investigate, and by preaching and writing to propagate, religious truth; that though the freedom I have used for this purpose was for some time disadvantageous to me, it was not long so, and that my present situation is such that I can with the greatest openness urge whatever appears to me to be the truth of the gospel, not only without giving the least offense, but with the entire approbation of those with whom I am particularly connected.

As to the dislike which I have drawn upon myself by my writings, whether that of the Calvinistic party, in or out of the Church of England, those who rank with rational Dissenters (but who have been exceedingly offended at my carrying my inquiries farther than they wished any person to do), or whether they be unbelievers, I am thankful that it gives less disturbance to me than it does to themselves; and that their dislike is much more than compensated by the cordial esteem and approbation of my conduct by a few, whose minds are congenial to my own, and especially that the number of such persons increases.

Birmingham, 1787

CONTINUATION TO 1795

When I wrote the preceding part of these memoirs, I was happy, as must have appeared in the course of them, in the prospect of spending the remainder of my life at Birmingham, where I had every advantage for pursuing my studies, both philosophical and theological; but it pleased the Sovereign Disposer of all things to appoint for me other removals, and the manner in which they were brought about was more painful to me than the removals themselves. I am far, however, from questioning the wisdom or the goodness of the appointments, respecting myself or others.

To resume the account of my pursuits, where the former part of the memoirs left it, I must observe that, in the prosecution of my experiments, I was led to maintain the doctrine of phlogiston against Mr. Lavoisier, and other chemists in France, whose opinions were adopted not only by almost all the philosophers of that country, but by those in England and Scotland also.[25] My friends, however, of the Lunar Society, were never satisfied with the anti-phlogistic doctrine. My experiments and observations on this subject were published in various papers in the *Philosophical Transactions.* At Birmingham I also published a new edition of my publications on the subject of air, and others connected with it, reducing the six volumes to three, which, with his consent, I dedicated to the Prince of Wales.

In theology, I continued my *Defences of Unitarianism,* until it appeared to myself and my friends that my antagonists produced nothing to which it was of any consequence to reply. But I did not, as I had proposed, publish any address to the bishops, or to the legislature, on the subject. The former I wrote, but did not publish. I left it, however, in the hands of Mr. Belsham,[26] when I came to America, that he might dispose of it as he should think proper.

The pains that I took to ascertain the state of early opinions concerning Jesus Christ, and the great misapprehensions I perceived in all the ecclesiastical historians, led

[25] See below, pp. 231-259.

[26] Thomas Belsham (1750-1829) was the leading English Unitarian in the generation after Priestley and Lindsey. Belsham succeeded Lindsey as pastor of the Essex Street Chapel in 1805. See Wilbur, *Unitarianism,* pp. 326-330.

me to undertake a *General History of the Christian Church to the Fall of the Western Empire,* which accordingly I wrote in two volumes octavo, and dedicated to Mr. Shore. This work I mean to continue.

At Birmingham I wrote the "Second Part" of my *Letters to a Philosophical Unbeliever,* and dedicated the whole to Mr. Tayleur, of Shrewsbury, who had afforded the most material assistance in the publication of many of my theological works, without which, the sale being inconsiderable, I should not have been able to publish them at all.

Before I left Birmingham, I preached a funeral sermon for my friend, Dr. Price, and another for Mr. Robinson, of Cambridge, who died with us on a visit to preach our annual charity-school sermon. I also preached the last annual sermon to the friends of the college at Hackney. All these three sermons were published.

About two years before I left Birmingham, the question about the Test and Corporation Acts was much agitated both in and out of Parliament.[27] This, however, was altogether without any concurrence of mine. I only delivered and published a sermon on the 5th of November, 1789, recommending the most peaceable method of pursuing our object. Mr. Madan, however, the most respectable clergyman in the town, preaching and publishing a very inflammatory sermon on the subject, inveighing in the bitterest manner against the Dissenters in general, and myself in particular, I addressed a number of *Familiar Letters to the Inhabitants of Birmingham* in our defense. This produced a reply from him, and other letters from me. All mine were written in an ironical and rather a pleasant manner, and in some of the last of them I introduced a farther reply to Mr. Burn, another clergyman in Birmingham, who had addressed to me *Letters on the Infallibility of the Apostolic Testimony Concerning the Person of Christ,* after replying to his first set of letters in a separate publication.

[27] The Test and Corporation Acts, which had been passed in the time of Charles II, excluded religious Dissenters from public office.

THE BIRMINGHAM RIOTS

From these small pieces I was far from expecting any serious consequences. But the Dissenters in general being very obnoxious to the court, and it being imagined, though without any reason, that I had been the chief promoter of the measures which gave them offense, the clergy, not only in Birmingham, but through all England, seemed to make it their business, by writing in the public papers, by preaching, and other methods, to inflame the minds of the people against me; and on occasion of the celebration of the anniversary of the French Revolution, on July 14, 1791, by several of my friends, but with which I had little to do, a mob, encouraged by some persons in power, first burned the meetinghouse in which I preached, then another meetinghouse in the town, and then my dwelling house, demolishing my library, apparatus, and, as far as they could, everything belonging to me. They also burned, or much damaged, the houses of many Dissenters, chiefly my friends, the particulars of which I need not recite, as they will be found in two *Appeals*, which I published on the subject, written presently after the riots.

Being in some personal danger on this occasion, I went to London; and so violent was the spirit of party which then prevailed, that I believe I could hardly have been safe in any other place.

There, however, I was perfectly so, though I continued to be an object of troublesome attention, until I left the country altogether. It showed no small degree of courage and friendship in Mr. William Vaughan to receive me into his house, and also in Mr. Salte, with whom I spent a month at Tottenham; but it showed more in Dr. Price's congregation, at Hackney, to invite me to succeed him, which they did, though not unanimously, some time after my arrival in London.

In this situation I found myself as happy as I had been at Birmingham; and, contrary to general expectation, I opened my lectures to young persons with great success, being attended by many from London; and though I lost some of the hearers, I left the congregation in a better situation than that in which I found it.

On the whole, I spent my time even more happily at Hackney than ever I had done before, having every advantage for my philosophical and theological studies, in some respects superior to what I had enjoyed at Birmingham, especially from my easy access to Mr. Lindsey, and my frequent intercourse with Mr. Belsham, professor of divinity in the New College, near which I lived. Never, on this side the grave, do I expect to enjoy myself so much as I did by the fireside of Mr. Lindsey, conversing with him and Mrs. Lindsey on theological and other subjects, or in my frequent walks with Mr. Belsham, whose views of most important subjects were, like Mr. Lindsey's, the same with my own.

I found, however, my society much restricted with respect to my philosophical acquaintance, most of the members of the Royal Society shunning me on account of my religious or political opinions, so that I at length withdrew myself from them, and gave my reasons for so doing in the preface to my *Observations and Experiments on the Generation of Air from Water,* which I published at Hackney; for, with the assistance of my friends, I had in a great measure replaced my apparatus, and had resumed my experiments, though after the loss of nearly two years.

Living in the neighborhood of the New College, I voluntarily undertook to deliver lectures to the pupils on the subject of "History and General Policy," which I had composed at Warrington, and also on "Experimental Philosophy, particularly including Chemistry," the "Heads" of which I drew up for this purpose, and afterwards published. In being useful to this institution, I found a source of considerable satisfaction to myself. Indeed, I have always had a high degree of enjoyment in lecturing to young persons, though more on theological subjects than on any other.

After the riots in Birmingham, I wrote *An Appeal to the*

Public on the subject, and that being replied to by the clergy of the place, I wrote a "Second Part," to which, though they had pledged themselves to do it, they made no reply; so that, in fact, the criminality of the magistrates, and other principal high churchmen at Birmingham, in promoting the riot, remains acknowledged. Indeed, many circumstances which have appeared since that time, show that the friends of the court, if not the prime ministers themselves, were the favorers of that riot, having, no doubt, thought to intimidate the friends of liberty by the measure.

To my *Appeal* I subjoined various "Addresses" that were sent to me from several descriptions of persons in England and abroad; and from them I will not deny that I received much satisfaction, as it appeared that the friends of liberty, civil and religious, were of opinion that I was a sufferer in that cause. From France I received a considerable number of addresses; and when the present National Convention was called, I was invited by many of the departments to be a member of it; but I thought myself more usefully employed at home, and that I was but ill qualified for a business which required knowledge which none but a native of the country could possess, and therefore declined the honor that was proposed to me.

But no addresses gave me so much satisfaction as those from my late congregation, and especially of the young persons belonging to it, who had attended my lectures. They are a standing testimony of the zeal and fidelity with which I did my duty with respect to them, and which I value highly.

Besides congratulatory addresses, I received much pecuniary assistance from various persons and bodies of men, which more than compensated for my pecuniary losses, though what was awarded me at the assizes fell two thousand pounds short of them; but my brother-in-law, Mr. John Wilkinson, from whom I had not at that time any expectation, in consequence of my son's leaving his employment, was the most generous on the occasion. Without any solicitation, he immediately sent me five hundred pounds, and afterwards transferred to me ten thousand pounds, which he had deposited in the French funds, and until that be productive, he allows me two hundred pounds per annum.

After the riots, I published my *Letters to the Sweden-borgian Society,* which I had composed and prepared for the press just before.

Mr. Wakefield living in the neighborhood of the College, and publishing at this time his objections to public worship, they made a great impression on many of our young men, and in his preface he reflected much on the character of Dr. Price. On both these accounts I thought myself called upon to reply to him, which I did in a series of *Letters to a Young Man.* But though he made several angry replies, I never noticed any of them. In this situation I also answered Mr. Evanson's *Observance on the Dissonance of the Evan-gelists,* in *A Second Set of Letters to a Young Man.* He also replied to me, but I was satisfied with what I had done, and did not continue the controversy.

Besides the *Sermon* which I delivered on my acceptance of the invitation to the meeting at Hackney, in the preface to which I gave a detailed account of my system of cate-chizing, I published two *Fast Sermons,* for the years 1793 and 1794, in the latter of which I gave my ideas of ancient prophecies, compared with the then state of Europe; and in the preface to it I gave an account of my reasons for leaving the country. I also published a *Farewell Discourse.*

But the most important of my publications in this situa-tion were a series of *Letters to the Philosophers and Poli-ticians of France on the Subject of Religion.* I thought that the light in which I then stood in that country gave me some advantage in my attempts to enforce the evidence of natural and revealed religion. I also published a set of *Discourses on the Evidences of Revealed Religion,* which I first delivered by public notice, and the delivery of which

was attended by great numbers. They were printed just
before I left England.

REMOVAL TO PENNSYLVANIA

As the reasons for this step in my conduct are given at
large in the preface to my *Fast Sermon,* I shall not dwell
upon them here. The bigotry of the country in general made
it impossible for me to place my sons in it to any advantage.
William had been some time in France, and on the breaking
out of the troubles in that country he had embarked for
America, where his two brothers met him. My own situation, if not hazardous, was become unpleasant, so that I
thought my removal would be of more service to the cause
of truth than my longer stay in England. At length, therefore, with the approbation of all my friends, without exception, but with great reluctance on my own part, I came to
that resolution, I being at a time of life in which I could not
expect much satisfaction as to friends and society, com-
parable to that which I left, in which the resumption of my
philosophical pursuits must be attended with great disadvantage, and in which success in my still more favorite pursuit, the propagation of Unitarianism, was still more uncertain. It was also painful to me to leave my daughter, Mr.
Finch having the greatest aversion to leave his relations
and friends in England.

At the time of my leaving England, my son, in conjunction with Mr. Cooper, and other English emigrants, had a
scheme for a large settlement for the friends of liberty in
general, near the head of the Susquehanna, in Pennsylvania;[28] and taking it for granted that it would be carried
into effect, after landing at New York, I went to Philadelphia, and thence came to Northumberland, a town the
nearest to the proposed settlement, thinking to reside there

[28] See Dumas Malone, *The Public Life of Thomas Cooper* (New
Haven, 1926), pp. 75-83.

until some progress had been made in it. The settlement was given up; but being here, and my wife and myself liking the place, I have determined to take up residence here, though subject to many disadvantages. Philadelphia was excessively expensive, and this comparatively a cheap place; and my sons, settling in the neighborhood, will be less exposed to temptation, and more likely to form habits of sobriety and industry. They will also be settled at much less expense than in or near a large town. We hope, after some time, to be joined by a few of our friends from England, that a readier communication will be opened with Philadelphia, and that the place will improve, and become more eligible in other respects.[29]

When I was at sea, I wrote some *Observations on the Cause of the Present Prevalence of Infidelity,* which I published, and prefixed to a new edition of the *Letters to the Philosophers and Politicians of France.* I have also published my *Fast and Farewell Sermons,* and my *Small Tracts* in defense of Unitarianism; also a *Continuation* of those letters, and a "Third Part" of *Letters to a Philosophical Unbeliever,* in answer to Mr. Paine's *Age of Reason.*

The *Observations on the Prevalence of Infidelity* I have much enlarged, and intend soon to print; but I am chiefly employed on the continuation of my *History of the Christian Church.*

Northumberland, March 24, 1795, in which I have completed the sixty-second year of my age.[30]

[29] The handsome white frame house which Priestley built in Northumberland is still standing. Now owned by the Commonwealth of Pennsylvania, it is open to visitors at regular hours.

[30] On Priestley's last years see Ira V. Brown, "Joseph Priestley: Exile in Pennsylvania," *American Heritage,* V (Spring, 1954), 12-15; and Elizabeth M. Geffen, *Philadelphia Unitarianism, 1796-1861* (Philadelphia, 1961).

Priestley's six years as a tutor at Warrington Academy (1761-1767) resulted in the production of various works stemming from the courses he taught and his interest in the principles of pedagogy. In 1765 he published An Essay on a Course of Liberal Education for Civil and Active Life, *in which he set forth something of his general philosophy of education. While Priestley did not use the term, it is clear that he was advocating in essence the introduction of "social studies" — history, government, and economics — into the academies and the universities. His insistence on including "Civil History" and "Civil Policy" in the curriculum was unusual for the time.[1] In the context of the prevailing classical curriculum of the period, he was really advocating a more "practical" education. In this essay Priestley also commented on his favorite teaching methods. The text used here represents the last of several revisions of the original work.[2] It was published in Philadelphia in 1803, the year before the author's death. This explains the several references to the United States.*

---

[1] On the importance of Priestley's work in this field see J. W. Ashley Smith, *The Birth of Modern Education: The Contribution of the Dissenting Academies, 1660-1800* (London, 1954), pp. 152-159.

[2] John T. Rutt, ed., *The Theological and Miscellaneous Works of Joseph Priestley* (25 vols., London, 1817-1832), XXIV, 7-25.

An Essay on a Course of
Liberal Education for Civil
and Active Life

It seems to be a defect in our present system of public education, that a proper course of studies is not provided for gentlemen who are designed to fill the principal stations of active life, distinct from those which are adapted to the learned professions. We have hardly any medium between an education for the countinghouse, consisting of writing, arithmetic, and merchants' accounts, and a method of institution in the abstract sciences; so that we have nothing liberal that is worth the attention of gentlemen whose views neither of these two opposite plans may suit.

Formerly, none but the clergy were thought to have any occasion for learning. It was natural, therefore, that the whole plan of education, from the grammar school to the finishing at the university, should be calculated for their use. If a few other persons, who were not designed for holy orders, offered themselves for education, it could not be expected that a course of studies should be provided for them only. And indeed, as all those persons who superintended the business of education were of the clerical order, and had themselves been taught nothing but the rhetoric, logic, and school-divinity, or civil law, which comprised the whole compass of human learning for several centuries, it could not be expected that they should entertain larger or more liberal views of education; and still less, that they should strike out a course of study for the use of men who were universally thought to have no need of study; and of whom few were so sensible of their own wants as to desire any such advantage.

Besides, in those days, the great ends of human society seem to have been but little understood. Men of the greatest rank, fortune, and influence, and who took the lead in all the affairs of state, had no idea of the great objects of wise and extensive policy; and therefore could never apprehend that any fund of knowledge was requisite for the most eminent stations in the community. Few persons imagined what were the true sources of wealth, power, and happiness, in a nation. Commerce was little understood, or even attended to; and so slight was the connection of the different nations of Europe, that general politics were very contracted. And thus, men's views being narrow, little previous furniture of mind was requisite to conduct them.

The consequence of all this was that the advances which were made to a more perfect and improved state of society were very slow; and the present happier state of things was brought about rather by an accidental concurrence of circumstances than by any efforts of human wisdom and foresight. We see the hand of Divine Providence in those revolutions which have gradually given a happier turn to affairs, while men have been the passive and blind instruments of their own felicity.

But the situation of things at present is vastly different from what it was two or three centuries ago. The objects of human attention are prodigiously multiplied; the connections of states are extended; a reflection upon our present advantages, and the steps by which we have arrived to the degree of power and happiness we now enjoy, has shown us the true sources of them; and so thoroughly awakened are all the states of Europe to a sense of their true interests that we are convinced the same supine inattention with which affairs were formerly conducted is no longer safe; and that, without superior degrees of wisdom and vigor in political measures, everything we have hitherto gained will infallibly be lost, and be quickly transferred to our more intelligent and vigilant neighbors. In this critical posture of affairs, more lights and superior industry are requisite, both to ministers of state, and to all persons who have any influence in schemes of public and national advantage; and consequently a different and a better furniture of mind is requisite to be brought into the business of life.

This is certainly a call upon us to examine the state of education in this country, and to consider how those years are employed which men pass previous to their entering into the world; for upon this, their future behavior and success must in a great measure depend. A transition which is not easy can never be made with advantage; and therefore it is certainly our wisdom to contrive that the studies of youth should tend to fit them for the business of manhood; and that the objects of their attention and turn of thinking in younger life should not be too remote from the destined employment of their riper years. If this be not attended to, they must necessarily be mere novices upon entering the great world, be almost unavoidably embarrassed in their conduct, and, after all the time and expense bestowed upon their education, be indebted to a series of blunders for the most useful knowledge they will ever acquire.

In what manner soever those gentlemen who are not of any learned profession, but who in other capacities have rendered the most important services to their country, came by that knowledge which made them capable of it, I appeal to themselves, whether any considerable share of it was acquired till after they had finished their studies at the university. So remote is the general course of study at places of the most liberal education among us from the business of civil life, that many gentlemen, who have had the most liberal education their country could afford, have looked upon the real advantage of such an education as very problematical, and have either wholly dispensed with it in their own children, or, if they have sent their sons through the usual circle of the schools, it has been chiefly through the influence of custom and fashion, or with a view to their forming connections which might be useful to them in future life. This appears by the little solicitude they show about their sons being grounded in those sciences in which they themselves might possibly have been considerable proficients, when they applied to them; but which, from their being foreign to the business of life in which they were afterwards engaged, they have now wholly forgotten.

Indeed, the severe and proper discipline of a grammar school is become a common topic of ridicule; and few young gentlemen, except those who are designed for some of the learned professions, are made to submit to the rigors of it. And it is manifest, that when no foundation is laid in a grammatical knowledge of the learned languages (which, in a large or public school, cannot be done without very strict discipline, and a severe application on the part both of the master and scholar), youth can be but ill qualified to receive any advantage from a university education. Young gentlemen themselves so frequently hear the learning which is taught in schools and universities ridiculed, that they often make themselves easy with giving a very superficial attention to it, concluding from the turn of conversation in the company they generally fall into, and which they expect to keep, that a few years will confound all distinction of learned and unlearned, and make it impossible to be known whether a man had improved his time at the university, or not.

These evils certainly call for redress; and let a person be reckoned a projector, a visionary, or whatever anybody pleases, that man is a friend of his country who observes and endeavors to supply any defects in the methods of educating youth. A well-meaning and a sensible man may be mistaken, but a good intention, especially if it be not wholly unaccompanied with good sense, ought to be exempted from censure. What has occurred to me upon this subject I shall, without any further apology, propose to my fellow citizens and fellow tutors, hoping that it will meet with a candid reception. It is true, I can boast no long or extensive experience in the business of education, but I have not been a mere spectator in this scene; which I hope may exempt me from the ridicule and contempt which have almost ever fallen upon the schemes of those persons who have written only from their closets; and, without any experience, have rashly attempted to handle this subject, in which, of all others, experiments only ought to guide theory, upon which hardly anything worth attending to can be advanced *a priori;* and where the greatest geniuses, for want of experience, have been the greatest visionaries, laying schemes the least capable of being reduced to practice, or the most absurd if they had been put in practice.

Let it be remembered, that the difficulty under present consideration is how to fill up with advantage those years which immediately precede a young gentleman's engaging in those higher spheres of active life in which he is destined to move. Within the departments of active life, I suppose to be comprehended all those stations in which a man's conduct will considerably affect the liberty and the property of his countrymen, and the riches, the strength, and the security of his country; the first and most important ranks of which are filled by gentlemen of large property, who have themselves the greatest interest in the fate of their country, and who are within the influence of an honorable ambition to appear in the character of magistrates and legislators in the state, or of standing near the helm of affairs, and guiding the secret springs of government.

The profession of law, also, certainly comes within the above description of civil and active life, if a man hope to be anything more than a practicing attorney; the profession of arms too, if a gentleman have any expectation of arriving at the higher ranks of military preferment; and the business of merchandise, if we look beyond the servile drudgery of the warehouse or countinghouse. Divines and physicians I consider to be interested in this subject only as gentlemen and general scholars, or as persons who converse and have influence with gentlemen engaged in active life, without any particular view to their respective professions.

PROPOSED NEW SUBJECTS

That the parents and friends of young gentlemen destined to act in any of these important spheres may not think a liberal education unnecessary to them, and that the young gentlemen themselves may enter with spirit into the enlarged views of their friends and tutors, I would humbly propose some new articles of academical instruction, such as have a nearer and more evident connection with the business of active life, and which may therefore bid fairer to engage the attention, and rouse the thinking powers of young gentlemen of an active genius. The subjects I would recommend are Civil History, and more especially the important objects of Civil Policy: such as the theory of laws, government, manufactures, commerce, naval force, etc., with whatever may be demonstrated from history to have contributed to the flourishing state of nations, to rendering a people happy and populous at home, and formidable abroad; together with those articles of previous information without which it is impossible to understand the nature, connections, and mutual influences of those great objects.

To give a clearer idea of the subjects I would propose to the study of youth at places of public and liberal education, I have subjoined plans of three distinct courses of lectures, which, I apprehend, may be subservient to this design, divided into such portions as, experience has taught me, may be conveniently discussed in familiar lectures of an hour each.

The first course is on the "Study of History" in general, and in its most extensive sense. It will be seen to consist of such articles as tend to enable a young gentleman to read history with understanding, and to reap the most valuable

fruits of that engaging study. I shall not go over the particulars of the course in this place; let the syllabus speak
for itself. Let it only be observed, that my view was not
merely to make history intelligible to persons who may
choose to read it for their amusement, but principally to
facilitate its subserviency to the highest uses to which it
can be applied; to contribute to its forming the able statesman, and the intelligent and useful citizen. It is true that
this is comprising a great deal more than the title of the
course will suggest. But under the head of "Objects of
Attention to a Reader of History," it was found convenient
to discuss the principal of those subjects which every gentleman of a liberal education is expected to understand,
though they do not generally fall under any division of the
sciences in a course of academical education; and yet, without a competent knowledge of these subjects, no person can
be qualified to serve his country except in the lowest capacities.

This course of lectures, it is also presumed, will be found
to contain a comprehensive system of that kind of knowledge which is peculiarly requisite to gentlemen who intend
to travel. For, since the great objects of attention to a reader
of history, and to a gentleman upon his travels, are evidently the same, it must be of equal service to them both,
to have their importance and mutual influences pointed
out to them.

It will likewise be evident to any person who inspects
this syllabus, that the subject of commerce has by no means
been overlooked. And it is hoped that when those gentlemen who are intended to serve themselves and their country in the respectable character of merchants have heard
the great maxims of commerce discussed in a scientifical
and connected manner, as they deserve, they will not easily
be influenced by notions adopted in a random and hasty
manner, and from superficial views of things, whereby they
might otherwise be induced to enter into measures seemingly gainful at present, but in the end prejudicial to their

country, and to themselves and their posterity, as members of it.

The next course of lectures, the plan of which is briefly delineated, is upon the "History of England," and is designed to be an exemplification of the manner of studying history recommended in the former course, in which the great uses of it are shown, and the actual progress of every important object of attention distinctly marked, from the earliest accounts of the island to the present time.

To make young gentlemen still more thoroughly acquainted with their own country, a third course of lectures (in connection with the two others) is subjoined, viz. on its "Present Constitution and Laws." But the particular uses of these two courses of lectures need not be pointed out here, as they are sufficiently explained in the introductory addresses prefixed to each of them.

That an acquaintance with the subjects of these lectures is calculated to form the statesman, the military commander, the lawyer, the merchant, and the accomplished country gentleman, cannot be disputed. The principal objection that may be made to this scheme is the introduction of these subjects into academies, and submitting them to the examination of youth, of the age at which they are usually sent to such places of education. It will be said by some that these subjects are too deep and too intricate for their tender age and weak intellects; and that, after all, it can be no more than an outline of these great branches of knowledge that can be communicated to youth.

To prevent being misunderstood, let it be observed, that I would not propose that this course of studies should be entered upon by a young gentleman till he be sixteen or seventeen years of age, or at least, and only in some particular cases, fifteen years; at which time of life, it is well known to all persons concerned in the education of youth, that their faculties have attained a considerable degree of ripeness, and that, by proper address, they are as capable of entering into any subject of speculation as they ever will be. What is there in any of the subjects mentioned above which requires more acuteness or comprehension than algebra, geometry, logic, or metaphysics; to which students are generally made to apply about the same age?

And if it be only an outline of political and commercial knowledge, etc., that can be acquired in the method I propose, let it be observed that it is nothing more than the rudiments of any science which can be taught in a place of education. The master of science is a character of which nothing more than the outline is ever drawn at an academy or the university. It is never finished but by assiduous and long continued application afterwards. And supposing that only the first rudiments, the grand, plain and leading maxims of policy, with respect to arts, arms, commerce, etc., be communicated to a young gentleman, if they be such maxims as he is really destined to pursue in life, is it not better that he have some knowledge of them communicated early, and at a time when it is likely to make the deepest and most lasting impression, than to be thrown into the practice without any regular theory at all? It is freely acknowledged, that the man of business is not to be finished at an academy, any more than the man of science. This character is not the child of instruction and theory only; but, on the other hand, neither is it the mere offspring of practice without instruction. And certainly, if a knowledge of these subjects be of any use, the earlier they are attended to (after a person is capable of attending to them to any purpose), and the more regular is the method in which they are taught, the greater chance there is for their being thoroughly understood.

When subjects which have a connection are explained in a regular system, every article is placed where the most light is reflected upon it from the neighboring subjects. The plainest things are discussed in the first place, and are made to serve as axioms, and the foundation of those which are treated of afterwards. Without this regular method of studying the elements of any science, it seems impossible ever to gain a clear and comprehensive view of it. But after a regular institution, any particular part of a plan of instruction may be enlarged at any time with ease, and without confusion. With how much more ease and distinctness would a person be able to deliver himself upon any subject of policy or commerce, who had had everything belonging to it explained to him in its proper connection, than another person of equal abilities who should only have considered the subject in a random manner, reading any treatise that might happen to fall in his way, or adopting his maxims from the company he might accidentally keep, and, consequently, liable to be imposed upon by the interested views with which men very often both write and speak. For these are subjects on which almost every writer or speaker is to be suspected; so much has party and interest to do with everything relating to them.

Since, however, these subjects do enter into all sensible conversation, especially with gentlemen engaged in civil life, it is a circumstance extremely favorable to the study of them, that conversation will come greatly in aid of the lectures the young gentlemen hear upon them. It cannot fail to rouse their attention, and increase their application to their studies, when they hear the subjects of them discussed by their fathers and the elder part of their friends and acquaintance, for whose understanding and turn of thinking they have conceived a great esteem. They will listen with greater attention to grave and judicious persons, and become much more fond of their company, when they are able to understand their conversation, and to enter occasionally into it; when they can say that such a sentiment or fact was advanced in their lectures, and that one of their fellow pupils or themselves made such a remark upon it. It is no wonder that many young gentlemen give but little attention to their present studies, when they find that the subjects of them are never discussed in any sensible conversations to which they are ever admitted. If studying these subjects only serve to give the generality of young gentlemen a taste for conversing upon them, and qualify them to appear to tolerable advantage in such conversations, the variety of lights in which they are viewed upon those occasions cannot fail to make them more generally understood; and the better these subjects are understood by the bulk of the nation, the more probable it is that the nation will be benefited by such knowledge.

If I were asked what branches of knowledge a young gentleman should in my judgment be master of before he can study this course with advantage, I would answer, that a knowledge of the learned languages is not absolutely necessary, but is very desirable; especially such an insight into Latin as may enable a person to read the easier classics, and supersede the use of a dictionary, with respect to those more difficult English words which are derived from the Latin. The student of this course should understand French very well; he should also be a pretty good accountant, be acquainted with the more useful branches of practical mathematics; and, if possible, have some knowledge of algebra and geometry, which ought to be indispensable in every plan of liberal education.

POSSIBLE OBJECTIONS

Some will be ready to object to these studies, that a turn for speculation unfits men for business. I answer, that nothing is more true, if those speculations be foreign to their employment. It is readily acknowledged, that a turn for poetry and the belles-lettres might hurt a tradesman; that the study of natural philosophy might interfere with the practice of the law; and metaphysics and the abstract sciences with the duty of a soldier. But it can never be said that a counselor can be unfitted for his practice by a taste for the study of the law, or that a commander would be the worse soldier for studying books written on the art of war; nor can it be supposed that a merchant would do less busi-

ness, or to worse purpose, for having acquired a fondness
for such writers as have best explained the principles of
trade and commerce, and for being qualified to read them
with understanding and judgment.

It must be allowed, that the mechanical parts of any employment will be best performed by persons who have no
knowledge or idea of anything beyond the mere practice.
When a man's faculties are wholly employed upon one
single thing, it is more probable that he will make himself
completely master of it; and, having no further or higher
views, he will more contentedly and more cheerfully give
his whole time to his proper object. But no man who can
afford the expense of a liberal education enters upon any
business with a view to spend his whole life in the mere
mechanical part of it, and in performing a task imposed
on him. A man of spirit will laudably aspire to be a master
in his turn; when he must be directed by his own lights,
and when he will find himself miserably bewildered, if he
have acquired no more knowledge than was sufficient for
him while he followed the direction of others. Besides, in
the case of merchandise, if one branch fail, there is no resource but in more extensive knowledge. A man who has
been used to go only in one beaten track, and who has had
no idea given him of any other, for fear of his being tempted to leave it, will be wholly at a loss when it happens that
that track can be no longer used; while a person who has
a general idea of the whole course of the country may be
able to strike out another and perhaps a better road than
the former.

I am aware of a different kind of objection, from another
quarter, which it behooves me not to overlook. The advocates for the old plan of education, and who dislike innovations in the number or the distribution of the sciences
in which lectures are given, may object to the admission
of these studies, as in danger of attracting the attention of
those students who are designed for the learned professions,
and thereby interfering too much with that which has been

found, by the experience of generations, to be the best for scholars, the proper subjects of which are sufficient to fill up all their time, without these supernumerary articles. I answer, that the subjects of these lectures are by no means necessary articles of a mere scholastic education; but that they are such as scholars ought to have some acquaintance with, and that without some acquaintance with them, they must on many occasions appear to great disadvantage in the present state of knowledge.

Time was when scholars might, with a good grace, disclaim all pretensions to any branch of knowledge, but what was taught in the universities. Perhaps they would be the more revered by the vulgar on account of such ignorance, as an argument of their being more abstracted from the world. Few books were written but by critics and antiquaries for the use of men like themselves. The literati of those days had comparatively little free intercourse but among themselves; the learned world and the common world being much more distinct from one another than they are now. Scholars by profession read, wrote, and conversed in no language but the Roman. They would have been ashamed to have expressed themselves in bad Latin, but not in the least of being guilty of any impropriety in the use of their mother tongue, which they considered as belonging only to the vulgar.

But those times of revived antiquity have had their use, and are now no more. We are obliged to the learned labors of our forefathers for searching into all the remains of antiquity, and illustrating valuable ancient authors; but their maxims of life will not suit the world as it is at present. The politeness of the times has brought the learned and the unlearned into more familiar intercourse than they had before. They find themselves obliged to converse upon the same topics. The subjects of modern history, policy, arts, manufactures, commerce, etc., are the general topics of all sensible conversation. Everything is said in our own tongue; little is even written in a foreign or dead language; and every British author is studious of writing with propriety in his native English. Criticism, which was formerly the great business of a scholar's life, is now become the amusement of a leisure hour, and this but to a few; so that a hundredth part of the time which was formerly given to criticism and antiquities, is enough in this age to gain a man the character of a profound scholar. The topics of sensible conversation are likewise the favorite subjects of all the capital writings of the present age, which are read with equal avidity by gentlemen, merchants, lawyers, physicians, and divines.

Now, when the course of reading, thinking, and conversation, even among scholars, is become so very different from what it was, is it not reasonable that the plan of even scholastic education should in some measure vary with it? The necessity of the thing has already in many instances forced a change, and the same increasing necessity will either force a greater and more general change, or we must not be surprised to find our schools, academies, and universities deserted, as wholly unfit to qualify men to appear with advantage in the present age.

In many private schools and academies, we find several things taught now which were never made the subjects of systematical instruction in former times; and in those of our universities, in which it is the interest of the tutors to make their lectures of real use to their pupils, and where lectures are not mere matters of form, the professors find the necessity of delivering themselves in English. And the evident propriety of the thing must necessarily make this practice more general, notwithstanding the most superstitious regard to established customs.

But let the professors conduct themselves by what maxims they please, the students will of course be influenced by the taste of the company they keep in the world at large, to which young gentlemen in this age have an earlier admission than they had formerly. How can it be expected that the present set of students for divinity should apply to the study of the dead languages with the assiduity of their fathers and grandfathers, when they find so many of the uses of those languages no longer subsisting? What can they think it will avail them to make the purity of the Latin style their principal study, for several years of the most improvable part of their life, when they are sensible that they shall have little more occasion for it than other gentlemen, or than persons in common life, when they have left the university? And how can it be otherwise, but that their private reading and studies should sometimes be different from the course of their public instructions, when the favorite authors of the public, the merits of whom they hear discussed in every company, even by their tutors themselves, write upon quite different subjects?

In such a state of things, the advantage of a regular, systematical instruction in those subjects which are treated of in books that in fact engage the attention of all the world, the learned least of all excepted, and which enter into all conversations, where it is worth a man's while to bear a part, or to make a figure, cannot be doubted. And I am of opinion that these studies may be conducted in such a manner as will interfere very little with a sufficiently close application to others. Students in medicine and divinity may be admitted to these studies later than those for whose real use in life they are principally intended; not till they be sufficiently grounded in the classics, have studied logic, oratory, and criticism, or anything else that may be deemed useful, previous to those studies which are peculiar to their respective professions; and even then, these new studies may be made a matter of amusement, rather than an article of business.

With respect to divines, it ought moreover to be considered that the same revolutions in the state of knowledge which call their attention to these new studies, have, in a great measure, furnished them with time for their application to them, by releasing them from several subjects, the study of which was formerly the great business of divines, and engrossed almost their whole time. And though new subjects have been started within the province of divinity, it does not appear to me that they require so much time and application as was usually given to those other studies, the use of which is now superseded. I mean principally school divinity, and the canon law; not to mention logic and metaphysics, which were formerly a more intricate business, and took up much more time than they do now.

Let a person but look over the table of contents to the works of Thomas Aquinas, which were read, studied, or commented upon, by all divines a few centuries ago; and he will be convinced that it must have required both more acuteness to comprehend the subjects of them, and more time to study and digest them in any tolerable manner, than it would require to become exceedingly well versed in all the branches of knowledge I would now recommend.

The canon law was not less complex than both the common and statute law of England; and every clergyman of eminence was under a necessity of understanding, not only the general principles and theory of that system, but even the minutiae of the practice. Good sense and a free access to the Scriptures have at length (assisted perhaps by an aversion to abstract speculations) thrown down the whole fabric of school divinity, and the rise of the civil above the ecclesiastical power in this realm has reduced the theory and practice of the English canon law within very narrow bounds. And as to the little that now remains in use, very few clergymen need trouble themselves about it. In this country a knowledge of the canon law cannot be said to be of any use, and that of the civil law of the Romans can only be interesting to curious and speculative persons, having no connection with any laws in the United States.

It is acknowledged that the attention of students in theology, and other learned professions, is much engaged by mathematical and philosophical studies which have been cultivated of late years. I rejoice in so valuable an accession to human science, and would be far from shortening the time that is given to them in places of liberal education. I rather wish there were more room for those studies in such places, and better provision for teaching them. But notwithstanding this, there is room enough for a small portion of time and attention to be given to the subjects I would here recommend; and it is not much of either that I would plead for in the case of gentlemen intended for the learned professions.

HIS TEACHING METHODS

The method in which those lectures may be taught to the most advantage, I apprehend to be the following; and experience has in some measure formed my judgment in this case.

Let the lecturer have a pretty full text before him, digested with care, containing not only a method of discoursing upon the subjects, but also all the principal arguments he adduces, and all the leading facts he makes use of to support his hypothesis. Let this text be the subject of a regular, but familiar discourse, not exceeding an hour at a time, with a class not exceeding twenty or thirty. Let the lecturer give his pupils all encouragement to enter occasionally into the conversation, by proposing queries, or making any objections or remarks that may occur to them. Let all the students have an opportunity of perusing this text, if not of copying it, in the intervals between the lectures, and let near half of the time for lecturing be spent in receiving from the students a minute account of the particulars of the preceding lecture, and in explaining any difficulties they might have met with in it, in order that no subject be quitted till the tutor be morally certain that his pupils thoroughly understand it.

Upon every subject of importance, let the tutor make references to the principal authors who have treated of it; and if the subject be a controverted one, let him refer to books written on both sides of the question. Of these references let the tutor occasionally require an account, and sometimes a written abstract. Lastly, let the tutor select a proper number of the most important questions that can arise from the subject of the lectures, and let them be proposed to the students as exercises, to be treated in the form of orations, theses, or dissertations, as he shall think fit. Moreover, if he judge it convenient, let him appoint rewards to those who shall handle the subject in the most judicious manner.

Young gentlemen designed for the learned professions need not be put upon these exercises, or reading all the authors referred to. It may be sufficient for them to attend the lectures as they are delivered. And as I would not advise that the lectures be given with shorter intervals between them than three days, they cannot interfere much with their application to their proper studies.

I think I could assign very satisfactory reasons for each of the directions I have laid down above; but I flatter myself they will suggest themselves, if not upon the bare perusal, at least upon any attempt to reduce them to practice. I shall only take notice of an objection that may be made to one particular article in this method.

Some may object to the encouragement I would give the students to propose objections at the time of lecturing. This custom, they may say, will tend to interrupt the course of the lecture, and promote a spirit of impertinence and conceit in young persons. I answer, that every inconvenience of this kind may be obviated by the manner in which a tutor delivers himself in lecturing. A proper mixture of dignity and freedom (which are so far from being incompatible, that they mutually set off one another) will prevent or repress all impertinent and unseasonable remarks, at the same time that it will encourage those which are modest and pertinent.

But suppose a lecturer should not be able immediately to give a satisfactory answer to an objection that might be started by a sensible student. He must be conscious of his having made very ridiculous pretensions, and having given himself improper airs, if it give him any pain to tell his class that he will reconsider a subject, or even to acknowledge himself mistaken. It depends wholly upon a tutor's general disposition, and his usual manner of address, whether he lose or gain ground in the esteem of his pupils by such a declaration. Every tutor ought to have considered the subjects on which he gives lectures with attention, but no man can be expected to be infallible. For my own part, I would not forego the pleasure and advantage which accrue both to my pupils and to myself, from this method, together with the opportunity it gives me of improving my lectures, by means of the many useful hints which are often started in this familiar way of discoursing upon a subject, for any inconvenience I have yet found to attend it, or that I can imagine may possibly attend it.

I cannot help flattering myself that were the studies I have here recommended generally introduced into places of liberal education, the consequence might be happy for this country in some future period. Many of the political evils, under which this and every country in the world labor, are not owing to any want of a love for our country, but to an ignorance of its real constitution and interests. Besides, the very circumstance of giving that attention which I would recommend to its constitution and interests, would unavoidably beget a love and affection for them, and might perhaps contribute more to produce, propagate, and inflame a spirit of patriotism, than any other circumstance. And certainly if there be the most distant prospect of this valuable end being gained by an application to these studies, it cannot fail to recommend them to every true lover of his country, in an age in which the minds of so many are blinded and misled by a spirit of faction; and, what is more alarming, when a taste for luxury and expense is so high, that there is reason to fear it may, in many cases, be superior to all other regards; and when in many breasts it already apparently threatens the utter extinction of a spirit of patriotism.

What was it that made the Greeks, the Romans in early ages, and other nations of antiquity, such obstinate patriots, that they had even no idea of any obligation superior to a regard for their country; but that the constant wars they were obliged to maintain with the neighboring nations kept the idea of their country perpetually in view, and always opposed to that of other nations? It is the same circumstance that gives our common soldiers and seamen more of the genuine spirit of patriotism than is felt by any other order of men in the community, notwithstanding they have the least interest in it. Now the course of instruction I would introduce would bring the idea of our country more early into the minds of British youth, and habituate them to a constant and close attention to it. And why should not the practice of thinking, reading, conversing, and writing, about the interest of our country answer the same purpose with the moderns that fighting for it did among the ancients?

It is a circumstance of particular consequence, that this enthusiastic love for our country would by this means be imbibed by persons of fortune, rank, and influence, in whom it might be effectual to the most important purposes; who might have it in their power, not only to wish well to their country, but to render it the greatest real services. Such men would not only, as is the case with private soldiers or seamen, be able to employ the force of a single arm in its defense, but might animate the hearts and engage the hands of thousands in its cause. Of what unspeakable advantage might be one minister of state, one military commander, or even a single member of parliament, who thoroughly understood the interests of his country, and who postponed every other interest and consideration to it!

This is not teaching politics to low mechanics and manufacturers, or encouraging the study of it among persons with whom it could be of no service to their country, and often a real detriment to themselves; though we may see in those persons how possible it is for the public passions to swallow up all the private ones, when the objects of them are kept frequently in view, and are much dwelt upon in the mind. The same zeal that is the subject of ridicule in persons of no weight or influence in the state would be most glorious and happy for their country in a more advantageous situation.

Some may perhaps object to these studies, as giving too much encouragement to that turn for politics which they may think is already immoderate in the lower and middle ranks of men among us. But must not political knowledge be communicated to those to whom it may be of real use, because a fondness for the study may extend beyond its proper bounds, and be caught by some persons who had better remain ignorant of it? Besides, it ought to be considered, that how ridiculous soever some may make themselves by pretensions to politics, a true friend of liberty will be cautious how he discourages a fondness for that kind of knowledge which has ever been the favorite subject of writing and conversation in all free states. Only tyrants and the friends of arbitrary power have ever taken umbrage at a turn for political knowledge, and political discourses, among even the lowest of the people. Men will study and converse about what they are interested in, especially if they have any influence; and though the ass in the fable was in no concern who was his master, since he could but carry his usual load; and though the subjects of a despotic monarch need not trouble themselves about political disputes and intrigues, which never terminate in a change of measures, but only of men; yet, in a free country, where even private persons have much at stake, every man is nearly interested in the conduct of his superiors, and cannot be an unconcerned spectator of what is transacted by them. With respect to influence, the sentiments of the lowest vulgar in England are not wholly insignificant, and a wise minister will ever pay some attention to them.

It is our wisdom, therefore, to provide that all persons, who have any influence in political measures, be well instructed in the great and leading principles of wise policy. This is certainly an object of the greatest importance. Inconveniences ever attend a general application to any kind of knowledge, and, no doubt, will attend this. But they are inconveniences which a friend to liberty need be under no apprehensions about.

What is said in this essay to recommend the study of the principles of general policy to Englishmen is much more applicable to Americans, as every individual has much more influence in public measures. In fact, the greatest attention is actually given to them by almost all persons in the United States. It is therefore the more necessary that they be well instructed in the true principles of government and general policy, that they may be the better qualified to give their votes on public occasions with real judgment, and without prejudice, to which members of free states are peculiarly liable; every competitor for power having an interest in biasing others in favor of himself and his peculiar principles.

I may possibly promise myself too much, from the general introduction of the studies I have recommended in this essay, into places of liberal education; but a little enthusiasm is always excusable in persons who propose and recommend useful innovations. I have endeavored to represent the state of education in this view as clearly and as fully as I have been able; and I desire my proposals for emendations to have no more weight than the fairest representation will give them in the minds of the cool and the unbiased.

Lectures on History
and General Policy

To meet the need he saw for "social studies," Priestley developed at Warrington a series of lectures on "history and general policy," on the history of England, and on the laws and constitution of England. The Lectures on History and General Policy *were prepared in 1761 but were not published until 1788. The first three lectures, only a small part of the entire work, gave Priestley's views on the uses of historical study.*[3]

THE INTRODUCTION

The study of history is more or less the employment of all persons of reading and education. This was, indeed, the earliest use that was made of letters. For the most ancient poems were almost entirely historical; and verse was first cultivated in preference to prose (which seems to be the most natural vehicle of history), as the best, because the most secure method of transmitting to posterity the knowledge of past events. In all ages the writing of history has employed the ablest men of all nations; and to this day hardly any writer enjoys a greater, a more extensive, and what will probably be a more lasting reputation, than a good historian.

The infinite variety there is in the subjects of history makes it inviting to persons of every disposition. It may be either trifling or serious. It supplies materials with equal ease and equal copiousness, for the sallies of mirth and the gravest disquisitions of philosophy. As everything comes under the denomination of history which informs us of any fact which is too remote in time or place to be the subject

---

[3] Text from Rutt, XXIV, 25-54.

of our personal knowledge, it is calculated for the use of persons of both sexes, and of men of all ranks and of all professions in life; because it cannot be presumed that a person of any profession, or in any situation, can of himself come at the knowledge of every fact which it is for his advantage to be acquainted with.

History is so connected with, and essential to, all kinds of knowledge, that the most superficial essay upon any subject whatever is hardly tolerable, unless some kind of historical facts be introduced or alluded to in it. The necessity of facts to moral writers, or those who write upon the theory of human nature, I need not mention. And certainly no person can be a good divine, much less undertake any part of the controversy with unbelievers, unless he be very well acquainted with history, civil as well as ecclesiastical. Indeed, more than half of the books of Scripture consist of history. And as all the prophecies of the Old and New Testament must be verified by history, none but a good historian can be a judicious commentator upon such important parts of the sacred writings.

Besides, an acquaintance with history is agreeable to us as sociable and conversable creatures; since it may be considered as a means of extending the power of conversation, and making the dead equally of the party with the living. Nay, as things are circumstanced, the dead contribute more largely to gratify our natural and eager curiosity to be informed of past and remote transactions.

In this field of history, therefore, which is open to every man of letters, and in which every man of taste and curiosity cannot fail to pass a great part of his leisure hours, it cannot but be desirable to have a guide (at least upon a person's first introduction into it), lest he should lose himself in the boundless variety it affords, and not be able to find those convenient eminences from which he will have the most easy and agreeable view of the objects it contains. In the character of this guide, gentlemen, I now offer you my best assistance.

The course of lectures we are now entering upon is intended to facilitate the study of history, both by directing you to the easiest methods of acquiring and retaining the knowledge of it, and making the proper use of it when you are possessed of it.

That the observations I have collected for this purpose may be the most intelligible and useful, I shall dispose of them in the following method: considering,

I. The general uses of history.

II. The sources of history.

III. What is necessary or useful to be known previous to the study of history.

IV. Directions for the more easy acquiring and retaining a knowledge of history.

V. Proper objects of attention to an historian. And under this head I shall consider the several subjects of general policy, or the circumstances that chiefly contribute to render civil societies secure, numerous, and happy, as being the most important of all objects of attention to readers of history.

VI. In the last place I would give you a general view of history, civil and ecclesiastical, but shall content myself with referring to Holberg,[4] or some other epitome of general history.

THE USES OF HISTORY

According to the method above laid down, I am first to consider the general uses of history. These may be exhibited under three heads: 1. History serves to amuse the imagination and interest the passions in general. 2. It improves the understanding. And, 3. It tends to strengthen the sentiments of virtue.

[4] Ludvig Holberg (1684-1754) was a Danish writer, the author of a variety of literary and historical works, including *An Introduction to Universal History* (English translation from the original Latin, London, 1755).

The first and lowest use of history is that it agreeably amuses the imagination and interests the passions. With these charms history captivates the generality of readers; and though I shall chiefly recommend it in another and a higher view, I think this is an advantage of history which is by no means inconsiderable, and by which a reader of the severest philosophy need not be ashamed to acknowledge himself influenced. To amuse the imagination, and give play to the passions in general, is almost the only and avowed scope of all works of fiction, both in prose and verse; and men of great genius and abilities are not thought to have thrown away their time to no purpose upon them. Whatever exercises does likewise improve and invigorate our faculties and dispose them for the more free and perfect discharge of their proper functions. Admitting, therefore, that the histories of Alexander the Great, of Charles XII of Sweden, or the conquest of Mexico, be read with no other view than the adventures of Telemachus, of Amadis de Gaul, or the conquest of Jerusalem; or that the voyages of Dampier, Sir Francis Drake, and Captain Cook, be put upon the same footing with those of Gulliver; I would not say the time spent in reading them was wholly lost. Whatever valuable impressions are made upon the mind by fictitious adventures, the same in kind, though perhaps generally not equal in degree, are made by real adventures; and facts, with whatever view and in whatever manner treasured up in the mind, are ready to be applied to any further and higher uses that they are capable of, whenever the person who is possessed of them is disposed to view them in any other light.

In this view all true history has a capital advantage over every work of fiction. Works of fiction are not in their nature capable, in general, of any other uses than the authors of them had in view, which must necessarily be very limited; whereas true history, being an exhibition of the conduct of Divine Providence, in which everything has, perhaps, infinite relations and uses, is an inexhaustible mine of the most valuable knowledge. Works of fiction resemble those machines which we contrive to illustrate the principles of philosophy, such as globes and orreries, the uses of which extend no further than the views of human ingenuity; whereas real history resembles the experiments made by the air pump, the condensing engine and electrical machine, which exhibit the operations of nature, and the God of nature himself, whose works are the noblest subject of contemplation to the human mind, and are the groundwork and materials of the most extensive and useful theories.

But, independent of any further use, we have many well-written histories, which, I think, are calculated to give as much pure entertainment, especially to a person of a reasonable age and experience, as the generality of novels and romances. Let a person of taste and just sentiment read the history of the life of Cicero, written by Middleton; the conquest of Mexico, or the voyage of Commodore Anson, or even such larger works as the histories of Herodotus, Thucydides, Livy, Philip de Comines, etc., and then judge. If the amazing and interesting scenes of fiction be worked up with more art, be more happily disposed to excite and interest the passions, and be more agreeably diversified with proper episodes, the very thought that it is fiction (the influence of which grows with our years) makes that artful disposition and those embellishments necessary; whereas the mere thought that we are listening to the voice of truth is able to keep the attention awake through many a dry and ill-digested narrative of facts.

The next and higher use of history is to improve the understanding and strengthen the judgment, and thereby fit us for entering upon life with advantage. "By contemplating the vast variety of particular characters and events," as Lord Bolingbroke[5] well observes; "by examining the

[5] Henry St. John, first Viscount Bolingbroke, lived from 1678 to 1751. An important figure in English politics during the reign of Queen Anne, he was the author of *The Idea of a Patriot King* (1749) and *Letters on the Study of History* (1752).

strange combination of causes different, remote, and seemingly opposite, that often concur in producing one effect; a man of parts may improve the study of history to its proper and principal use; he may sharpen the penetration, fix the attention of his mind, and strengthen his judgment; he may acquire the faculty and the habit of discerning quicker and looking further, and of exerting that flexibility and steadiness which are necessary to be joined in the conduct of all affairs that depend on the concurrence or opposition of other men." Judgment, as well as our other powers, must improve by exercise. Now history presents us with the same objects which we meet with in the business of life. They must consequently excite the same kind of reflections, and give the same exercise to our thoughts, and thus produce the same turn of mind. History, therefore, may be called anticipated experience. By this means we begin our acquaintance with mankind sooner, and bring into the world, and the business of it, such a cast of thought and temper of mind, as is acquired by passing through it; which will make us appear to more advantage in it, and not such mere novices upon our introduction into it, as we should otherwise be. As Lord Bolingbroke again observes, "There are certain general principles, and rules of life and conduct, which always must be true, because they are conformable to the invariable nature of things. He who studies history as he would study philosophy, will soon distinguish and collect them; and by doing so, will soon form to himself a general system of ethics and politics on the surest foundations, on the trial of these principles and rules in all ages, and on the confirmation of them by universal experience."

The impressions which this anticipated knowledge of the world makes upon us, it is certain, will not be so deep as those which are the result of our own personal acquaintance with it; and our judgment of things, and maxims of conduct, formed in this manner, will not be so firmly riveted in our minds. But then they will have the advantage of being more correct, and of being a better guide to us, than anything we could have learned from our own random experience upon our entering the world. The reason is that the examples which history presents to us are generally complete. The whole is before us. We see men and things at their full length, as we may say; and we likewise generally see them through a medium which is less partial than that of experience. Whereas in real life every scene opens very slowly; we see therefore but a very small part of a thing at one time, and are consequently liable to be deceived into a very fallacious judgment of it; particularly considering how distorted even those imperfect views of things are by the relation of everything to self, which it is impossible to keep out of sight in things in which we ourselves are concerned.

In this view, history is generally the only faithful instructor of princes, particularly absolute princes. It is so much the interest of abler men than themselves to impose upon them, and to swell their ideas of their own importance, that, without the aid of history, it is almost impossible they should ever form any just notion of men or things at all. But in history, princes may see their predecessors treated without flattery or ceremony; and therefore, by the help of common sense, they may see, as in a glass, in what light their own characters and conduct will appear to posterity. Nay, they may depend upon it, that some historians will rate them as much too low as their contemporaries have rated them too high. Of what avail have been the fulsome flatteries of Velleius Paterculus to the character of Tiberius, or his favorite Sejanus; or even the refined praises of Virgil and Horace, to the character of Augustus himself? Posterity at length sees their real characters, through all their artful disguises, and only thinks the worse of men for laying persons of wit and ingenuity under a necessity of acting a part so unworthy of themselves. All future kings of France may see many very free censures upon the character and conduct of their predecessor Louis XIV in Voltaire, notwithstanding the writer cannot conceal his partiality for his hero and his nation.

But, indeed, to men in all stations, instructions for their own conduct may be conveyed in the clearest and most cogent manner through the example of others. Suetonius relates that Augustus used to transcribe instructive passages of historians, and send them to those of his officers who had need of admonition.

We may easily be sensible of the importance of history to the advancement of knowledge in general, as well as of political knowledge in particular, if we consider that the most exalted understanding is nothing more than a power of drawing conclusions, and forming maxims of conduct, from known facts and experiments, of which necessary materials of knowledge the mind itself is wholly barren. How then can knowledge be gained without experience? And very scanty and dear-bought would be the wisdom that was the result of the experience of one man, or of one age only. How slow then must have been the progress that mankind would have made in wisdom, and in improvements of all kinds, before, by some means or other, one age could be made acquainted with the observations of their ancestors!

It was requisite, therefore, in order to the improvement of human kind and of human conduct, and to give mankind clear and comprehensive views of their interest, together with the means of promoting it, that the experience of some ages should be collected and compared, that distant events should be brought together; and so the first rise, entire progress, and final conclusion of schemes, transactions, and characters, should be seen, as it were, in one unbroken view, with all their connections and relations. Without this, no adequate judgment could be formed of them, such as would enable an intelligent person to determine how far the same or the like undertakings would bear to be repeated or amended. Without these advantages, therefore, the improvements of human life, notwithstanding the greatest perfection and extent of our intellectual powers, would be at a stand. There might be conjecture and enterprise, but there could be no certainty or rational expectation of success.

Consequently, without history, the advantages of our rational nature must have been rated very low; and the more complete, the more exact and comprehensive is our furniture of historical facts, the more materials of knowledge, and consequently of power and happiness, are we possessed of. For Lord Bacon has justly remarked, that "knowledge is power"; and certainly all the excellence of human nature, all the advantage we have above the brutes, is derived from the use of our intellectual powers. Since, with respect to the powers of body, and an instinctive capacity of defending and providing for themselves, they have greatly the advantage of us.

Political knowledge, it will be said, is useful only to politicians and ministers of state. But besides that, it is a matter of reasonable curiosity to examine into the springs of the great wheel of government, on the just balance and regular motions of which our temporal security and happiness depend; and though political affairs be almost wholly, but not entirely, out of the sphere of private persons under an arbitrary government; yet "in free governments," as it is admirably said by Lord Bolingbroke, "the public service is not confined to those whom the prince appoints to different posts in the administration under him. — It can never be impertinent nor ridiculous therefore, in such a country, for men of all degrees to instruct themselves in those affairs wherein they may be actors, or judges of those that act, or controllers of those that judge"; and from some one or other of these classes no subject of Great Britain is wholly excluded.

HISTORY REMOVES PREJUDICES

It is not unworthy of our notice, when we consider in what respects the knowledge of history improves the understand-

ing, that it tends to free the mind from many foolish prejudices, particularly an unreasonable partiality for our own
country, merely as our own country, which makes a people
truly ridiculous in the eyes of foreigners. It was a want of
acquaintance with history that made the Chinese mandarins
express their astonishment to find their country make so
small a figure in a map of the world which the Jesuits
showed them. And through the same ignorance, the Sam-
oyedes, a people inhabiting the northern parts of Siberia,
whom Le Bruyn describes as the lowest and worst provided for of all the human race, wondered that the Czar
of Muscovy did not choose to live among them.

National prejudices likewise produce a most unreasonable
aversion to foreign nations and foreign religions, which
nothing but an acquaintance with history can cure. The
misfortune is that it is too often the interest of particular
persons and parties to promote those prejudices. The Moors
of Africa were surprised to find their first Christian captives
in the shape of men; and our very signs do to this day bear
the traces of the extravagant opinion of the size and the
strength of the Saracens, which they who returned from the
crusades propagated among their ignorant countrymen.

The knowledge of history operates no less favorably and
effectually, in removing the prejudices that may have been
entertained in favor of ancient or modern times, by giving
a just idea of the advantages and disadvantages of mankind
in all ages.

Far am I, however, from imagining that the consequence
of studying history will be an indifference to our own country. On the contrary, I think it one of the greatest advantages arising from the study of history, to an inhabitant of
Great Britain, that he will generally lay down his book
more thoroughly satisfied with his own situation; and will
be, from rational conviction, and not from blind prejudice,
a more zealous friend to the interest of his country than
before. But this is much more true of an American citizen,

especially as he cannot but have a higher sense of his own influence and importance.

Indeed, so apparent are the superior advantages of our constitution and laws, if not of our manners and customs, over those of most other nations, that there are few foreigners who do not give ours the preference to their own. Montesquieu, one of the first of philosophical politicians — that is, those who have treated of laws and government with a just regard to the principles of human nature, and the situation and wants of mankind — is in raptures, and almost quits the style of philosophy whenever he treats of our constitution. And Voltaire, who is exceedingly partial to the power and glory of France, cannot help doing the same justice to the superior excellence of our government. Indeed, as a man of a free and bold turn of thinking, you will be sensible that he could not have done otherwise, when we come to analyze the British constitution, and to show from what its excellence results; though at the same time I shall not fail to point out some radical and very considerable defects in it.

Under the head of prejudices, I shall just mention a pleasant but not unimportant observation of Mr. Hume, viz. that the fair sex "may learn from history — that love is not the only passion that governs the male world"; which from the reading of novels, frequenting the theater, and even the general turn of polite conversation, they might otherwise imagine.

But the capital advantage we derive from history under this head is that from this source only can be derived all future improvements in the science of government. And if the well-being of society be our object, this is, after all, the most important of all sciences. For certainly more substantial benefit results to society from the proper balance of the several powers of a state, or even from one wise law respecting the liberties and properties of men, than could be derived from all the other sciences put together. I except, however, the sciences, if they may be so called, of morality and religion.

Human nature, with the various interests and connections of men in a state of society, is so complex a subject that nothing can be safely concluded *a priori* with respect to it. Everything that we can depend upon must be derived from facts. All the plans of government laid down by the wisest of the ancients, as Plato, Aristotle, and Cicero, are, without exception, defective in many capital instances; and notwithstanding the further lights that More and Harrington might have derived from the history of many centuries after them, neither the *Utopia* of the former, nor the *Oceana* of the latter, would bear to be reduced to practice. The former is visionary even to a proverb.

This grand science is still in its infancy. Men of the greatest reflection and experience could not pretend to pronounce, with any degree of certainty, what, for instance, would be the consequence of any considerable change in our own constitution and government, or that of other nations. And do we not frequently see that our ablest ministers of state, who give the closest attention to the internal policy of the kingdom, are obliged to change their measures, in consequence of being disappointed in their expectations from them? This makes it so extremely hazardous to introduce any material change into an established form of government. No human sagacity can foresee what inconvenience might arise from it.

So important is this science of government, that nothing can be more worthy of the study of those who have sufficient abilities, and who are friends of mankind; and the only foundation on which men who think, and who are not carried away by their own imaginations, will build any conclusions is historical facts. Hypotheses built upon arguments *a priori* are least of all tolerable. Here observation and experience are the only safe guides.

As all other sciences have made very rapid advances in the present age, the science of government bids fair to keep pace with them. Many ingenious men have of late turned their thoughts to this subject, and valuable treatises upon it have been published both in this country and abroad. But what is of much more value, we have now a vast stock of important facts before us, for our contemplation. The old governments of Europe are arrived to a considerable degree of maturity. We may rather say they are growing into decay; so that their several advantages and defects are become sufficiently conspicuous; and the new governments in North America, and especially those of France and Poland, are so many new experiments, of which political philosophers cannot fail to make the greatest use. Time has also weakened and removed many prejudices in favor of pretended rights to power and peculiar modes of government; so that the only proper object of government, the happiness of the people, is now almost universally seen and alone attended to.

For want of acquaintance with history, we are apt to pronounce *a priori*, many things to be impossible, which in fact really exist, and are very safe. Thus the king of Siam could not be made to believe that the Venetians had no king, any more than that water could have the hardness of stone, and bear men and carriages.

I shall conclude this head with adding that the knowledge of history contributes to enlarge the mind by the acquaintance we are thereby enabled to form with all those objects which, in the course of these lectures, will be pointed out as worthy of peculiar attention to an historian, the knowledge of which is equally useful for speculative or practical purposes; so that philosophers and politicians may equally avail themselves of it.

HISTORY STRENGTHENS VIRTUE

The third use of history is that it tends to strengthen the sentiments of virtue. That this is the tendency of an acquaintance with history will be evident, if we consider in what manner virtuous impressions are actually made upon the mind. How do we acquire a love for virtue, but by frequently viewing it in those points of light in which it appears desirable to us, and in a situation of mind in which no bias is laid upon us in favor of vice?

It cannot be denied by any who maintain that virtue is its own sufficient reward in this life, that even a just and well-conducted knowledge of the world would have this happy effect. It is only a partial acquaintance with it, seeing things in an unfair point of light, and with minds prejudiced by prospects of pleasure, interest, or false notions of honor, that prevents that happy consequence from taking place universally. Now, to study history is to come at the knowledge of the world in the most favorable circumstances. Historians are the best guides and tutors we can take with us in our travels. They show us the whole of transactions and characters, before a partial view of them can have had time to make unfavorable impressions on our minds; and all the reflections they make upon men and things are uniformly dictated by a sense of virtue and honor. Even Machiavelli himself, though his very name conveys the idea of baseness and villainy as a politician, "discovers," as Mr. Hume observes, "a true sentiment of virtue in his History of Florence."

In such company, and in the hands of such able and faithful conductors, what reason have we to be alarmed to see our friends introduced to a knowledge of mankind? There is certainly a great difference between a person's being admitted to see the figure which Alexander the Great, or Charles XII, made at the head of their conquests, to view the court of Dionysius, of Nero, or of Louis XIV, in all their splendor, and seeing the figure their whole lives make in the annals of history. In the former situation the incautious mind of a young man might be in danger of being captivated with the charms of ambition, voluptuousness, or magnificence; but looking upon the same objects from the more advantageous situation in which history places us, we must certainly be equally struck with their vanity and folly, and conceive a disgust and aversion to them. It is with the knowledge of the world, as Pope says it is with learning:

There shallow draughts intoxicate the brain,
And drinking largely sobers us again.

The only reason why a young person cannot be safely trusted with viewing the vices, as well as the virtues, that are in the world, is, that if left to himself in real life, vice may be so circumstanced as to be but too inviting to his inexperienced mind; but in history, vice never appears tempting. Indeed, whatever be the disposition of historians themselves, if they give a faithful view of things as they have really come to pass, they cannot help giving a representation favorable to virtue. So consistent is the order of Divine Providence, that if the scheme be fairly and completely represented, we may depend upon it that nothing will be exhibited from which it may be justly concluded that vice is eligible upon the whole. Contrary, therefore, to what may be apprehended from a promiscuous acquaintance with the world, through the glass of history, vices may be viewed as safely as virtues. Nay, they both equally teach wisdom and good morals. It is even impossible to say which of them inculcates the important lesson with more force. The excesses of a Nero, and the goodness of a Marcus Aurelius, have the same good effect in history.

Thus it appears, by arguing as it were *a priori*, from the lights in which characters and events are seen in history, that it must have an effect that is favorable to virtue. I shall now demonstrate the same thing more particularly, by showing what scenes history actually exhibits that have this happy tendency.

HISTORY TEACHES BY EXAMPLES

In the first place, history, by displaying the sentiments and conduct of truly great men, and those of a contrary character, tends to inspire us with a taste for solid glory and real greatness; and convinces us that it does not consist in what the generality of mankind are so eager in pursuit of.

We can never imagine, if we derive our instruction from history, that true greatness consists in riches; when we see that some of the most distinguished characters in the annals of mankind were formed and lived in poverty, men who showed their contempt of riches by refusing to improve the opportunities they had of amassing wealth. Not to mention Cincinnatus, Fabricius, and other Romans, in the early ages of that city, honored for their poverty, but who had no opportunity of acquiring what we should call riches — Scipio Aemilianus, who might have engrossed almost all of the wealth of Carthage, never made a single acquisition in all his life. The great Philopoemen generally went in a very plain dress, and without any servant or attendants. The emperors Nerva, Trajan, Antoninus, and Aurelius, sold their palaces, their gold and silver plate, their valuable furniture, and all the superfluities they could dispense with, which their predecessors had heaped up, and banished all expenses and delicacies from their tables with the greatest severity.

These princes, together with Vespasian, Pertinax, Alexander Severus, Claudius the Second, and Tacitus, who were raised to the empire by their merit, and whom all ages have admired as the greatest and the best of princes, were ever fond of the greatest plainness in their apparel, furniture, and outward appearance. The ruins of Hadrian's country seat are still to be seen, and it does not appear to have exceeded the bigness of one of our common houses. Even Augustus himself, during a reign of near fifty years, never changed his apartment or furniture. We see the same just turn of thinking in the famous Cornelia, daughter of the great Scipio. When a lady of her acquaintance desired very importunately to see her toilet, she deferred satisfying her curiosity till her children, who were the famous Gracchi, came from school, and then only said, "En! haec ornamenta mea sunt." (These are my ornaments!)

When temperance, frugality, and a just sense of greatness are graced with such names as these I have mentioned,
shall we be in any danger of abandoning ourselves to excess
in imitation of the infamous Nero, whose golden palace,
Herodian says, was as large as all the rest of the city of
Rome, and whose extravagance in other respects was in
proportion to it; of Caligula, of the mad Commodus, or the
beastly Heliogabalus? Do we admire Lucullus the more
for the idea that Cicero gives us of his expensive table? Or
can we think Marc Antony to be commended for having a
succession of grand entertainments always ready, that whenever he was disposed to eat he might never wait half an
hour?

Can we think that honors and preferment constitute true
greatness, when we see in history that the most worthy men
have generally declined them? Tacitus and Probus, who
did so much honor to their stations, were both advanced
to the empire against their inclinations; and in how much
fairer a point of light do their characters stand than that
of those sons of ambition, who waded through seas of blood
to come at it!

The extravagancies of Alexander the Great in killing his
best friends, the cruelties of the Spaniards in America, the
ruin of Sweden by Charles XII, are certainly more proper
to show the folly and madness of unbounded ambition, than
their victories are to dazzle our minds with their glare.
How we regret that unhappy turn of mind, when we consider what valuable members of society their abilities would
have rendered such men as Julius Caesar and Pompey, had
they jointly employed them to raise the glory of their country; and that the expenses of Louis XIV, in preparations for
destruction, were more than sufficient to have founded
many numerous colonies, and to have put them into a
flourishing condition.

Nothing so effectually cures a man of the absurd pride
of birth and family, as seeing some of the greatest men in
history, such as Tamerlane, Cardinal Ximenes, and Pope

Sixtus the Fifth, rise from low beginnings; and we are always charmed to see truly great men, who were possessed of the advantages of birth, waive all pretenses to merit on that account. Even Vespasian laughed at those who pretended to derive his descent from Hercules.

An excessive passion for fame, as an end of action, reduces a man very low in the light of history. How much does the letter which Cicero wrote to Lucceius, and which unfortunately for him yet remains (in which he almost insists upon his praising him at the expense of truth, in the history of his consulship), sink that great man in our esteem! On the contrary, how prodigiously does the character of Cato rise upon us by a few words of Sallust, "Esse, quam videri, bonus malebat!" (He rather chose to be, than to seem, good.) And the vanity of Nero upon his excelling in music, and of Commodus on his dexterity in killing wild beasts, completely expose the affectation of excelling in what is out of our proper sphere. The same maxim is conveyed by Philip, when he asked his son Alexander if he was not ashamed to play on a musical instrument so well as he did.

In how different a light do those men appear in history, who are greedy to engross praise to themselves, and those who contribute heartily to the reputation of others! An instance of the former we see in Claudius, who made an idle expedition to finish the conquest of Britain; of the latter, in Marcus Aurelius, who denied himself the pleasure of attending his sister Lucilla (whom he had married to Lucius Verus) into the East, lest his presence should give a check to the growing reputation of his son-in-law, and seem to draw upon himself the honor of putting an end to an important war, to the other's prejudice. And history does the most ample recompense to those who have generously sacrificed their own reputation to the public good. Thus Fabius Maximus, to his immortal honor, notwithstanding the provoking insults he received from Minucius, rescued him from the hands of Hannibal, setting aside his resentment, and consulting only his zeal for the interest of his country.

We conceive more clearly what true greatness of mind is, at the same time that our hearts are more filled with admiration of it, and burn with a stronger passion for it, by a simple narration of some incidents in history, than by the most elaborate and philosophically exact description of it. What can give us a clearer idea of the noble sentiments of strict honor and integrity than Marshal Turenne's refusing a sum of money, which was offered him if he would not march his army through a certain territory, because he had not intended to march that way? Does not every person's heart strongly feel the sentiments of benevolence when he hears the good Titus exclaiming that he had lost a day, because he had done no person a good office in it? If a person be capable of forming any idea of greatness of mind in forgiving injuries, he will do it from hearing the following reply that Louis XII made to a courtier who pressed him to punish a person who had offended him before he came to the throne: "It belongs not to the King of France to revenge the injuries offered to the Duke of Orleans." Or, lastly, what can give so just an idea of the true spirit and magnanimity of a soldier, as the reply that Viscount Doree made to Charles IX of France, when he received an order from him to massacre the Huguenots, "I desire your majesty would employ me in what is possible"?

The last example leads me to a second observation, which is that history enables us to form just ideas of the dignity and the weakness of human nature, both of which are extremely useful to us in life. The one inspires us with the noble ambition of rising above the level of our species; and the other view, without destroying, tempers that ambition with no more than a due degree of humility and diffidence; which, in fact, equally contributes to the same end. What I mean will be more clearly understood by a few examples.

How can we conceive a more just or a more exalted idea of a sense of true honor and heroism, than by reading such

stories as that of the behavior of the Earl of Peterborough
at the famous siege of Barcelona? While he was settling
the terms of capitulation with the Spanish commander, news
was brought that, contrary to the suspension of arms agreed
upon between them, a party of the allied troops had broken
into the town. The earl told the Spanish general, that if he
would give him leave to enter the town with his English
troops, he would drive out his allies, and then return to
finish the capitulation, which he actually performed.

I shall say nothing of the fabulous story of Curtius, who
is said to have leaped into a gulf, or of Codrus, who procured his own death to save his country, since instances of
equal courage in braving death are by no means uncommon
in our own times. At the siege of Turin, one Mica is said
to have fired a mine, and purposely destroyed himself with
the enemy. And how many commanders of ships have purposely blown them up rather than strike their colors! These,
it may be said, are the effects of a refined sense of honor,
which is acquired in a highly improved state of society. But
we may see what may be called the native strength of the
mind, in the North American Indians, with whom, when
prisoners, it is very common to refuse dying by their own
hands, on purpose to show the honor of their country, in
supporting the tortures which they know are prepared for
them.

Facts like these, together with those which show the extent of genius in such men as Aristotle, Archimedes, and
Sir Isaac Newton, give us high ideas of the dignity of human nature, and the capacity of the human mind. But the
other side of the picture, which history with equal faith-
fulness presents to us, gives us a most affecting and equally
instructive view of our deplorable weakness and frailty,
exemplified in the greatest of men.

Hardly anything gives us a more affecting view of the
weakness and inconsistency to which the mind of man is
liable, than to see men of sound and clear understandings
in most respects, and of upright, honest hearts, fall into

sentiments that lead to gross and painful superstitions. A most remarkable instance of this was Pascal, one of the greatest geniuses and best men that ever lived. He with many others entertained a notion that God made men miserable here, in order to their being happy hereafter; and in consequence of this, he imposed upon himself the most disagreeable mortifications. He even ordered a wall to be built before a window of his study, from which he thought he had too agreeable a prospect. He also wore a girdle full of sharp points next to his skin, and while he was eating or drinking anything that was grateful to his appetite, he was constantly pricking himself, that he might not be sensible of any pleasure. His sister too, who was a woman of fine sense and great piety, actually died of thirst, as she thought, to the glory of God. It was certainly through a weakness of the same nature in the ingenious and excellent Fénelon, that he submitted without reserve to the arbitrary sentence of the Pope, when he condemned a book that he published. He even preached to condemn his own book, and forbade his friends to defend it.

They have not only been good men and of a truly religious turn of mind who have been subject to such groundless superstitions, but the most vicious and abandoned also. Both kinds of instances show the weakness to which human nature is liable. But whereas a good man who is a slave to superstition is an object of the greatest compassion, a wicked man in the same situation is rather a subject of ridicule. What, for instance, can be more completely ridiculous than Louis XI of France, a man who made no conscience of any villainy, going always covered with relics, and wearing a leaden image of the Virgin Mary in his hat, of which it is said he asked pardon for his murders before they were committed? The same prince made a deed of the earldom of Bolloigne to the Virgin Mary.

Even the sentiments of morality, which of all others one would expect to find the most invariable and uncorrupted, are found greatly perverted, and intermixed with notions that are foreign and even contrary to morality, in the minds of some whole nations. Thus the Tartars, with whom it is a sin and a capital crime, as Voltaire says, to put a knife into the fire, to lean against a whip, to beat a horse with a bridle, or to break one bone with another, think it no sin, in some cases, to break their word, to plunder, and commit murder. The same Arab who, if he find you at his door claiming hospitality, would receive you as his brother, and conduct you the next day, would not have scrupled to rob and murder you, as his lawful prey, if he had met you in the desert an hour before. To give instances of the weakness and inconsistency in the human mind which history presents us with, were endless. These are sufficient to give us an idea how affecting and useful such views are, and at the same time how entertaining to a speculative mind.

PROVIDENCE IN HISTORY

Thirdly, history tends to strengthen the sentiments of virtue, by the variety of views in which it exhibits the conduct of Divine Providence, and points out the hand of God in the affairs of men. For certainly whatever suggests to us the idea of a Divine Being, either in the end or means of great events, must be favorable to piety and virtue.

That the world has a governor, or superintendent, is just as evident as that it had a maker. For no person does anything without some design, or without intending to make some use of it. A telescope is made to be used for the better distinguishing distant objects, the eye itself for seeing things at a moderate distance from us, and, no doubt, men and the world for some end or other.

And as the same Being that made the greatest things made the smallest things also, all being parts of the same system, some use, no doubt, is made of everything, even what appears to us the most inconsiderable; so that, as our Saviour observed, a sparrow falls not to the ground without

God, and the very hairs of our heads are numbered. Also, as nothing was made, so nothing can come to pass, without the knowledge, the appointment, or permission of God. Something, therefore, is intended by everything that happens, as well as by everything that is made. But in little things a design is not so apparent as in greater and more striking things. Though, therefore, the hand of God be really in everything that happens, and that is recorded in history, our attention is more forcibly drawn to it in great events, and especially in things which happen in a manner unexpected by us; in events in which the hand of man is least seen, the hand of God is most easily seen and acknowledged; though, in fact, it is equally concerned in everything; men and their schemes and exploits being only instruments in his hand, employed as the most fit means to execute his purposes.

How can we help acknowledging the hand of God when we see great and important events brought about by seemingly trifling and inconsiderable means, or by means which seem to have little or no relation to the end; as when our King James and both houses of Parliament were rescued from destruction by a letter which a conspirator sent with a view to save one of the members of the House of Lords for whom he had a friendship?

Who would have imagined that the desire which Henry VIII had to be divorced from his wife would have brought about the Reformation in England? The indiscretion of a Portuguese priest, who would not give place to one of the king's officers in Japan, and the obstinacy of the Jesuits in refusing to give up the house which a nobleman had given them, when his son claimed it back again, occasioned the extirpation of the Roman Catholic religion in that country.

But what most of all shows the hand of Providence, and the weakness and shortsightedness of men, are great events being brought about contrary to the intention of the persons who were the chief instruments of them, and by the very means which were intended to produce a contrary event.

Thus persecution has always been the means of promoting the persecuted religion; insomuch that it is become a common proverb, that "the blood of the martyrs is the seed of the church." Thus likewise, Athens, Lacedaemon, Carthage, Rome, and many other states have been ruined by their own successes. Philip II of Spain, by his intolerable oppression, was the cause of the freedom of the states of Holland. Such has often been the consequence of wicked men overacting their parts. Thus also the senate of Rome was once saved by Catiline's making the signal for the massacre too soon.

With what satisfaction may a person who has an eye to Divine Providence read such a passage as the following in Machiavelli: — that Borgia had so well conducted his measures, that he must have been master of Rome and of the whole ecclesiastical estate, after the death of his father, but that it was impossible for him to foresee that he himself would be at the point of death at the very time that Alexander his father finished his life! They were both poisoned at an entertainment, by a mistake of the waiter, who served them with the wine which was to have taken off their enemies.

It is no uncommon thing, in the history of Divine Providence, that persons being known to have abilities shall have been the means of keeping them in obscurity, while others have been advanced in consequence of their seeming insignificance. If Augustus had shown any capacity as a statesman or general, any greatness of soul, or anything in the least enterprising, at first, he would probably never have been master of the Roman Empire. But while Cicero and Antony, in their turns, thought to make a tool of him, they, unknown to themselves, increased his power and influence at the expense of their own.

In this view it is very amusing and useful to consider to what a different purpose the labor, powers, and works of men and nations have been employed, from what was originally thought of and intended; as, that the Romans, after all their conquests of other nations, should be often gov-

erned by savage and tyrannical barbarians, such as Maximin
and others; and that that city, the mistress of the world,
which was built by Romulus, and whose power was enlarged by such men as Camillus, Scipio Africanus, Marius,
Sylla, Caesar, Pompey, and Trajan, should now be in subjection to the Pope, and the seat of a power totally different
from what had before resided in it, and of which the founders could have no conception. How far was Constantine
from foreseeing that Constantinople would be the capital
of the Turkish empire, and the principal support of a religion opposite to that which he established! How far, also,
were the heads of the Grecian commonwealths from foreseeing that their country, the seat of arts and liberty, would
ever become the most ignorant and enslaved of all the states
of Europe!

A regard to Divine Providence is likewise extremely useful to heighten our satisfaction in reading history, and throw
an agreeable light upon the most gloomy and disgusting
parts of it. With a view to this, the most disagreeable objects in history will bear to be looked upon with satisfaction.
And could we see every event in all its connections and most
distant influences, we should no doubt perfectly acquiesce
in everything that comes to pass under the government of
God; in seeing that all evils lead to, and terminate in, a
greater good. But in many cases we see events which give
us pain at first sight, and which occasion much regret and
disappointment to those who give more scope to their passions than to their reflection while they are reading; which,
nevertheless, if we look no further than the next and immediate consequences, we shall be thoroughly satisfied and
pleased with.

No person conversant with the ancient classical historians,
and who has thereby acquired a classical taste and classical
notions of liberty, but regrets that Rome, in the height of
its glory, should fall under the power of masters. But it is
because he does not consider that all the provinces of the
vast Roman empire were most miserably oppressed and

plundered by the republican governors, who had little to fear from courts of justice; but were relieved and happy under the government of persons who lived in constant fear of being accused of maladministration, to an inexorable master. Nay, the provinces were not much less happy under Tiberius and Nero, than under Trajan and the Antonines.

A reader of Thucydides is apt to be extremely mortified at the ill treatment of Alcibiades, and the defeat of the Athenians before Syracuse. But it is because he does not think what would probably have been the consequence of the success of that expedition; namely, the slavery of Greece, and, from the nature of its government, the confusion and slavery of Athens too. As success naturally points out our favorite hero to us, we cannot help conceiving a violent indignation against Hanno, for taking no more care to send recruits to Hannibal after the battle of Cannae. But justly did he and all Carthage dread the power of Hannibal, when master of Rome, who was able to change the whole form of their government even when he was conquered.

These obvious remarks I mention here to show the necessity of thought and reflection in reading history. Further observations of this kind, and such as are less obvious, I shall reserve for another part of this course of lectures, in which I shall endeavor to enter a little further into the views and conduct of Divine Providence in the government of the world.

HISTORY PREPARES FOR ADVERSITY

In the fourth place, history, in the misfortunes and hardships to which the most distinguished personages have been reduced, gives us a deep conviction of the instability of all human things, and prepares our minds to submit to adversity with more patience and resignation, as to a condition from which we see none are exempt. Even the mis-

fortunes and disappointments of brave and good men, who
have brought themselves into difficulties in consequence of
their generous attempts in favor of the liberties and best
interests of mankind, do not, as exhibited in history, in the
least tend to slacken our zeal in the same glorious cause;
at the same time that they make us more prudent in the
choice and prosecution of our measures to attain the same
end, and dispose us to yield to disappointment with a better grace. That an acquaintance with history has this effect,
I appeal to what any person feels after reading of the un-
timely end of Agis, Cato, Brutus, Hampden, and the great
Algernon Sydney. The honorable mention that will to the
end of the world be made of such glorious though unfortu-
nate men as these, will raise up more friends to the same
great interests; while their misfortunes will only serve to
make those friends more prudent, and therefore, probably,
more successful in their endeavors.

But, independently of these martyrs of liberty raising up
more and more successful patrons of it, the consideration of
the remarkable reverses of fortune, in the history of considerable personages, has a fine effect upon the human
mind. It wonderfully softens and calms it, and gives it an
excellent temper for encountering with the vicissitudes of
life. What other sensations do we feel, while we read that
Henrietta, daughter of Henry IV of France, and wife to
Charles I of England, was reduced to the utmost extremity
of poverty; and that her daughter, who was afterwards married to a brother of Louis XIV, is said to have lain in bed
for want of fuel to keep her warm, while the people of Paris,
blind with rage, paid no attention to their sufferings? The
same kind of sensations we feel when we read of the great
and successful general Belisarius (if the story be true) beg-
ging his bread; of Cortez, the renowned conqueror of Mexico, living unknown and in disgrace in Spain, and scarce
able to get to speak to his master, Charles V, though when
the king asked who the fellow was that was so clamorous
to speak to him, he cried out, "I am one who have gotten

your majesty more provinces than your father left you towns." He afterwards served in a rank little higher than that of a common soldier, on the coast of Barbary.

Fifthly, these great reverses of fortune, and calamities of men in high stations, at the same time that they are hardly ever known to discourage men of ability and spirit from undertaking the public service when regularly called to it, may justly make persons who are born to private stations, and who have no opportunity of rising above them, content with their situation. The many who have abdicated royalty, as Christiana, Queen of Sweden; Charles V, Emperor of Germany; Victor Amadeus, King of Sardinia; John Casimir, King of Poland; and others, convince us that crowns do not always sit easy; and that persons in high stations have need of a strong sense of honor and integrity to make their fatigues and misfortunes tolerable.

It is no unuseful sentiment that we collect from reading that Richelieu shortened his days by the uneasiness with which he was devoured in the fulness of his power. What Voltaire says of Louis XIV, is an excellent memento to the ambitious: that he saw all his family perish by premature deaths; that though, towards the close of his life, he appeared in public as usual, in private, the pain of his many misfortunes pierced him to the heart, and threw him into convulsions; that he met with domestic losses at the conclusion of an unsuccessful war, and before he was sure of obtaining a peace, and at a time when a famine had wasted his kingdom; and that he lost in the minds of his subjects, during the last three years of his life, all the respect and esteem he had gained by his great actions.

The advantage of preferring a private situation, especially to entering into the views of faction, we see in the security and long life of Atticus, in the most distracted times of the Roman history; and in Richard Cromwell, who lived to a great age, contented and happy, whereas his father never knew what happiness was. The history of very few great statesmen can match that of Cardinal Fleury, of whom we read that his schemes were crowned with success from the year 1726 to 1742; that he lived ninety years, and preserved his faculties unimpaired to the last; which makes his historian say that if ever there was a happy man upon earth, it was doubtless Cardinal Fleury.

Lastly, those observations on the tempers and manners of men, which we may collect every day from common life, affect us much more strongly when we see them exemplified in the history of great personages. We see, for instance, every day, that almost all persons who are entrusted with power, abuse it. But this is better exemplified in kings and ministers of state. We see again, that men in low circumstances are apt to be despised, and that court is always paid to the great and the powerful. But this maxim receives a stronger confirmation, and makes a deeper impression, than any occurrence in private life could occasion, when we think what court was paid to Oliver Cromwell by all the princes of Europe; while Charles II, then in exile, could not obtain an interview with the ministers of either France or Spain, at the Treaty of the Pyrenees, though he made a journey on purpose to obtain it.

It is a common and just observation, that, through the inconstancy of our nature, men are liable to conceive hasty and unreasonable disgust at their situation, and yet, when they have changed it, wish to resume it; and this we see exemplified in private life almost every day. But ever so many examples of this kind do not make so great an impression upon us as the history of Victor Amadeus, King of Sardinia, who abdicated the crown through mere caprice; but found, as some historian says, that the company of his mistress, who was become his wife, devotion, and the tranquility of retirement, could not satisfy a soul occupied during fifty years with the affairs of Europe. He was desirous of regaining the throne even by force, and afterwards died in confinement.

How incapable riches and power are to satisfy the mind of man is an observation which few persons, in the course of their own experience, have not seen occasion to make. But the sentiment makes a deeper impression upon us when we see it exemplified in the history of statesmen and conquerors, and as it is beautifully exhibited in a conversation which passed between Pyrrhus and his minister Cyneas, before their expedition into Italy. The minister asked the king what he proposed to do when he had subdued the Romans. He answered, "Pass into Sicily." "What then?" said the minister. "Conquer the Carthaginians," replies the king. "And what follows that?" says the minister. "Be sovereign of Greece, and then enjoy ourselves," said the king. "And why," replied the sensible minister, "can we not do this last even now?"

To add one instance more: We see the vanity of the living, in their boundless provision for futurity, and in the dissipation of the large fortunes of covetous persons, by the extravagance of their heirs. But it does not affect us near so much as when we are reading in history that the riches which Sixtus V amassed in his pontificate, and those which Henry IV of France had with great difficulty saved, were squandered away within less than a year after their deaths; also, that the treasure which Henry VII of England had raised by every art of extortion, went almost as fast.

Thus we have seen how, by history, our minds are agreeably entertained, our passions are exercised, and our judgments are formed, so as either to fit us for the business of life, or furnish us with materials for science; how sentiments of virtue are acquired, and the best moral maxims of conduct are most deeply impressed upon our minds. All these advantages result from history as a study. There are other advantages resulting to mankind from it, in a different manner, as only one instrument of recording transactions. How imperfect, for instance, without history, would be our knowledge of genealogies, and consequently of the order of important successions; and how precarious would be the advantage resulting from conventions and treaties of all kinds, if all the articles of them were reposited only in the memory of the contracting parties! We read that the boundaries of some of the Grecian states were once determined by a verse of Homer, who, in his description of Greece, relates what they were in his time.

The preceding account of the uses of history will assist us in determining what has formerly been a subject of debate among the critics; namely, at what age history is proper to be read.

Considering the various uses to which the study of history has been shown to be subservient, I see no reason why we should hesitate to pronounce that it can neither be begun too early, nor continued too late. If history amuse the imagination, exercise and improve the passions, inspire a taste for true glory, just sentiments of, and a love for, virtue, and thereby form the temper, and prepare men for conversing with the world — what can be more proper for young persons? And since the mind cannot be too well furnished in these respects, and men cannot have too large a stock of this anticipated experience, the study of it must be useful while there remains anything of the part we have to act on the theater of the world. Moreover, since history furnishes materials for the finest speculations and the most important sciences, it cannot but be of service while we make any use of our intellectual faculties.

Since history may be considered as containing examples of the sciences of morals and politics chiefly, no doubt a person who has studied these sciences is qualified to read history with more pleasure and advantage. But then it must likewise be considered that it is impossible to be master of these sciences without a knowledge of history. Their influences and uses are reciprocal. Thus the person who has studied the grammar of any language will read authors who have written in it, with more ease and advantage. But grammars could never have been made without a previous knowledge of the languages for which they were made, nor even learned, without the use of examples borrowed from those languages.

That young persons are not capable of making a right use of historical examples in a moral respect was obviated when the advantages of history above experience were mentioned. If what was said there be considered, it will appear much safer for a child to be treated with a piece of history, than to hear the common news of the town he lives in. It is certain that neither in the one nor the other is exact justice done to the characters of men in the events of their lives. But in history it is done much more completely than it is within the compass of any particular person's observation.

A proper regard, no doubt, ought to be had to the age, experience, and previously acquired knowledge, as well as the intended sphere of life, of the persons to whom particular histories are recommended. It would be very preposterous to advise any person to begin the study of history with such writers as Polybius or Tacitus, and to end with Livy, Quintus Curtius, or Cornelius Nepos. Common sense will direct that histories which tend chiefly to amuse the imagination, or enforce the plainest instructions in morals, ought rather to be recommended to young persons, who will both have the most relish for such works, and to whom they will be of the greatest use; and that histories which furnish more exercise for the judgment should be reserved for an age in which that faculty is riper. However, there can be no great inconvenience in young persons being indulged in reading almost all histories promiscuously. Their natural disposition and previous acquirements will direct them to what they are most capable of profiting by, and the higher uses of the same works may be safely left to be reaped at a second perusal, in a more advanced stage of life. No general history is better calculated for the use of young persons than that of Rollin.[6]

[6] Charles Rollin (1661-1741) was a French educator and author, whose *Histoire Ancienne* in thirteen volumes was translated into English and published in London between 1738 and 1740.

A Course of Lectures on the Theory of Language, and Universal Grammar

From his experience in teaching at Warrington, Priestley wrote two books on grammar: The Rudiments of English Grammar *(1761) and* A Course of Lectures on the Theory of Language, and Universal Grammar *(1762). The next selection, Lecture XII of the latter work, illustrates Priestley's interest in the history of language.[7] There were a total of nineteen lectures in the series.*

OF THE REGULAR GROWTH AND CORRUPTION OF LANGUAGES

Languages, like all other arts which owe their cultivation, if not their invention, to men, which subsist by their use of them, and are daily subject to human caprice, cannot be expected to continue long in the same state. Whether ancient or modern, whether simple or complex in their structure, they have a kind of regular growth, improvement, and declension; and are moreover liable to many intermediate fluctuations. No internal constitution can preserve them either from the general revolutions, or the particular accidents.

The regular growth of languages proceeds from the necessity of giving names to new objects, new ideas, and new combinations of ideas; combinations existing, either in nature, or formed in the imagination. Hence the language of those nations hath ever grown copious whose situation and occasions were such as brought them acquainted with various scenes of nature, or obliged them to have recourse to the improvements of art.

[7] Text from Rutt, XXIII, 191-199.

The private life and policy of the Hebrews, living under an absolute monarchy, and whose religion forbade them the use of the arts of painting and statuary, and the immediate design of which was to keep them clear of all connection with neighboring nations, was too uniform to afford them many opportunities or occasions of enlarging or embellishing their language.

Whereas the Greeks — divided into a great number of separate communities, perpetually vying with each other in power, policy, commerce, and arts; most of the states republics, where all kinds of honors and emoluments were the prize of eloquence; whose private policy abounded with such institutions as games, festivals, etc., which drew a vast concourse of people together, and where men distinguished themselves by their talents in public speaking; where not only public consultations were held for the general utility of Greece, but poems, and even histories, were recited in public — could not fail giving particular attention to their language. And Athens, whose constitution was a more perfect democracy, and in other respects afforded more scope for the use of language, and where the rewards of literary excellence were more certain and more inviting, was deemed to be in a more especial manner the seat of eloquence in Greece. The Athenians in general valued themselves upon their exquisite taste for the purity and propriety of their language, and among them the arts of oratory were held in reputation, and flourished long after polite literature was totally forgotten in every other part of Greece.

Next to the Athenians, the inhabitants of the seaport towns of Asia Minor, addicted to commerce, subject to frequent revolutions, and peculiarly connected with Athens, distinguished themselves for their skill in the powers of language.

Universally, in countries where there were no arts to exercise the inventive faculties of men, and to augment and diversify their stock of ideas, nor any other inducement to excel in the use of speech, language has been very barren, and in every respect ill adapted to express the ideas of more cultivated minds. What the poems were that Ovid wrote in the Getic language, we are not informed; but certain we may be, from the nature of things, that they must have fallen infinitely short of his Latin compositions; if not in delicacy of sentiment, at least in accuracy and ease of expression.

The progress of human life in general is from poverty to riches, and from riches to luxury and ruin. In architecture, structures have always been at first heavy and inconvenient, then useful and ornamental, and lastly, real propriety and magnificence have been lost in superfluous decorations. Our very dress is at first plain and awkward, then easy and elegant, and lastly, downright fantastical. Stages of a similar nature may be observed in the progress of all human arts; and language, being liable to the same influences, has undergone the same changes. Whenever a language has emerged from its first rough state of nature, and has acquired a sufficient *copia* of significant and harmonious terms, arbitrary and whimsical ideas of excellence have been superadded to those which were natural and becoming, till at length the latter have been entirely sacrificed to the former.

I shall exemplify these observations by a short history of the revolutions of the Roman language. About the time of the first Punic War, when the inscription upon the *Columna Rostrata* was written, the Latin tongue seems to have been very barbarous, and void of that regularity and harmony which it was afterwards distinguished by. In consequence of more extensive connections with foreign countries and states; in consequence of the Romans having more power, wealth, and influence to contend for among themselves, and especially upon the introduction of the Grecian arts and sciences; all the chief men of the state applied themselves with indefatigable assiduity to the cultivation of their language, and in one age it arrived to all the perfection it ever attained.

In this state it continued till the dissolution of the Commonwealth; after which time, when little use was made of the *Rostrum*, and judicial proceedings took a form which left little to the pleader; when, in short, the practice of oratory did not bring along with it those honors and advantages that had formerly attended it; in those circumstances, persons addicted to letters having no occasion for the ancient manly and free eloquence, fell, through an affectation of novelty, into a number of trifling and puerile refinements in style: analogies, instead of being fetched from nature, were borrowed from language itself; and verbal conceits and turns were admired for true wit and just sentiment. Afterwards, upon the irruption of the northern barbarians, the language itself became mixed and adulterated, as well as the taste of the writers corrupted; universal confusion was introduced, and the old Roman tongue entirely lost.

There are certain limits beyond which the growth of a language cannot extend. Whatever be the improvements in human life and the human mind; let men's acquaintance with the powers of nature and art be ever so extensive; their ideas and those combinations and relations of them which it will be at all convenient to express by words, cannot be infinite. When, therefore, a people have words and modifications of words sufficient for the occasions they have for the use of them, for the language to grow still more copious, and to have words and modifications to express more things and relations than they could attend to, were absurd and burdensome. Trees, in the most proper soil and climate, grow but to a certain height; and when arrived to their full size, all the redundant juices serve only to nourish various excrescences, as funguses, mosses, etc., which deform and waste them. In like manner, all the pains that we bestow upon a language, when it is sufficiently perfect for all the uses of it, serve only to disfigure it, to lessen its real value, and encumber it with useless rules and refinements, which embarrass the speaker or writer, and are of no advantage to the hearer or reader.

The time in which a language arrives at its perfection, it is natural to conjecture, will be when the people that speak it have occasion to make the greatest use of it; which will be when their power and influence abroad, and when arts, sciences, and liberty at home, are at the greatest height. As these grow less considerable, the language will naturally contract itself with the occasions of it, if it be not preserved by writing.

When a language is complete in all its parts, and the grammar of it has received its last improvement, the introduction of a few new terms, suited to casual new ideas and occurrences, and adjusted to the established rules, does not deserve the name of an improvement in the language. We do not call an oak that is grown to its full size more perfect for an additional leaf or acorn. Perhaps one entire century favorable to the polite arts may have been sufficient, in general, to bring any language to its perfection.

Before a language has acquired a sufficient number of modifications and forms of speech, different forms must necessarily be adopted by different persons; but the best forms of speech, the most commodious for use, and the most agreeable to the analogy of the language, will at length establish themselves, and become universal, by their superior excellence; and at the time that a language has begun to be spoken and written with uniformity, it may be taken for granted to be arrived to its maturity and perfection; for, till a sufficient number of forms have become universal, different forms will occur to different persons, and the language will be written with great dissimilarity. The English language, in particular, cannot be said to have been fixed till about the reign of Queen Anne. Before that time, every writer adopted what words he thought proper from foreign tongues. Only a small part of them have since that period been in use; but they are now perfectly incorporated with the language, and our most licentious writers of any reputation are very sparing in introducing others.

In general, those writings which have contributed to fix

a language are deemed classical in a country; and a studied imitation of them by succeeding writers tends still more to promote a perfect uniformity in writing.

The progress of a language towards perfection may be considerably accelerated by the labors of persons who give their attention to it; if they study the analogy of the language, recommend phrases that are agreeable to it, and detect and expose those that are improper. While literary critics keep within these bounds, and their opinions are left to recommend themselves by their own weight, they do a very important service to a language; but when their decisions have the sanction of any authority, and forms of speech are adopted because recommended by them, and not on account of the reasons that might be alleged in their favor, since all men, and all bodies of men, are fallible, the interposition of their authority is in danger of contributing to establish phrases and constructions which the more mature judgment of after ages would see reason to correct; and though the spirit of men will assert their liberty in rejecting what they do not approve, such undue influence may keep a language much longer in an imperfect state than it otherwise would have been.

All the real service that any men, or bodies of men, can do to a language, is to analyze it into its parts, to show distinctly what are the materials and composition of it, and thereby make the whole structure of it perfectly understood. For when, by the judicious disposition of everything belonging to a language, all its analogies are seen at one view, it will presently appear what is redundant, deficient, or ambiguous, in the words or construction of it.

Before an improvement can be made of anything, its present powers must be perfectly known. Before we can improve upon nature, by an artificial combination of its powers, the laws of nature must be understood; and they are only to be understood by a careful observation of what does in fact take place in consequence of them. A digest of these observations makes a system of natural philosophy.

In like manner, to improve upon a language, observations must be made upon the manner in which words are actually used in it. A methodical enumeration of the rules and laws of its construction is the grammar of it; as a dictionary is that which contains all the words of a language, and an account of all the senses in which they are used. If the language be a dead one, the remains only of the writers of it can be made use of; if it be a living one, the forms of conversation must not be wholly overlooked. In the former case, no innovations can be made. Those who wrote in the language while it was a living one, will be accounted the standards of it; and even their imperfections must be adopted by all who use it after them; unless (as has been thought of with respect to some of the dead languages) mankind should agree to form a more perfect and philosophical language out of the remains of it; in which case, it could no longer be considered as a dead, but as a revived and living language.

In modern and living languages, it is absurd to pretend to set up the compositions of any person or persons whatsoever as the standard of writing, or their conversation as the invariable rule of speaking. With respect to customs, laws, and everything that is changeable, the body of a people, who, in this respect, cannot but be free, will certainly assert their liberty in making what innovations they judge to be expedient and useful. The general prevailing custom, whatever it happen to be, can be the only standard for the time that it prevails. And in a case that admits of no authority to control a man's actions, it is in vain to pretend that any person may not attempt to introduce whatever he thinks to be an improvement. Indeed, the fear of becoming ridiculous is sufficient to prevent many very extravagant and absurd proposals.

The chief thing to be attended to in the improvement of a language is the analogy of it. The more consistent are its principles, the more it is of a piece with itself, the more commodious it will be for use; and it cannot be looked upon as any great or alarming innovation, merely to disuse some constructions that clash with others, and to confine one's self to one sense of any single word or phrase.

That immense and valuable performance of Mr. Johnson's contains an account of almost all the senses in which all the words of the English language are used; and it is very possible, from little more than the examples he has given, from our best writers, of the use of every word in every sense, to compose a grammar of all the varieties of manner in which words are used, both as to their inflection and disposition, which, together with the *Dictionary,* would be a complete system of our language as now used.

Merely to drop what, from a view of such a system, were apparently useless and inconvenient, would make the language as perfect as the general nature of it would admit. To introduce into it all that, upon the same view, would appear to be wanting to it, might seem too great an innovation, to alter its nature and character, and make another language; and if it were thought necessary to form a new language, it were better to begin from the first, upon the most philosophical principles, than take for the foundation of it any of the imperfect languages now in use.

A Course of Lectures on Oratory and Criticism

A Course of Lectures on Oratory and Criticism was prepared while Priestley was a tutor at Warrington but was not published until 1777. This eighteenth-century textbook of rhetoric consists of thirty-five lectures and runs more than two hundred pages in length. While its importance in the history of elocution is not great, it offers an interesting sidelight on Priestley's versatile career and is particularly striking in view of the speech defect from which he suffered, described in his Memoirs, *above, p. 16. Lecture I and part of Lecture XV are presented here.*[8]

THE INTRODUCTION
AND THE DISTRIBUTION OF THE SUBJECT

The use of speech is common to all mankind. For we find none of the human race but who are capable of expressing their ideas, sentiments, and intentions to others, in a more or less adequate manner, by words; and this capacity was necessary to that mutual intercourse and free communication without which beings of our social nature could not be happy.

It is the province of art to improve upon nature, by adding to her powers and advantages; and, for the exercise of our intellectual and active powers, all the gifts of nature are little more than the bare unwrought materials of those accomplishments, from which result the dignity and refined happiness of social life.

Thus, oratory is the natural faculty of speech improved by art; whereby the use of it is perfected, facilitated, and

[8] Text from Rutt, XXIII, 260-263, 340-343.

extended, and, consequently, its value and influence greatly increased. And the excellence of this art is the more generally acknowledged, and its effects the more admired, because, language being common to us all, all men can the more easily conceive both the importance and the difficulty of the improvements of which it is capable.

Very few persons ever find themselves at a loss to deliver a single sentence or two at a time; because they are able to see at one view the whole of what they intend to say. But it is not common to find a person able to acquit himself with propriety in a speech of considerable length, even though he prepare himself by digesting beforehand all that he intends to say; because the order and connection of sentiment, and variety of diction, necessary in a continued speech, are not easily carried in memory; and it requires a very extraordinary invention and recollection to speak long, in a proper and graceful manner, quite extempore. Nor can a person, without the assistance of art and instruction, even compose a set discourse upon any subject; because it requires greater exactness in the use of words, more accuracy of method, and variety of transition, than persons uninstructed and unused to composition can be masters of. For this reason, we see many persons who make a good figure in conversation, by no means able to make a speech, or a composition of any considerable length. It is in this respect, where the powers of nature fail us, in expressing our sentiments to advantage, that we have recourse to the art of oratory.

It may not be amiss, at the entrance upon these *Lectures on Oratory and Criticism,* to promise one caution; which is, that we must not expect too much from the art; since this can do little for us in comparison of what must be the fruit of our own previous application to science. The art of oratory can only consist of rules for the proper use of those materials which must be acquired from various study and observation, of which, therefore, unless a person be possessed, no art of oratory can make him an orator.

In order to speak or write well upon any subject, it is necessary that that subject be thoroughly understood, that every argument which is to be used be previously collected, and the value of it ascertained. How absurd, for instance, would it be to imagine that a person who had never studied law, government, and history, should be enabled, by the art of oratory, to make a political harangue, or write a dissertation upon the constitution of a state! With what success would an orator, who had not studied the law, undertake the defense of a client? Or a person wholly unacquainted with morals or theology, attempt to speak from the pulpit? Whatever subject, therefore, any person intends to write or speak upon, he must, by applying to the proper sources, acquire a perfect knowledge of it, before he can expect any assistance from the art of oratory, as such.

Moreover, let a person be ever so perfect a master of his subject, he could not be taught to speak or write about it with propriety and good effect, without being previously instructed in the principles of grammar, that is, without a knowledge of the inflection of words, and of the structure of sentences, in the language he makes use of.

It is necessary, likewise, as far as reasoning is concerned, that a person be, in some sense, a logician before he be an orator; since it is by the rules of logic that we judge of everything relating to arguments, their perspicuity or confusion, their fallacy or their force. More especially is it of consequence to every orator whose business is with men, to be well acquainted with human nature, that, knowing the passions, prejudices, interests, and views of those he has to do with, he may know how to address them accordingly.

But notwithstanding this be treated of in many books written on the subject of oratory, and particularly by Aristotle, there is no more reason why we should encumber a system of oratory with it, than that we crowd into it the elements of any other science, or branch of knowledge, that the orator may have occasion for. Besides, those plain principles of human actions with which the orator has to do are obvious to common reflection, and must have occurred to every person before he has lived to the age in which he has any occasion for the art of oratory. For this part of the furniture of an orator, therefore, let the student have recourse to ethical treatises, as far as they unfold the principles of human nature; let him study authentic histories of human characters and conduct; and let him principally attend to the emotions of his own heart. However, that knowledge of human nature, which is necessary to understand the rationale of the ornaments of style, will not be excluded a place in these *Lectures,* but will be explained pretty much at large in the third part of the course.

Supposing a man, therefore, to be perfectly acquainted with the subject on which he proposes to speak or write, that he is not deficient in the knowledge of grammatical propriety, and that by logic, natural or artificial, he can judge of the force or fallacy of any argument that occurs, or is proposed to him; it is asked, what assistance he may expect from the art of oratory, in carrying his design into execution in the most advantageous manner? In this case, all that remains to be done is:

1. To assist him in the habit of recollection, or to direct him which way to turn his thoughts, in order to find the arguments and illustrations with which his mind is already furnished; and likewise, when a general topic, or head of discourse, is found, in what manner to confirm or illustrate it, in order to have materials for the bulk or body of the discourse. In this manner oratory may assist the invention; but it is not in finding things with which the mind was wholly unacquainted, but in readily recollecting, and judiciously selecting, what is proper for his purpose, out of the materials with which the mind was previously furnished.

2. The art of oratory teaches in what order to dispose of those topics. It shows what disposition of the materials of a discourse will give them the greatest force, and contribute the most to produce the effect intended by it.

3. To contribute still farther to the effect of a discourse, the art of oratory teaches what style, or manner of expression, will best become, adorn, and recommend it.

4. If the discourse is to be pronounced, the art of oratory teaches what tone of voice, or what gestures of the body, will best become, and add grace to the delivery of it.

The four great objects, therefore, that fall within the province of the orator, are, recollection, method, style, and elocution. Of these I shall treat in the order in which they are here mentioned.

OF FORMS OF ADDRESS
ADAPTED TO GAIN BELIEF

. . . The perfection of speaking is, certainly, to speak extempore. All men must, in a greater or less degree, have tried their talent this way, and have found the difficulty of succeeding in it. Hence people listen with a continued wonder while a person is delivering himself fluently without notes, and their admiration concurs with the fore-mentioned causes to attach them to the speaker, to his sentiments and views. Can we imagine it possible that the primitive Christians, the first reformers, and, I may add, the founders of our modern sects, such as the Independents, Quakers, and Methodists, could ever have attained to so great a degree of popularity, without the talent of haranguing extempore? Can we, then, wonder at the success of a judicious and happy imitation of those extempore forms of address?

As a caution against making too free with these very bold forms of address, which are adapted to show that a man is in earnest, and confident of the goodness of his cause, I would advise that no one appeal to another, unless it be morally certain that the person he appeals to, and boldly expostulates with, will really take his part, or, at least, that it will be generally allowed that he ought to do it. Otherwise he exposes his own vain confidence, and betrays the cause he espouses.

Let no person venture to exclaim and apostrophize, unless the importance, as well as the goodness of his cause, will justify it. These strong, natural emotions, are not to be counterfeited. To these arcana of nature it is hardly possible that artifice should have access; and if the circumstances and occasions of the address will not justify such vehemence of style, a man makes himself ridiculous by attempting the imposition. Besides, direct exclamations and apostrophes to persons not present, or to things inanimate, though ever so just, ought to be used very sparingly; since, if they produce their natural and full effect, they raise the attention to such a degree as cannot be kept up long.

It is, likewise, proper that all Englishmen in particular should be informed that a person of a liberal education in this country can hardly ever be in such a situation, as will not render the imitation of some of the boldest, the most successful, and admired strokes of Roman, not to say Grecian eloquence, extremely improper and ridiculous. The English pulpit, the English bar, and the English senate, require an eloquence more addressed to the reason, and less directly to the passions, than the harangues of a Roman pleader, or the speech of a Roman senator. Our hearers have generally more good sense and just discernment, at least they are naturally more cool and phlegmatic; both which qualities check a propensity to strong emotions; and marks of great vehemence must appear absurd in a speaker, when the audience is unmoved, and sees nothing to occasion such emotion.

An audience, indeed, that is wholly illiterate, may have all their passions actuated by means of admiration or astonishment, and mechanical communication; but then there are few English audiences composed wholly of persons of so little reading and reflection as makes that practicable. And it is hardly possible that a person whose reading has lain among modern English books, or has conversed with persons of a liberal education, should not have acquired more delicacy of taste, than to be taken with that gross and direct address to the passions, which Cicero adopted with applause. The refinement of modern times requires that we speak, upon all occasions, with more temper, and use more address in raising the passions.

If a person adopt any of the forms of address which derive their beauty, force, and efficacy, from their seeming to be extemporary, as well as those which express great earnestness and vehemence; all his gestures, the air of his countenance, and his whole manner, should correspond to them; because certain gestures and motions of the countenance universally accompany natural vehemence, and genuine extemporary expression. When these things, which have so strong a connection in nature, are not united, the whole must appear extremely unnatural, the imperfect artifice will be easily seen through, and the imposter be deservedly exposed.

If a person never attempt these forms of speech but when his temper really corresponds to and dictates them, he will seldom fail in point of propriety; because the state of mind being strongly associated with those correspondent motions, they are excited mechanically and justly. No attention can supply the place of this. The external expressions of passion, with all their variations, corresponding to the different degrees of their emotions, are too complex for any person in the circumstances of a public speaker to be able to attend to them. Or, were it possible, the difference between a genuine automatic and a voluntary motion, is sufficiently apparent. All motions that are automatic have a quickness and vigor which are lost when they become voluntary; witness sighing, laughing, the gestures peculiar to anger, etc., and the same when imitated. The difference is too apparent to escape any person's observation.

If these observations be sufficiently attended to, they will deter any prudent and considerate person from attempting phrases and modes of address, expressive of earnestness, when they do not really feel those emotions, which will, of themselves, suggest the proper attitudes and gestures corresponding to them.

These cautions are given in this place, because they peculiarly relate to those forms of address which express earnestness, extreme confidence in the goodness of one's cause, and that quick conception and animated delivery natural to extemporary speaking, which have now been explained. They are, indeed, applicable, but not in the same degree, to the remaining forms of address which are adapted to gain belief.

Although Priestley's writings on political theory were not extensive, they made a significant contribution to the tradition of political liberalism both in England and in America. His chief work in this field was An Essay on the First Principles of Government *(1768). It revealed the influence of earlier political theorists, notably John Locke and Jean Jacques Rousseau, but it in turn was a molding influence on later political thinkers, notably Jeremy Bentham, who acknowledged indebtedness to it for the famous phrase "the greatest happiness of the greatest number."* [1] *Priestley's* Essay on Government *was widely read in the young American republic and was especially recommended by Thomas Jefferson.* [2] *The following extracts from Sections I, II, and V of this work are noteworthy not only as pleas for political and religious liberty but also as illustrations of the eighteenth-century confidence in social progress and human perfectibility.* [3]

[1] Harold J. Laski, *Political Thought in England, from Locke to Bentham* (New York and London, 1920), pp. 190-196.

[2] Wilson O. Clough, ed., *Our Long Heritage: Pages from the Books Our Founding Fathers Read* (Minneapolis, 1955), pp. 251-254 and 261; see also Clinton Rossiter, *Seedtime of the Republic: The Origin of the American Tradition of Political Liberty* (New York, 1953), pp. 358-360.

[3] Text of selections from John T. Rutt, ed., *The Theological and Miscellaneous Works of Joseph Priestley* (25 vols., London, 1817-1832), XXII, 8-13, 54-57, 64-67, 71-72. For a thorough discussion of the political milieu in which Priestley moved, consult the excellent study by Caroline Robbins, *The Eighteenth-Century Commonwealthman* (Cambridge, Mass., 1959).

OF THE FIRST PRINCIPLES OF GOVERNMENT
AND THE DIFFERENT KINDS OF LIBERTY

Man derives two capital advantages from the superiority of his intellectual powers. The first is that, as an individual, he possesses a certain comprehension of mind, whereby he contemplates and enjoys the past and the future, as well as the present. This comprehension is enlarged with the experience of every day; and by this means the happiness of man, as he advances in intellect, is continually less dependent on temporary circumstances and sensations.

The next advantage resulting from the same principle, and which is, in many respects, both the cause and effect of the former, is that the human species itself is capable of a similar and unbounded improvement; whereby mankind in a later age are greatly superior to mankind in a former age, the individuals being taken at the same time of life. Of this progress of the species, brute animals are more incapable than they are of that relating to individuals. No horse of this age seems to have any advantage over other horses of former ages; and if there be any improvement in the species, it is owing to our manner of breeding and training them. But a man at this time, who has been tolerably well educated, in an improved Christian country, is a being possessed of much greater power to be, and to make happy, than a person of the same age, in the same or any other country, some centuries ago. And, for this reason, I make no doubt that a person some centuries hence will, at the same age, be as much superior to us.

The great instrument in the hand of Divine Providence, of this progress of the species towards perfection, is society, and, consequently, government. In a state of nature the powers of any individual are dissipated by an attention to a multiplicity of objects. The employments of all are similar. From generation to generation every man does the same that every other does, or has done, and no person begins where another ends; at least, general improvements are exceedingly slow and uncertain. This we see exemplified in all barbarous nations, and especially in countries thinly inhabited, where the connections of the people are slight, and consequently, society and government very imperfect; and it may be seen more particularly in North America and Greenland. Whereas a state of more perfect society admits of a proper distribution and division of the objects of human attention. In such a state, men are connected with and subservient to one another; so that, while one man confines himself to one single object, another may give the same undivided attention to another object.

Thus the powers of all have their full effect; and hence arise improvements in all the conveniences of life, and in every branch of knowledge. In this state of things, it requires but a few years to comprehend the whole preceding progress of any one art or science; and the rest of a man's life, in which his faculties are the most perfect, may be given to the extension of it. If, by this means, one art or science should grow too large for an easy comprehension, in a moderate space of time, a commodious subdivision will be made. Thus all knowledge will be subdivided and extended; and knowledge, as Lord Bacon observes, being power, the human powers will, in fact, be enlarged; nature, including both its materials and its laws, will be more at our command; men will make their situation in this world abundantly more easy and comfortable; they will probably prolong their existence in it, and will grow daily more happy, each in himself, and more able (and, I believe, more disposed) to communicate happiness to others. Thus whatever was the beginning of this world, the end will be glorious and paradisiacal, beyond what our imaginations can now conceive. Extravagant as some may suppose these views to be, I think I could show them to be fairly suggested by the true theory of human nature, and to arise from the natural course of human affairs. But, for the present, I waive this subject, the contemplation of which always makes me happy.

Government being the great instrument of this progress of the human species towards this glorious state, that form of government will have a just claim to our approbation which favors this progress, and that must be condemned in which it is retarded. Let us, then, my fellow citizens, consider the business of government with these enlarged views, and trace some of the fundamental principles of it, by an attention to what is most conducive to the happiness of mankind at present, and most favorable to the increase of this happiness in futurity; and, perhaps, we may understand this intricate subject, with some of its most important circumstances, better than we have done; at least, we may see some of them in a clearer and stronger point of light.

To begin with first principles, we must, for the sake of gaining clear ideas on the subject, do what almost all political writers have done before us; that is, we must suppose a number of people existing, who experience the inconvenience of living independent and unconnected; who are exposed, without redress, to insults and wrongs of every kind, and are too weak to procure themselves many of the advantages, which they are sensible might easily be compassed by united strength. These people, if they would engage the protection of the whole body, and join their force in enterprises and undertakings calculated for their common good, must voluntarily resign some part of their natural liberty, and submit their conduct to the direction of the community; for without these concessions, such an alliance, attended with such advantages, could not be formed.

Were these people few in number, and living within a

small distance of one another, it might be easy for them to assemble upon every occasion, in which the whole body was concerned; and everything might be determined by the votes of the majority, provided they had previously agreed that the votes of a majority should be decisive. But were the society numerous, their habitations remote, and the occasions on which the whole body must interpose frequent, it would be absolutely impossible that all the members of the state should assemble, or give their attention to public business. In this case, though, with Rousseau, it be a giving up of their liberty, there must be deputies, or public officers, appointed to act in the name of the whole body; and, in a state of very great extent, where all the people could never be assembled, the whole power of the community must necessarily, and almost irreversibly, be lodged in the hands of these deputies. In England, the king, the hereditary lords, and the electors of the House of Commons, are these standing deputies; and the members of the House of Commons are again the temporary deputies of this last order of the state.

In all states, great or small, the sentiments of that body of men in whose hands the supreme power of the society is lodged must be understood to be the sentiments of the whole body, if there be no other method in which the sentiments of the whole body can be expressed. These deputies, or representatives of the people, will make a wrong judgment, and pursue wrong measures, if they consult not the good of the whole society, whose representatives they are; just as the people themselves would make a wrong judgment, and pursue wrong measures, if they did not consult their own good, provided they could be assembled for that purpose. No maxims or rules of policy can be binding upon them, but such as they themselves shall judge to be conducive to the public good. Their own reason and conscience are their only guide, and the people, in whose name they act, their only judge.

In these circumstances, if I be asked what I mean by

liberty, I should choose, for the sake of greater clearness, to divide it into two kinds, political and civil; and the importance of having clear ideas on this subject, will be my apology for the innovation. Political liberty, I would say, consists in the power which the members of the state reserve to themselves, of arriving at the public offices, or, at least, of having votes in the nomination of those who fill them; and I would choose to call civil liberty, that power over their own actions, which the members of the state reserve to themselves, and which their officers must not infringe.

Political liberty, therefore, is equivalent to the right of magistracy, being the claim that any member of the state has, to have his private opinion or judgment become that of the public, and thereby control the actions of others; whereas civil liberty extends no farther than to a man's own conduct, and signifies the right he has to be exempt from the control of the society, or its agents; that is, the power he has of providing for his own advantage and happiness. It is a man's civil liberty which is originally in its full force, and part of which he sacrifices when he enters into a state of society; and political liberty is that which he may, or may not acquire in the compensation he receives for it. For he may either stipulate to have a voice in the public determinations, or as far as the public determination takes place, he may submit to be governed wholly by others. Of these two kinds of liberty, which it is of the greatest importance to distinguish, I shall treat in the order in which I have mentioned them.

OF POLITICAL LIBERTY

In countries where every member of the society enjoys an equal power of arriving at the supreme offices, and consequently of directing the strength and the sentiments of the whole community, there is a state of the most perfect political liberty. On the other hand, in countries where a man is, by his birth or fortune, excluded from these offices, or from a power of voting for proper persons to fill them; that man, whatever be the form of the government, or whatever civil liberty, or power over his own actions he may have, has no power over those of another; he has no share in the government, and therefore, has no political liberty at all. Nay, his own conduct, as far as the society does interfere, is, in all cases, directed by others.

It may be said that no society on earth was ever formed in the manner represented above. I answer, it is true; because all governments whatever, have been, in some measure, compulsory, tyrannical, and oppressive in their origin; but the method I have described must be allowed to be the only equitable and fair method of forming a society. And since every man retains, and can never be deprived of his natural right (founded on a regard to the general good) of relieving himself from all oppression, that is, from everything that has been imposed upon him without his own consent, this must be the only true and proper foundation of all the governments subsisting in the world, and that to which the people who compose them have an unalienable right to bring them back.

It must necessarily be understood, therefore, whether it be expressed or not, that all people live in society for their mutual advantage; so that the good and happiness of the members, that is, the majority of the members of any state, is the great standard by which everything relating to that state must finally be determined.[4] And though it may be supposed, that a body of people may be bound, by a voluntary resignation of all their interests, to a single person, or to a few, it can never be supposed that the resignation is obligatory on their posterity; because it is manifestly contrary to the good of the whole that it should be so.

[4] This is the sentence which so greatly impressed Bentham. See Charles W. Everett, *The Education of Jeremy Bentham* (New York, 1931), pp. 38, 47.

I own it is rather matter of surprise to me, that this great object of all government should have been so little insisted on by our great writers who have treated of this subject, and that more use has not been made of it. In treating of particular regulations in states, this principle necessarily obtruded itself; all arguments in favor of any law being always drawn from a consideration of its tendency to promote the public good; and yet it has often escaped the notice of writers in discoursing on the first principles of society, and the subject of civil and religious liberty.

This one general idea, properly pursued, throws the greatest light upon the whole system of policy, morals, and, I may add, theology too. To a mind not warped by theological and metaphysical subtilties, the Divine Being appears to be actuated by no other views than the noblest we can conceive, the happiness of his creatures. Virtue and right conduct consist in those affections and actions which terminate in the public good; justice and veracity, for instance, having nothing intrinsically excellent in them, separate from their relation to the happiness of mankind; and the whole system of right to power, property, and everything else in society, must be regulated by the same consideration; the decisive question, when any of these subjects are being examined, being what is it that the good of the community requires?

OF RELIGIOUS LIBERTY
AND TOLERATION IN GENERAL

The most important question concerning the extent of civil government is whether the civil magistrate ought to extend his authority to matters of religion; and the only method of deciding this important question, as it appears to me, is to have recourse at once to first principles, and the ultimate rule concerning everything that respects a society, viz. whether such interference of the civil magistrate appear to be for the public good. And as all arguments *a priori*, in matters of policy, are apt to be fallacious, fact and experience seem to be our only safe guides. Now these, as far as our knowledge of history extends, declare clearly for no interference in this case at all, or, at least for as little as is possible. Those societies have ever enjoyed the most happiness, and have been, *caeteris paribus*, in the most flourishing state, where the civil magistrates have meddled the least with religion, and where they have the most closely confined their attention to what immediately affects the civil interests of their fellow citizens.

Civil and religious matters (taking the words in their usual acceptation) seem to be so distinct, that it can only be in very uncommon emergencies, where, for instance, religious quarrels among the members of the state rise very high, that the civil magistrate can have any call or pretense for interfering with religion.

It is, indeed, impossible to name any two things, about which men are concerned, so remote in their nature, but that they have some connections and mutual influences; but where I asked what two things I should think to be in the least danger of being confounded, and which even the ingenuity of man could find the least pretense for involving together, I should say, the things that relate to this life, and those that relate to the life to come. Defining the object of civil government, in the most extensive sense, to be the making provision for the secure and comfortable enjoyment of this life, by preventing one man from injuring another in his person or property; I should think the office of the civil magistrate to be in no great danger of being encroached upon, by the methods that men might think proper to take to provide for their happiness after death.

All the civil societies we enter into in this life will be dissolved by death. When this life is over, I shall not be able to claim any of the privileges of an Englishman; I shall not be bound by any of the laws of England, nor shall I owe any allegiance to its sovereign. When, therefore, my situation in a future life shall have no connection with my privileges or obligations as an Englishman, why should those persons who make laws for Englishmen interfere with my conduct with respect to a state to which their power does not extend? Besides, we know that infinite mischiefs have arisen from this interference of government in the business of religion; and we have yet seen no inconvenience to have arisen from the want or the relaxation of it.

The fine country of Flanders, the most flourishing and opulent then in Europe, was absolutely ruined, past recovery, by the mad attempt of Philip II to introduce the Popish Inquisition into that country. France was greatly hurt by the revocation of the Edict of Nantes; whereas England was a great gainer on both occasions, by granting an asylum for those persecuted, industrious people; who repaid us for our kindness by the introduction of many useful arts and manufactures which were the foundation of our present commerce, riches, and power.

Pennsylvania flourished much more than New England, or than any other of the English settlements in North America, evidently in consequence of giving more liberty in matters of religion, at its first establishment. Holland has found its advantage in the indulgence she gives to a great variety of religious persuasions. England has also been much more flourishing and happy, since the establishment, as it may properly enough be styled, of the Dissenting method of worship, by what is commonly called the Act of Toleration. And all the sensible part of Europe concur in thinking, both that the Polish dissidents have a right to all the privileges of other Polish citizens; and that it would be much happier for that country if their claims were quietly admitted, and none but interested bigots opposed their demands.

If we look a little farther off from home, let it be said, what inconvenience did Genghis Khan, Tamerlane, and other eastern conquerers, ever find from leaving religion to its natural course in the countries they subdued, and from having Christians, Mahometans, and a variety of pagans under the same form of civil government? Are not both Christianity and Mohammedanism, in fact, established (the former, at least, fully tolerated) in Turkey; and what inconvenience, worth mentioning, has ever risen from it?

Pity it is, then, that more and fairer experiments are not made; when, judging from what is past, the consequences of unbounded liberty, in matters of religion, promise to be so very favorable to the best interests of mankind.

I am aware that the connection between civil and religious affairs will be urged for the necessity of some interference of the legislature with religion; and, as I observed before, I do not deny the connection. But as this connection has always been found to be the greatest in barbarous nations and imperfect governments, to which it lends an useful aid; it may be presumed that it is gradually growing less necessary; and that, in the present advanced state of human society, there is very little occasion for it. For my own part, I have no apprehension but that, at this day, the laws might be obeyed very well without any ecclesiastical sanctions, enforced by the civil magistrate.

Not that I think religion will ever be a matter of indifference in civil society; that is impossible, if the world be understood in its greatest latitude, and by religion we mean that principle whereby men are influenced by the dread of evil or the hope of reward from any unknown and invisible causes, whether the good or evil be expected to take place in this world or another; comprehending enthusiasm, superstition, and every species of false religion, as well as the true. Nor is such an event at all desirable; nay, the more just motives men have to the same good actions, the better; but religious motives may still operate in favor of the civil laws, without such a connection as has been formed between them in ecclesiastical establishments; and I think this end would be answered even better without that connection.

In all the modes of religion which subsist among mankind, however subversive of virtue they may be in theory, there is some salvo for good morals; so that, in fact, they enforce the more essential parts, at least, of that conduct which the good order of society requires. Besides, it might be expected that if all the modes of religion were equally protected by the civil magistrate, they would all vie with one another which should best deserve that protection. This, however, is, in fact, all the alliance that can take place between religion and civil policy, each enforcing the same conduct by different motives. Any other "alliance between church and state" is only the alliance of different sorts of worldly-minded men, for their temporal emolument.

———

It will be said that a regard to liberty itself must plead for one exception to the principles of toleration. The Papists, it is alleged, are such determined enemies to liberty, civil and ecclesiastical, and so effectually alienated from the interests of a Protestant country and government, that Protestants, who have a regard for their own safety, and the great cause in which they are engaged, cannot tolerate them. If they do it, it is at their own peril; so that the persecution of Papists is, in fact, nothing more than a dictate of self-preservation.

This plea, I own, is plausible; and two centuries ago it is no wonder it had considerable weight; but persecution by Protestants, in this enlightened age, appears so utterly repugnant to the great principle of their cause, that I wish they would view it in every point of light, before they seriously adopt any such measure. And I cannot help thinking that the result of a more mature consideration of this subject will not be to render evil for evil to our old mother church, but rather a more indulgent treatment than we have as yet vouchsafed to afford her.

In the first place, I cannot imagine that the increase of Popery in these kingdoms will ever be so considerable as to give any just alarm to the friends of liberty. All the address and assiduity of man cannot, certainly, recommend so absurd a system of faith and practice to any but the lowest and most illiterate of our common people, who can never have any degree of influence in the state. The number of Popish gentry must grow less; partly through the influence of fashion, and partly through the conviction of those who have a liberal education, which will necessarily throw Protestant books into their hands.

The French translator of Warburton's *Alliance*,[5] in an address to Cardinal Fleury (in which he recommends such a system of church establishment and toleration as this of the Bishop of Gloucester), observes that the number of Roman Catholics in England diminishes every day, and that the only reason why they are not so good subjects in this country as they are in Holland is that they are under more restraints here.

If the Popish priests and missionaries have the success which it is pretended they have, I am almost persuaded that the most effectual arguments they have employed for this purpose have been drawn from the rigor of our present laws respecting the Papists. They tell the people that, conscious of the weakness of our cause, we dare not give them full liberty to teach and exercise their religion; knowing that the excellency of it is such, that if it were publicly exhibited, it would attract universal admiration; and that what we are not able to silence by argument, we suppress by force.

Besides, the traces and remains of Popery are so striking in the Book of Common Prayer, and in the whole of our ecclesiastical establishment, that the derivation of it from the Popish system cannot be concealed; and hence it may not be difficult for an artful Papist to persuade many of the common people to quit the shadow, and have recourse to the substance; to abandon the interests of an apostate child, and adopt that of its ancient and venerable parent.

[5] William Warburton (1698-1779) was a churchman and theologian whose *Alliance Between Church and State* (1736), defending the church-state connection, was strongly attacked by Priestley. See Laski, *Political Thought*, pp. 118-120 and 192.

Let the Church of England, then, before it be too late, make a farther reformation from Popery, and leave fewer of the symbols of the Romish Church about her; and the ideas of her members being more remote from everything that has any connection with Popery, the Popish missionaries will have much more difficulty in making them comprehend and relish it. A convert to Popery from any of the sects of Protestant Dissenters (who are farther removed from the Popish system than the Church of England) is rarely heard of. And this effect is not owing to any particular care of their ministers to guard their hearers against Popery; but because the whole system of their faith and practice is so contrary to it that even the common people among them would as soon turn Mahometans, or pagans, as become Papists.

Instead, then, of using more rigor with the Papists, let us allow them a full toleration. We should, at least, by this means, be better judges of their number and increase. And I also think they would be much less formidable in these circumstances, than they are at present. If they be enemies, an open enemy is less dangerous than a secret one. And if our ecclesiastical establishment must not be reformed, and removed farther from Popery, let the clergy, as the best succedaneum for such an effectual antidote against their poison, show more zeal in the discharge of their parochial duties, and give more attention to their flocks. Half the zeal which the Papists employ to make converts, would be more than sufficient to prevent any from being made. Whose business is it to counteract the endeavors of the Popish emissaries, but those whom the state has appointed the guardians of the people in spiritual matters; and what is their calling in the aid of the civil power, but an acknowledgment of a neglect of their proper duty?

It may be said that the particular situation of this country should be a motive with all the friends of our happy constitution, to keep a watchful eye over the Papists; since a Popish religion may, at length, fix a Popish pretender upon

the throne of these kingdoms. Seriously as this argument
for persecution might have been urged formerly, I cannot
help thinking that, ever since the last rebellion [1745], the
apprehension on which it is grounded is become absolutely
chimerical, and therefore that it does not deserve a serious
answer. After the Pope himself has refused to acknowledge
the heir of the Stuart family to be king of England, what can
a Papist, as such, have to plead for him? And, for my own
part, I make no doubt, there are men of good sense among
the Popish gentry, at least, and persons of property of that
persuasion, as well as among persons of other religious
professions; and therefore, that if they lay under fewer civil
disadvantages, they would not only cheerfully acquiesce in,
but would become zealously attached to our excellent form
of free government; and that, upon any emergency, they
would bravely stand up for it, Protestant as it is, in opposition to any Popish system of arbitrary power whatever.

Some persons, of narrow minds, may be ready to admit of
a plea for the toleration of all sects of Protestants. They may
bear them some degree of good will, as brethren, or at least,
as distant relations, though the blood in their veins be not
equally pure with their own; but, in order to demonstrate
that there may be a licentiousness in toleration, and that we
must stop somewhere, they say, "What must we do with
heathens and atheists?" I answer, the very same that you,
Christians, would wish that heathens and atheists, in your
situation, should do to you, being in theirs. If your party
has been so long in power that you cannot, even in supposition, separate the idea of it from that of the authority which
has been so long connected with it, read the history of the
primitive church, and see what it was that the first Christians wished and pleaded for, under the pagan emperors.
Read the ancient Christian apologies; and do the infidels
of the present age the justice to put them, or at least part of
them, into their mouths.

An Address to Protestant Dissenters

Quite consistently, in the light of his convictions about political liberty, Joseph Priestley was extremely sympathetic to the American cause in the pre-Revolutionary controversy. He was closely associated with Benjamin Franklin in the years just before the outbreak of war, and Franklin encouraged him to publish his anonymous Address to Protestant Dissenters of All Denominations, on the Approaching Election of Members of Parliament, with Respect to the State of Public Liberty in General and of American Affairs in Particular *(London, 1774).*[6] *Part I of this pamphlet urged Dissenters to vote for candidates favoring the removal of religious discrimination from the statute books, and Part II, the following selection, presented the American case against the British government.*[7]

My Fellow Citizens:

As your late representatives have acted as if they were the representatives of all North America, and in that assumed capacity have engaged in measures which threaten nothing less than the ruin of the whole British Empire, it were greatly to be wished that their successors might learn by their example to know themselves better, and keep within their proper province. This is a business of so much consequence, that I cannot help subjoining a few plain considerations relating to it. It is true that I can advance nothing new upon the subject, but I shall endeavor to comprise the merits of the case in a very small compass, which may give it a chance of being better understood; and some advantage may arise from the same things being said in a different manner, and upon a different occasion.

[6] Carl Van Doren, *Benjamin Franklin* (Garden City, 1941), p. 481.
[7] Text of selection from Rutt, XXII, 483-498.

The minds of many, indeed, are so obstinately shut against conviction, and they are so blindly bent on pushing the vindictive schemes of the present ministry, without regard to reason or consequence, that I despair of making any impression upon them. But I wish to address myself to those who have not yet taken their part, or who, though they may have been deceived by the false lights in which this affair has been represented, are cool enough to attend to what may be said on the other side. On such I should think that some impression might be made by three considerations; one drawn from the nature and history of our constitution, another from the nature of things and the principles of liberty in general, and the third from the effects which the oppression of America may have on the liberties of this country.

It has ever been a fundamental maxim in our government that the representatives of the people should have a voice in enacting all the laws by which they are governed, and that they should have the sole power of giving their own money. Without these privileges there can be no true British liberty. These maxims were so well understood, and were held so inviolable in all former times, that though all the kings of this country, since the conquest, have had several realms, or principalities, subject to them, each has always had its separate legislative body, its separate laws, and its separate system of taxation; and no one of them ever thought of laying a tax upon another.

When the Kings of England were likewise Dukes of Normandy, and held other principalities in France, the English Parliament never thought of making laws for the Normans, or the Normans for the English; and still less did either of them presume to tax the other. Scotland, though united under one head with England, had its own system of laws and taxation, altogether independent of the English, till the union of the parliaments of both the nations. Wales also, and several counties palatine, taxed themselves, without any control from the Parliament of England; and so does Ireland to this day. So independent were all these governments of one another, though the same king had a negative upon the resolutions of them all, that when a man fled from any one of the realms, and took refuge in another, he was as effectually exempted from the jurisdiction of the country he had left, as if he had gone into the dominions of another prince; so that no process at law commenced in the former could affect him.

Agreeably to these ideas, it could not but have been understood, that when many of our ancestors, the old Puritans, quitted the realm of England, they freed themselves from the laws of England. Indeed they could have had no other motive for leaving this country; and how could they have expected any relief from taking refuge in America, if they had found in that country, or carried with them the same laws and the same administration by which they were aggrieved in this? But going into a country which was out of the realm of England, and not occupied, they found themselves at first without any laws whatever. But they enacted laws for themselves, voluntarily choosing, from their regard to the country from which they came, to have the same common head and center of concord, the King of Great Britain; and therefore submitted to his negative upon all their proceedings. They adopted as many of the laws of England as they chose, but no more; and if they had preferred the laws of Scotland, those of Ireland, or those of any foreign country, they were at liberty to have done it.

These colonists also provided for the expenses of their own separate governments, granting the king aids for that purpose, according to their own judgment and ability, without the interference of the English Parliament, till the fatal period of the Stamp Act, which was absolutely an innovation in our constitution, confounding the first and fundamental ideas belonging to the system of different realms subject to the same king, and even introduced a language quite new to us; viz. that of America being subject to England. For America was never thought to be within the realm of England, any more than Scotland or Ireland. If there have been any exceptions to this system of legislation, or taxation, with respect to America, it has been the exercise of tyranny, and it has not been the less so for having been disguised, or having passed without suspicion.

According to the language that was universally in use till of late years, to say that America was subject to England would have been considered as equally absurd with saying that it was subject to Ireland or to Hanover, that is, the subject of subjects; all being equally subject to one king, who is himself subject to the laws, and who is no longer our legal and rightful king, than he is so. In this great principle the very essence of our liberty, and the independent liberty of each part of the common empire, consists.

Secondly, with respect to the principles of liberty in general, I would observe, that if any realm or country be taxed by another, the people so taxed have no proper liberty left, but are in a state of as absolute despotism as any of which we read in history, or of which we can form an idea; since the same foreign power that can take one penny from them without their consent, may take the last penny that they have; so that, in fact, they have no property at all of their own, everything they have being at the mercy of others. This would be the case with England, if we were taxed at the pleasure of the king, or by the Parliament of Ireland, or by the houses of representatives of America; it would be the case of the Irish if they were taxed by the English; and therefore it will be the case of the Americans, if they be taxed by us.

It is said that Leeds, Manchester, and other large towns in England send no representatives to Parliament, and yet are taxed by it. But there is this very essential and obvious difference between their case and that of the Americans; viz. that those who tax Leeds, Manchester, etc. always tax themselves at the same time, and in the same proportion; and while this is the case, those towns have no reason to be apprehensive of partiality or oppression. To make the cases parallel, let the Parliament lay a separate tax on the towns that send no representatives, and exempt from such tax those that do send members. In this case I doubt not but that the unrepresented towns would complain as loudly as the Americans do now, who see that we assume a power of loading them, and easing ourselves; and that we are endeavoring to establish a principle, which will at once give us all the property they have. If there be in nature a justifiable case of resistance to government, it is this; and if the Americans have anything of the spirit of Englishmen, they will risk everything, rather than submit to such a claim. They are willing to be our fellow subjects having the same common head; but are not willing to be our slaves.

It is alleged that we have protected the Americans, and that they ought to pay for that protection; but have we not also protected Ireland, and the electorate of Hanover, without pretending either to make laws for them, or to tax them? What we may do, or attempt to do when this new doctrine shall have been established in the case of the Americans, is as yet unknown. Any favor that we do the Americans, certainly gives us a claim upon their gratitude, but it does not make them our slaves. Besides, they have, in many respects, made abundant requital, and we were actually reaping a rich harvest for the little we have sowed in that fruitful soil. But our present ministry resemble the man who would kill the hen that laid the golden eggs, in order that he might come at all the treasure at once; and the event will equally disappoint them both. Or rather, they resemble the dog who, by catching at the shadow, lost the substance.

Many persons of this country are so grossly ignorant as to imagine that while we are heavily taxed for the welfare of the common empire, and have even incurred a prodigious debt on that account, the Americans pay nothing at all. But have not the Americans their own separate governments to support, as well as we have ours, and do they not tax themselves for that purpose, and do we help them to bear any part of those taxes? If they incur debts, as they sometimes do, do they not discharge them as well as they can? And should we not laugh at them, if they should pretend to have any demand upon us for the payment of them? Should we not also treat the Irish with the same contempt in the same case?

In a common cause the Americans have always been ready to exert themselves with as much zeal as we have shown; nay, by our own acknowledgment, they have done more. For at the close of the last war, we voluntarily voted them large sums of money, because we were sensible that they had exerted themselves even beyond their ability. But their exertions were voluntary, as was our acknowledgment.

As to the conduct of the present ministry with respect to America, it is no part of my present argument; but I cannot help observing that it must give pain to every reasonable man to see an English parliament so readily giving their sanction to measures so exceedingly absurd and ruinous. Admitting that the East India Company has been injured by some of the inhabitants of Boston, reasonable people would have contented themselves with demanding satisfaction, and would not have punished the innocent with the guilty, by blocking up their port.[8]

An offense of this nature could not in reason or equity draw upon them the abolition of their charter; which demonstrates that none of the colonies have the least security for so much as the form of a free constitution, all being at the mercy of a foreign power.

An offense of this kind did not require that a fleet of eleven ships of war, and eight regiments should be sent thither, with a power to commit all crimes and murders with impunity, and that the wretched inhabitants should be compelled, upon every accusation, to leave their friends, and submit to a trial, and consequently an iniquitous trial, in a foreign country; an instance of oppression which, of itself, is absolutely intolerable, and which it cannot be conceived

[8] A reference to the Boston Port Act, one of the notorious "Intolerable Acts" of 1774.

that any person who has arms in his hands, and the spirit of a man within him, can possibly submit to.

What man, finding that the government of his country provided him no satisfaction for the murder of a near relative or friend (which will necessarily be the case, when a trial cannot be had upon the spot, or without crossing the Atlantic Ocean, whither he cannot carry his witnesses, and still less his feelings), will not think himself not only excusable, but even bound in conscience to take his own satisfaction, and engage his private friends to assist him in procuring blood for blood?

I need not ask any Englishman how the Americans (whom prelatical tyranny drove from this country, and who are grown numerous, strong, and high-spirited under a very different treatment) must feel in these circumstances; especially when, at the same time, they see the boundaries of Canada extended, and made a perfect arbitrary government, as a model, no doubt, for their own in due time, and a check upon them till that time.[9] It is what he himself would feel in the same circumstances.

Lastly, do you imagine, my fellow citizens, that we can sit still, and be the idle spectators of the chains which are forging for our brethren in America, with safety to ourselves? Let us suppose America to be completely enslaved, in consequence of which the English court can command all the money, and all the force of that country; will they like to be so arbitrary abroad, and have their power confined at home; especially as troops in abundance can be transported in a few weeks from America to England; where, with the present standing army, they may instantly reduce us to what they please? And can it be supposed that the Americans, being slaves themselves, and having been enslaved by us, will not, in return, willingly contribute their aid to bring us into the same condition?

These consequences appear to me so very obvious, that I think none but the absolutely infatuated can help seeing

[9] A reference to the Quebec Act.

them. Indeed the infatuation is of so gross a nature, and of so dangerous a kind, that I cannot help thinking it resembles that which usually precedes the downfall of states; and it calls to my mind the Latin proverb, "Quem Deus vult perdere prius dementat."

Philip II and the kingdom of Spain, at the height of its power, so as to threaten Europe with universal monarchy, were under a like infatuation. That proud and obstinate prince imagined that he could easily reduce the Belgic provinces, by writing dispatches from his closet. But the thing that was really effected by all his orders, his generals, his fleets, and his armies, after a bloody war of many years, was the independency of those provinces, and the ruin of Spain.

We too affect to speak with the same contempt of the people of North America, though the disparity of forces between Great Britain and them is nothing, compared with the apparent disparity between those of Spain and the Belgic provinces.

Also, because the Americans have more of the appearance of religion than ourselves, we ridicule them as hypocrites. But if they be such hypocrites as the puritanical party in England (whom the royalists diverted themselves with stigmatizing in the same manner) in the time of the civil war, true valor and perseverance will go hand in hand with their hypocrisy; and the history of our approaching contest will teach mankind the same lesson with our last, and show the different effects of sobriety and profligacy in soldiers. The king began with a manifest advantage in point of discipline and generals; and so may we in this war. But it soon appeared that generals and discipline are more easily acquired than principles; and in the course of two or three years, the superiority of the parliamentary forces was as great in one respect as in the other.

To pursue this subject would carry me far beyond the bounds of my present purpose. I shall therefore return to it, by earnestly advising to oppose, at the next election, every candidate, who, in the present Parliament, has concurred in the late atrocious attempts to establish arbitrary power over so great a part of the British Empire, to the imminent hazard of our most valuable commerce, and of that national strength, security, and felicity, which depend on union and on liberty. If you make any terms with your future representatives, do not forget to require of them, to do by others as they would have others do by them. It is only by justice, equity, and generosity, that nations, as well as individuals, can expect to flourish; and by the violation of them, both single persons and states, in the course of the righteous providence of God, involve themselves in disgrace and ruin.

Letters to the
Right Honourable Edmund Burke

The outbreak of the French Revolution evoked in England a remarkable series of controversial political tracts. Priestley's friend Dr. Price *inaugurated the debate with* A Discourse on the Love of Our Country, *delivered in London on November 4, 1789, at a meeting commemorating the Glorious Revolution. This address demanded political reform and religious freedom in England and hailed the French Revolution as a landmark in the advance of liberty. In reply to Price, Edmund Burke published his famous* Reflections on the French Revolution, *taking a critical view of the proceedings in France and defending the traditional loyalty to Church and King. Burke's work in turn was refuted in a variety of books and pamphlets, of which the most important was Tom Paine's* The Rights of Man. *Among Burke's critics was Joseph Priestley.[10] Two of his* Letters to the Right Honourable Edmund Burke *(1791) are included here.[11] Letter I is an attempt to justify the actions of the French National Assembly. Letter XIV, the last, is a lyrical picture of the utopian prospects which Priestley and other English liberals read into the dramatic events in France. Priestley's sympathy for the French Revolution, added to his opposition to the Established Church and his denial of the doctrine of the Trinity, resulted in the destruction of his house, his library, and his laboratory by a mob in the famous Birming-*

[10] On the general background of this controversy see Philip A. Brown, *The French Revolution in English History* (London, 1918), and Alfred Cobban, ed., *The Debate on the French Revolution, 1789-1800* (London, 1950).

[11] Text from Rutt, XXII, 152-157, 236-244.

*ham riots of July 14, 1791 — the second anniversary of the
fall of the Bastille.*[12]

THE GENERAL PRINCIPLES
OF THE FRENCH REVOLUTION

Dear Sir:

I do not wonder that the late Revolution in the French
government has excited your attention, and that of a great
part of the nation. It is, as you justly say, "all circumstances
taken together, the most astonishing that has hitherto happened in the world." It is, therefore, a most interesting
object both to philosophical and practical politicians. It
behooves them particularly to consider the principles on
which it has been made, that if the conduct of the leaders
in the business has been right, and if the scheme promises
to be beneficial to the country, it may, as far as their situations are similar, be imitated in other countries; and that, if
their conduct has been wrong, and the result of it unpromis-
ing, the example may serve to deter others from any attempt
of the like kind.

But though there is nothing extraordinary in this Revolution having excited so much of your attention, I am surprised
that you should be so much alarmed and disturbed at it.
You appear to me not to be sufficiently cool to enter into
this serious discussion. Your imagination is evidently heated,
and your ideas confused. The objects before you do not
appear in their proper shapes and colors; and, without
denying them, you lose sight of the great and the leading
principles on which all just governments are founded, principles which I imagined had been long settled, and universally assented to, at least by all who are denominated Whigs,
the friends of our own revolution, and of that which has

[12] On the riots see Anne Holt, *A Life of Joseph Priestley* (London,
1931), pp. 145-178.

lately taken place in America. To this class of politicians you, Sir, have hitherto professed to belong, and traces of these principles may be perceived in this work of yours.

Notwithstanding "the sacredness," as you call it, "of an hereditary principle of succession in our government," you allow of "a power of change in its application in cases of extreme emergency"; adding, however, that "the change should be confined to the peccant part only." Nor do you deny that the great end and object of all government, that which makes it preferable to the state of anarchy, is the good of the people. It is better for them, and they are happier in a state of society and government. For the same reason, you must allow that that particular form of government which is best adapted to promote the happiness of any people is the best for that people.

If you admit thus much, you must also allow that, since every private person is justified in bettering his condition, and indeed commended for it, a nation is not to be condemned for endeavoring to better theirs. Consequently, if they find their form of government to be a bad one, whether it was so originally, or became so through abuse or accident, they will do very well to change it for a better. A partial change, no doubt, will be preferable to a total one, if a partial change will be sufficient for the purpose. But if it appear that all attempts to mend an old constitution would be in vain, and the people prefer a new one, their neighbors have no more business to find fault with them than with any individual who should think it more advisable to pull down an old and inconvenient house, and build another from the foundation, rather than lay out his money in repairs. Nations, no doubt, as well as individuals, may judge wrong. They may act precipitately, and they may suffer in consequence of it; but this is only a reason for caution, and does not preclude a right of judging and acting for themselves, in the best manner that they can.

"The very idea," you say, "of the fabrication of a new government is enough to fill us with disgust and horror." It is, no doubt, far from being a thing desirable in itself; but it may nevertheless be necessary; and for all the evils arising from the change, you should blame, not the framers of the new government, but the wretched state of the old one, and those who brought it into that state. That some very material change was wanting in the old government of France, you cannot deny, after allowing, that in that country "the unlimited power of the sovereign over the persons of his subjects" was "inconsistent with law and liberty." On other occasions, I believe you have expressed yourself in a stronger manner than this. If law and liberty were wanting in the old constitution, "the peccant part" must have been the very foundation of it; so that nothing effectual could have been done short of taking down the whole.

If these incontrovertible principles and facts be admitted, I can see no reason for your exclaiming so violently as you do against the late Revolution in France. Besides, whatever has been done, and in whatever manner it has been done, if the nation itself, whom alone it concerns, do not complain, we have no business to complain for them, any farther than the interest we take in the welfare of others may lead us to feel for the distresses which we apprehend their folly and precipitancy may bring upon them. I shall, however, briefly consider the principal of your objections to this revolution.

You consider the present National Assembly of France as usurpers, assuming a power that does not belong to them. "I can never," you say, "consider this Assembly as anything else than a voluntary association of men, who have availed themselves of circumstances to seize upon the power of the state. They have not the sanction and authority of the character under which they first met. They have assumed another, of a very different nature, and have completely altered and inverted all the relations in which they originally stood. They do not hold the authority they exercise under any constitutional law of the state. They have departed from the instructions of the people by whom they were sent, which instructions, as the Assembly did not act in virtue of any ancient usage or settled law, were the sole source of their authority."

Now, Sir, even allowing this to be true; admitting this National Assembly to have had no regular summons to meet, or to do any business at all; supposing them to have been men who rose out of the earth, or who dropped down from the clouds, or that nobody could tell whence they came, and that, without any authority whatever, they took upon themselves to frame a new constitution of government for the French nation; if the nation really approve of it, acquiesce in it, and actually adopt it, it becomes from that time their own act, and the Assembly can only be considered as the proposers and advisers. It is the acquiescence of the people that gives any form of government its proper sanction, and that legalizes it. Changes of government cannot be brought about by established forms and rules, because there is no superior power to prescribe those rules. There are no supreme courts comprehending these great objects. Also, the cases occur so rarely, and they are so unlike to one another, that it would be to no purpose to look for precedents.

Now, that the French Revolution is justifiable on this plain principle is evident from the single circumstance of the National Assembly having continued their sittings without molestation, and from their decrees having been actually obeyed, for something more than a year at least. This Assembly does not consist, I believe, of more than about one thousand persons, and at first they had no army at their command; whereas at present the whole force of the state is in their hands. This force could not have been transferred from the king to them, without the consent both of the army, and of the nation which supports that army. As the nation does not complain of this translation of power, it is evident they do not think themselves aggrieved, and that the change has been made with their approbation. Here, then, we see all the marks of a legal government, or a government that is really the choice of the people. I do not say what difficulties may hereafter arise (which if they do, they will probably be the effect of their former government) to induce them to change their opinion; for neither that nation nor any other is omniscient and infallible.

Without examining into the former system of government, or the administration of it, we may take for granted that it must have become extremely odious to the country in general, from the almost universal and the very hearty concurrence with which the Revolution was brought about. A whole people is not apt to revolt, till oppression has become extreme, and been long continued, so that they despair of any other remedy than that desperate one. The strength of an established government, especially when it is in few hands, and has a large standing army at its command, is almost infinite; so that many nations quietly suffer every evil, and the country becomes in a manner desolate, without their making any attempt to relieve themselves. This is the case in all the Turkish dominions, and is said to be very nearly so in Spain and other countries. Whenever, therefore, we see a whole nation, or a great majority of it, rising, as one man, against an old government, and overturning it, we may safely conclude that their provocation was great, and their cause good.

An oppressed people do not, however, in general see anything more than what they immediately feel. All they think of is to shake off the load which they can no longer bear; and having thought of nothing but the particular evil that galled them, they are very apt, in their future settlement, to guard against that only, without attending to the whole of their new situation, and the greater evils that may possibly arise from it. Whether the French have done so or not, time must discover. But if the people in general be well informed and well disposed, they may make many experiments of new forms of government without much inconvenience; and though beginning with a very imperfect one, they may adopt a very good one at the last.

Was it not predicted that the Americans, on their breaking

off from this country, would run into universal confusion, and immediately fall to cutting one another's throats? But though that disruption was a violent one, and was effected by a war which drained all their resources, they never suffered for want of government. When the war was over they bore very contentedly several imperfect and disjointed forms; and now, having taken much time to deliberate on the subject, they have adopted a more comprehensive one. But of this they only propose to make trial, and if it should not answer, they will, no doubt, endeavor to improve upon it.

Now, why may not this be the case with the French, especially as they have no enemies to contend with, and interrupt their proceedings. I do not, I own, distinctly perceive the wisdom of several parts of the frame of government at present adopted by the National Assembly, owing, probably, to my not being master of the whole system, and many of the remarks that you have made upon it may, for anything that I know, be very just; but not being a judge of their circumstances, and consequently of all their reasons, I presume that they could not at the time have done better. In future time, however, whatever it be that is now deficient may be supplied. And considering the apparent strength of the ancient French government, and the great numbers that depended upon it (far more, I should imagine, than upon the court and ministry in this country), I wonder that the Revolution was brought about with so much ease, and so little bloodshed.

I am, &c.

OF THE PROSPECT
OF THE GENERAL ENLARGEMENT
OF LIBERTY, CIVIL AND RELIGIOUS, OPENED
BY THE REVOLUTION IN FRANCE

Dear Sir:

I cannot conclude these *Letters,* without congratulating, not you, Sir, or the many admirers of your performance, who have no feeling of joy on the occasion, but the French nation and the world (I mean the liberal, the rational, and the virtuous part of the world), on the great Revolution that has taken place in France, as well as on that which some time ago took place in America. Such events as these teach the doctrine of liberty, civil and religious, with infinitely greater clearness and force than a thousand treatises on the subject. They speak a language intelligible to all the world, and preach a doctrine congenial to every human heart.

These great events, in many respects unparalleled in all history, make a totally new, a most wonderful and important era in the history of mankind. It is, to adopt your own rhetorical style, a change from darkness to light, from superstition to sound knowledge, and from a most debasing servitude to a state of the most exalted freedom. It is a liberating of all the powers of man from that variety of fetters by which they have hitherto been held. So that, in comparison with what has been, now only can we expect to see what men really are, and what they can do.

The generality of governments have hitherto been little else than a combination of the few against the many; and to the mean passions and low cunning of these few, have the great interests of mankind been too long sacrificed. Whole nations have been deluged with blood, and every source of future prosperity has been drained, to gratify the caprices of some of the most despicable, or the most execrable, of the human species. For what else have been the generality of kings, their ministers of state, or their mistresses, to whose wills whole kingdoms have been subject? What can we say of those who have hitherto taken the lead in conducting the affairs of nations, but that they have commonly been either weak or wicked, and sometimes both? Hence the common reproach of all histories, that they exhibit little more than a view of the vices and miseries of mankind. From this time, therefore, we may expect that it will wear a different and more pleasing aspect.

Hitherto, also, infinite have been the mischiefs in which

all nations have been involved on account of religion, with which, as it concerns only God and men's own consciences, civil government, as such, has nothing to do. Statesmen, misled by ignorant or interested priests, have taken upon them to prescribe what men should believe and practice, in order to get to heaven, when they themselves have often neither believed nor practiced anything under that description. They have set up idols, to which all men, under the severest penalties, have been compelled to bow; and the wealth and power of populous nations, which might have been employed in great and useful undertakings, have been diverted from their proper channels, to enforce their unrighteous decrees. By this means have mankind been kept for ages in a state of bondage worse than Egyptian, the bondage of the mind.

How glorious, then, is the prospect, the reverse of all the past, which is now opening upon us, and upon the world! Government, we may now expect to see, not only in theory and in books, but in actual practice, calculated for the general good, and taking no more upon it than the general good requires; leaving all men the enjoyment of as many of their natural rights as possible, and no more interfering with matters of religion, with men's notions concerning God and a future state, than with philosophy or medicine.

After the noble example of America, we may expect, in due time, to see the governing powers of all nations confining their attention to the civil concerns of them, and consulting their welfare in the present state only; in consequence of which they may all be flourishing and happy. Truth of all kinds, and especially religious truth, meeting with no obstruction, and standing in no need of heterogeneous supports, will then establish itself by its own evidence; and whatever is false and delusive, all the forms of superstition, every corruption of true religion, and all usurpation over the rights of conscience, which have been supported by power or prejudice, will be universally exploded, as they ought to be.

Together with the general prevalence of the true principles of civil government, we may expect to see the extinction of all national prejudice and enmity, and the establishment of universal peace and good will among all nations. When the affairs of the various societies of mankind shall be conducted by those who shall truly represent them, who shall feel as they feel, and think as they think; who shall really understand and consult their interests, they will no more engage in those mutually offensive wars, which the experience of many centuries has shown to be constantly expensive and ruinous. They will no longer covet what belongs to others, which they have found to be of no real service to them, but will content themselves with making the most of their own.

The very idea of distant possessions will be even ridiculed. The East and the West Indies, and everything without ourselves will be disregarded, and wholly excluded from all European systems; and only those divisions of men and of territory will take place, which the common convenience requires, and not such as the mad and insatiable ambition of princes demands. No part of America, Africa, or Asia, will be held in subjection to any part of Europe, and all the intercourse that will be kept up among them, will be for their mutual advantage.

The causes of civil wars, the most distressing of all others, will likewise cease, as well as those of foreign ones. They are chiefly contentions for offices, on account of the power and emoluments annexed to them. But then the nature and uses of all civil offices shall be well understood, the power and emoluments annexed to them will not be an object sufficient to produce a war. Is it at all probable that there will ever be a civil war in America about the presidentship of the United States? And when the chief magistracies in other countries shall be reduced to their proper standard, they will be no more worth contending for than they are in America. If the actual business of a nation be done as well for the small emolument of that presidentship, as the similar business of other nations, there will be no apparent reason why more should be given for doing it.

If there be a superfluity of public money, it will not be employed to augment the profusion, and increase the undue influence, of individuals, but in works of great public utility, which are always wanted, and which nothing but the enormous expenses of government and of wars, chiefly occasioned by the ambition of kings and courts, have prevented from being carried into execution. The expense of the late American war only would have converted all the waste grounds of this country into gardens. What canals, bridges, and noble roads, what public buildings, public libraries, and public laboratories, etc., etc., would it not have made for us! If the pride of nations must be gratified, let it be in such things as these, and not in the idle pageantry of a court, calculated only to corrupt and enslave a nation.

Another cause of civil wars has been an attachment to certain persons and families, as possessed of some inherent right to kingly power. Such were the bloody wars between the houses of York and Lancaster, in this country. But when, besides the reduction of the power of crowns within their proper bounds (when it will be no greater than the public good requires), that kind of respect for princes which is founded on mere superstition (exactly similar to that which has been attached to priests in all countries) shall vanish, as all superstition certainly will before real knowledge, wise nations will not involve themselves in war for the sake of any particular persons, or families, who have never shown an equal regard for them. They will consider their own interest more, and that of their magistrates, that is, their servants, less.

Other remaining causes of civil war are different opinions about modes of government, and differences of interests between provinces. But when mankind shall be a little more accustomed to reflection, and consider the miseries of civil war, they will have recourse to any other method of deciding their differences, in preference to that of the sword. It was taken for granted, that the moment America had thrown off the yoke of Great Britain, the different states would go to war among themselves, on some of these accounts. But the event has not verified the prediction, nor is it at all probable that it ever will. The people of that country are wiser than such prophets, in this.

If time be allowed for the discussion of differences, so great a majority will form one opinion that the minority will see the necessity of giving way. Thus will reason be the umpire in all disputes, and extinguish civil wars as well as foreign ones. The empire of reason will ever be the reign of peace.

This, Sir, will be the happy state of things, distinctly and repeatedly foretold in many prophecies, delivered more than two thousand years ago; when the common Parent of mankind will cause "wars to cease to the ends of the earth"; when men "shall beat their swords into plough-shares, and their spears into pruning-hooks"; when "nation shall not lift up sword against nation, neither shall they learn war any more." *Isa.* ii. 4; *Micah* iv. 3. This is a state of things which good sense, and the prevailing spirit of commerce, aided by Christianity and true philosophy, cannot fail to effect in time. But it can never take place while mankind are governed in the wretched manner in which they now are. For peace can never be established but upon the extinction of the causes of war, which exist in all the present forms of government, and in the political maxims which will always be encouraged by them. I mention this topic in a letter to you, on the idea that you are a real believer in revelation, though your defense of all church establishments, as such, is no argument in favor of this opinion; the most zealous abettors of them, and the most determined enemies of all reformation, having been unbelievers in all religion, which they have made use of merely as an engine of state.

In this new condition of the world, there may still be kings, but they will be no longer sovereigns, or supreme lords, no human beings to whom will be ascribed such titles as those of most sacred, or most excellent majesty. There will be no more such a profanation of epithets, belonging to God only, by the application of them to mortals like ourselves. There will be magistrates, appointed and paid for the conservation of order, but they will only be considered as the first servants of the people, and accountable to them. Standing armies, those instruments of tyranny, will be unknown, though the people may be trained to the use of arms, for the purpose of repelling the invasion of barbarians. For no other description of men will have recourse to war, or think of disturbing the repose of others; and till they become civilized, as in the natural progress of things they necessarily must, they will be sufficiently overawed by the superior power of nations that are so.

There will still be religion, and of course ministers of it; as there will be teachers of philosophy; and practitioners in medicine; but it will no longer be the concern of the state. There will be no more lord bishops, or archbishops, with the titles and powers of temporal princes. Every man will provide religion for himself; and therefore it will be such as, after due inquiry and examination, he shall think to be founded on truth, and best calculated to make men good citizens, good friends, and good neighbors in this world, as well as to fit them for another.

Government, being thus simple in its objects, will be unspeakably less expensive than it is at present, as well as far more effectual in answering its proper purpose. There will then be little to provide for besides the administration of justice, or the preservation of the peace, which it will be the interest of every man to attend to, in aid of government.

They are chiefly our vices and follies that lay us under contribution, in the form of the taxes we now pay; and they will, of course, become superfluous, as the world grows wiser and better. It is a most unreasonable sum that we now pay for the single article of government. We give, perhaps, the amount of one half our property, for the secure enjoyment of the rest, which, after all, for want of a good police, is very insecure.

However, the enormous debts which our present systems of government, and the follies of our governors, have entailed upon us, like all other evils in the plan of Providence, promise to be eventually the cause of the greatest good, as necessary means of bringing about the happy state of things above described. And the improvement of Europe may serve as an example to the rest of the world, and be the instrument of other important changes, which I shall not dwell upon in this place.

By means of national debts, the wheels of several European governments are already so much clogged that it is impossible they should go on much longer. We see our taxes, even without war, continually increasing. The very peace establishment of France could not be kept up any longer, and the same must soon be the situation of other nations. All the causes which have operated to the augmentation of these debts continue to operate, and with increased force; so that our approach to this great crisis of our affairs is not equable, but accelerated. The present generation has seen the debt of this nation rise from a mere trifle to an amount that already threatens ruin. And will not the next generation, if not the present, see this ruin?

If the present change of the French government, brought on, to use a phrase of yours, "by fiscal difficulties," has been attended with such an interruption of their manufactures, such a stagnation of their commerce, and such a diminution of their current specie, as has greatly added to the difficulties of that country; what are we to expect, in a similar crisis, in this country, which depends so much more upon manufactures and commerce than France ever did, and which has far less resource within itself?

If you, Sir, together with your old or your new friends, can steer the ship of the state through the storm which we all see to be approaching, you will have more wisdom and steadiness than has yet been found in any who have hitherto been at the head of our affairs. And if, in these circumstances, you can save the church, as well as the state, you will deserve no less than canonization, and St. Edmund will be the greatest name in the calendar. But great occasions call forth, and in a manner create, great and unknown ability, as we have lately seen in the history of the American Revolution. A good Providence also governs the world, and therefore we need not despair.

If the condition of other nations be as much bettered as that of France will probably be, by her improved system of government, this great crisis, dreadful as it appears in prospect, will be a consummation devoutly to be wished for, and though calamitous to many, perhaps to many innocent persons, will be eventually most glorious and happy.

To you, Sir, all this may appear such wild declamation as your treatise appears to me. But speculations of this kind contribute to exhilarate my mind, as the consideration of the French Revolution has contributed to disturb and distress yours; and thus is verified the common proverb, which says, "One man's meat is another man's poison." If this be a dream, it is, however, a pleasing one, and has nothing in it malignant, or unfriendly to any. All that I look to promises no exclusive advantage to myself, or my friends; but an equal field for every generous exertion to all, and it makes the great object of all our exertions to be the public good.

I am, dear Sir,

Your very humble servant,

J. PRIESTLEY

Birmingham, Jan. 1, 1791.

On visits to London while teaching at Warrington, about the year 1766, Priestley made the acquaintance of two scientists already known for their work with electricity — John Canton and Benjamin Franklin. With their encouragement he decided to write an historical account of the development of this science. The result was his History and Present State of Electricity *(1767), the first of his major scientific treatises. In the course of writing this book Priestley began to make some experiments himself — "to ascertain several facts which were disputed"[1] — and as a result made some valuable discoveries of his own.*

Three selections have been made from this extensive work. First is the preface, which is a characteristic expression of the faith of the Enlightenment in the possibilities of progress through science. The second passage includes Priestley's account of Franklin's kite experiment, which is the most complete and circumstantial source of information on this famous episode.[2] The final extract tells of one of Priestley's own contributions to the understanding of electricity — his discovery that charcoal is a good conductor.[3]

[1] Quotation from Priestley's *Memoirs*, above, p. 32. On Priestley's preparation for research in physics and chemistry see the challenging article by Robert E. Schofield, "The Scientific Background of Joseph Priestley," in *Annals of Science*, XIII (September, 1957), 148-163.

[2] On the authenticity of this account see Carl Van Doren, *Benjamin Franklin* (Garden City, N. Y., 1941), pp. 164-168.

[3] Texts from original edition (London, 1767), pp. i-xxiii, 158-160, 170-184, and 598-608.

The History and Present State
of Electricity

PREFACE

In writing the *History and Present State of Electricity*, I flatter myself that I shall give pleasure, as well to persons who have a taste for natural philosophy in general, as to electricians in particular; and I hope the work will be of some advantage to the science itself. Both these ends would certainly be answered in a considerable degree, were the execution at all answerable to the design.

The history of electricity is a field full of pleasing objects, according to all the genuine and universal principles of taste, deduced from a knowledge of human nature. Scenes like these, in which we see a gradual rise and progress in things, always exhibit a pleasing spectacle to the human mind. Nature, in all her delightful walks, abounds with such views, and they are in a more especial manner connected with everything that relates to human life and happiness; things, in their own nature, the most interesting to us. Hence it is, that the power of association has annexed crowds of pleasing sensations to the contemplation of every object, in which this property is apparent.

This pleasure, likewise, bears a considerable resemblance to that of the sublime, which is one of the most exquisite of all those that affect the human imagination. For an object in which we see a perpetual progress and improvement is, as it were, continually rising in its magnitude; and moreover, when we see an actual increase, in a long period of time past, we cannot help forming an idea of an unlimited increase in futurity; which is a prospect really boundless, and sublime.

The pleasures arising from views exhibited in civil, natural, and philosophical history are, in certain respects, different from one another. Each has its advantages, and each its defects; and both their advantages and defects contribute to adapt them to different classes of readers.

Civil history presents us with views of the strongest passions and sentiments of the human mind, into which every man can easily and perfectly enter; and with such incidents, respecting happiness and misery, as we cannot help feeling would alarm and affect us in a very sensible manner; and therefore, we are at present alarmed and affected by them to a considerable degree. Hence the pleasure we receive from civil history arises, chiefly, from the exercise it affords our passions. The imagination is only entertained with scenes which occasionally start up, like interludes, or episodes, in the great drama to which we are principally attentive. We are presented, indeed, with the prospect of gradual improvement during the rise of great empires; but, as we read on, we are obliged to contemplate the disagreeable reverse. And the history of most states presents nothing but a tedious uniformity, without any striking events to diversify and embellish the prospect. Besides, if a man have any sentiment of virtue and benevolence, he cannot help being shocked with a view of the vices and miseries of mankind; which, though they be not all, are certainly the most glaring and striking objects in the history of human affairs. An attention, indeed, to the conduct of Divine Providence, which is ever bringing good out of evil, and gradually conducting things to a more perfect and glorious state, tends to throw a more agreeable light on the more gloomy parts of history, but it requires great strength of mind to comprehend those views; and, after all, the feelings of the heart too often overpower the conclusions of the head.

Natural history exhibits a boundless variety of scenes, and yet infinitely analogous to one another. A naturalist has, consequently, all the pleasure which the contemplation of uniformity and variety can give the mind; and this is one of the most copious sources of our intellectual pleasures. He is likewise entertained with a prospect of gradual improvement, while he sees every object in nature rising by due degrees to its maturity and perfection. And while new plants, new animals, and new fossils are perpetually pouring in upon him, the most pleasing views of the unbounded power, wisdom, and goodness of God are constantly present to his mind. But he has no direct view of human sentiments and human actions; which, by means of their endless associations, greatly heighten and improve all the pleasures of taste.

The history of philosophy enjoys, in some measure, the advantages both of civil and natural history, whereby it is relieved from what is most tedious and disgusting in both. Philosophy exhibits the powers of nature, discovered and directed by human art; it has, therefore, in some measure, the boundless variety with the amazing uniformity of the one, and likewise everything that is pleasing and interesting in the other. And the idea of continual rise and improvement is conspicuous in the whole study, whether we be attentive to the part which nature, or that which men are acting in the great scene.

It is here that we see the human understanding to its greatest advantage, grasping at the noblest objects, and increasing its own powers, by acquiring to itself the powers of nature, and directing them to the accomplishment of its own views; whereby the security, and happiness of mankind are daily improved. Human abilities are chiefly conspicuous in adapting means to ends, and in deducing one thing from another by the method of analogy; and where shall we find instances of greater sagacity, than in philosophers diversifying the situation of things, in order to give them an opportunity of showing their mutual relations, affections, and influences; deducing one truth and one discovery from another, and applying them all to the useful purposes of human life.

If the exertion of human abilities, which cannot but form a delightful spectacle for the human imagination, give us pleasure, we enjoy it here in a higher degree than while we are contemplating the schemes of warriors, and the stratagems of their bloody art. Besides, the object of philosophical pursuits throws a pleasing idea upon the scenes they exhibit; whereas a reflection upon the real objects and views of most statesmen and conquerors cannot but take from the pleasure, which the idea of their sagacity, foresight, and comprehension would otherwise give to the virtuous and benevolent mind. Lastly, the investigation of the powers of nature, like the study of natural history, is perpetually suggesting to us views of the divine perfections and providence, which are both pleasing to the imagination, and improving to the heart.

But though other kinds of history may, in some respects, vie with that of philosophy, nothing that comes under the denomination of history can exhibit instances of so fine a rise and improvement in things as we see in the progress of the human mind in philosophical investigations. To whatever height we have arrived in natural science, our beginnings were very low, and our advances have been exceeding gradual. And to look down from the eminence, and to see, and compare all those gradual advances in the ascent, cannot but give the greatest pleasure to those who are seated on the eminence, and who feel all the advantages of their elevated situation. And considering that we ourselves are, by no means, at the top of human science; that the mountain still ascends beyond our sight, and that we are, in fact, not much above the foot of it, a view of the manner in which the ascent has been made cannot but animate us in our attempts to advance still higher, and suggest methods and expedients to assist us in our further progress.

Great conquerors, we read, have been both animated, and also, in a great measure, formed by reading the exploits of former conquerors. Why may not the same effect be expected from the history of philosophy to philosophers? May not even more be expected in this case? The wars of many of those conquerors, who received this advantage from history, had no proper connection with former wars; they were only analogous to them. Whereas the whole business of philosophy, diversified as it is, is but one; it being one and the same great scheme, that all philosophers, of all ages and nations have been conducting, from the beginning of the world; so that the work being the same, the labors of one are not only analogous to those of another, but in an immediate manner subservient to them; and one philosopher succeeds another in the same field, as one Roman proconsul succeeded another, in carrying on the same war, and pursuing the same conquests, in the same country. In this case an intimate knowledge of what has been done before us cannot but greatly facilitate our future progress, if it be not absolutely necessary to it.

These histories are evidently much more necessary in an advanced state of science, than in the infancy of it. At present philosophical discoveries are so many, and the accounts of them are so dispersed, that it is not in the power of any man to come at the knowledge of all that has been done, as a foundation for his own inquiries. And this circumstance appears to me to have very much retarded the progress of discoveries.

Not that I think philosophical discoveries are now at a stand. On the other hand, as quick advances seem to have been made of late years as in any equal period of time past whatever. Nay, it appears to me, that the progress is really accelerated. But the increase of knowledge is like the increase of a city. The building of some of the first streets makes a great figure, is much talked of, and known to everybody; whereas the addition of, perhaps, twice as much building, after it has been swelled to a considerable size, is not so much as taken notice of, and may be really unknown to many of the inhabitants. If the additions which have been made to the buildings of the city of London, in any single year of late, had been made two or three centuries ago, it could not have escaped the observation of historians; whereas, now, they are so scattered, and the proportion they bear to the whole city is so small, that they are hardly noticed. For the same reason, the improvements that boys make at school, or that young gentlemen make at an academy, or the university, are more taken notice of than all the knowledge they acquire afterwards, though they continue their studies with the same assiduity and success.

The history of experimental philosophy, in the manner in which it ought to be written, to be of much use, would be an immense work; perhaps more than any man ought to undertake; but it were much to be wished, that persons who have leisure, and sufficient abilities, would undertake it in separate parts. I have executed it, in the best manner I have been able, for that branch which has been my own favorite amusement; and I shall think myself happy, if the attempt excite other persons to do the like for theirs.

I cannot help thinking myself to have been peculiarly fortunate in undertaking the history of electricity at the most proper time for writing it, when the materials were neither too few, nor too many to make a history; and when they were so scattered as to make the undertaking highly desirable, and the work peculiarly useful to Englishmen.

I likewise think myself peculiarly happy in my subject itself. Few branches of natural philosophy would, I think, make so good a subject for a history. Few can boast such a number of discoveries, disposed in so fine a series, all comprised in so short a space of time, and all so recent, the principal actors in the scene being still living.

With several of these principal actors it has been my singular honor and happiness to be acquainted; and it was their approbation of my plan, and their generous encouragement that induced me to undertake the work. With gratitude I acknowledge my obligations to Dr. Watson, Dr. Franklin, and Mr. Canton, for the books, and other materials with which they have supplied me, and for the readiness with which they have given me any information in their power to procure.[4] In a more especial manner am I obliged to Mr. Canton, for those original communications of his, which will be found in this work, and which cannot fail to give a value to it, in the esteem of all the lovers of electricity. My grateful acknowledgments are also due to the Rev. Mr. Price, F. R. S., and to the Rev. Mr. Holt, our professor of natural philosophy at Warrington, for the attention they have given to the work, and for the many important services they have rendered me with respect to it.

To the gentlemen above-mentioned the public is, likewise, indebted for whatever they may think of value in the original experiments which I have related of my own. It was from conversing with them that I was first led to entertain the thought of attempting anything new in this way, and it was their example, and favorable attention to my experiments, that animated me in the pursuit of them. In short, without them, neither my experiments, nor this work would have had any existence.

The historical part of the work, the reader, I hope, will find to be full and circumstantial, and at the same time succinct. Every new fact, or important circumstance, I have noted as it arose; but I have abridged all long details, and have carefully avoided all digressions and repetitions. For this purpose, I have carefully perused every original author to which I could have recourse; and every quotation in the margin points to the authority that I myself consulted, and from which the account in the text was actually taken. Where I could not procure the original authors, I was obliged to quote them at second hand, but the reference will always show where that has been done. That I might

[4] Sir William Watson (1715-1787) was a physician, naturalist, and electrical experimenter active in the Royal Society. John Canton (1718-1772) was a London schoolmaster and scientist of distinction. See Leslie Stephen and Sidney Lee, eds., *Dictionary of National Biography* (63 vols., London, 1885-1901), LX, 45-47 and VIII, 456-457.

not misrepresent any writer, I have generally given the reader his own words, or the plainest translation I could make of them; and this I have done, not only in direct quotations, but where, by a change of person, I have made the language my own.

I made it a rule to myself, and I think I have constantly adhered to it, to take no notice of the mistakes, misapprehensions, and altercations of electricians; except so far as, I apprehended, a knowledge of them might be useful to their successors. All the disputes which have no way contributed to the discovery of truth, I would gladly consign to eternal oblivion. Did it depend upon me, it should never be known to posterity that there had ever been any such thing as envy, jealousy, or caviling among the admirers of my favorite study. I have, as far as my best judgment could direct me, been just to the merits of all persons concerned. If any have made unjust claims, by arrogating to themselves the discoveries of others, I have silently restored them to the right owner, and generally without so much as giving a hint that any injustice had ever been committed. If I have, in any case, given a hint, I hope it will be thought, by the offending parties themselves, to be a very gentle one; and that it will be a memento, which will not be without its use.

I think I have kept clear of any mean partiality towards my own countrymen, and even my own acquaintance. If English authors are oftener quoted than foreign, it is because they were more easily procured; and I have found a difficulty I could not have expected, in procuring foreign publications upon this subject.

I find it impossible to write a preface to this work without discovering a little of the enthusiasm which I have contracted from an attention to it, by expressing my wishes that more persons of a studious and retired life would admit this part of experimental philosophy into their studies. They would find it agreeably to diversify a course of study, by mixing something of action with speculation, and giving some employment to the hands and arms, as well as to the head. Electrical experiments are, of all others, the cleanest, and the most elegant, that the compass of philosophy exhibits. They are performed with the least trouble, there is an amazing variety in them, they furnish the most pleasing and surprising appearances for the entertainment of one's friends, and the expense of instruments may well be supplied by a proportionable deduction from the purchase of books, which are generally read and laid aside, without yielding half the entertainment.

The instruction we are able to get from books is, comparatively, soon exhausted; but philosophical instruments are an endless fund of knowledge. By philosophical instruments, however, I do not here mean the globes, the orrery, and others; which are only the means that ingenious men have hit upon to explain their own conceptions of things to others and which, therefore, like books, have no uses more extensive than the views of human ingenuity; but such as the air pump, condensing engine, pyrometer, etc. (with which electrical machines are to be ranked) and which exhibit the operations of nature, that is of the God of nature himself, which are infinitely various. By the help of these machines, we are able to put an endless variety of things into an endless variety of situations, while nature herself is the agent that shows the result. Hereby the laws of her action are observed, and the most important discoveries may be made; such as those who first contrived the instrument could have no idea of.

In electricity, in particular, there is the greatest room to make new discoveries. It is a field but just opened, and requires no great stock of particular preparatory knowledge; so that any person who is tolerably well versed in experimental philosophy may presently be upon a level with the most experienced electricians. Nay, this history shows that several raw adventurers have made themselves as considerable as some who have been, in other respects, the greatest philosophers. I need not tell my reader of how great weight this consideration is, to induce him to provide himself with an electrical apparatus.[5] The pleasure arising from the most trifling discoveries of one's own far exceeds what we receive from understanding the much more important discoveries of others; and a mere reader has no chance of finding new truths, in comparison of him who now and then amuses himself with philosophical experiments.

Human happiness depends chiefly upon having some object to pursue, and upon the vigor with which our faculties are exerted in the pursuit. And, certainly, we must be much more interested in pursuits wholly our own, than when we are merely following the track of others. Besides, this pleasure has reinforcements from a variety of sources, which I shall not here undertake to trace; but which contribute to heighten the sensation, far beyond anything else of this kind that can be experienced by a person of a speculative turn of mind.

It is a great recommendation of the study of electricity that it now appears to be, by no means, a small object. The electric fluid is no local, or occasional agent in the theater of the world. Late discoveries show that its presence and effects are everywhere, and that it acts a principal part in the grandest and most interesting scenes of nature. It is not, like magnetism, confined to one kind of bodies, but everything we know is a conductor or nonconductor of electricity. These are properties as essential and important as any they are possessed of, and can hardly fail to show themselves wherever the bodies are concerned.

Hitherto philosophy has been chiefly conversant about the more sensible properties of bodies; electricity, together with chemistry, and the doctrine of light and colors, seems to be giving us an inlet into their internal structure, on

[5] The "electrical machines" of the eighteenth century are described in *Benjamin Franklin's Experiments: A New Edition of Franklin's "Experiments and Observations on Electricity,"* ed. by I. Bernard Cohen (Cambridge, Mass., 1941), pp. 28-36. The introduction to this work contains an excellent sketch of the development of electrical science up to Priestley's time.

which all their sensible properties depend. By pursuing this new light, therefore, the bounds of natural science may possibly be extended beyond what we can now form an idea of. New worlds may open to our view, and the glory of the great Sir Isaac Newton himself, and all his contemporaries, be eclipsed by a new set of philosophers, in quite a new field of speculation. Could that great man revisit the earth, and view the experiments of the present race of electricians, he would be no less amazed than Roger Bacon, or Sir Francis would have been at his. The electric shock itself, if it be considered attentively, will appear almost as surprising as any discovery that he made; and the man who could have made that discovery, by any reasoning *a priori,* would have been reckoned a very great genius; but electrical discoveries have been made so much by accident, that it is more the powers of nature, than of human genius, that excite our wonder with respect to them. But if the simple electric shock would have appeared so extraordinary to Sir Isaac Newton, what would he have said upon seeing the effects of a modern electrical battery, and an apparatus for drawing lightning from the clouds! What inexpressible pleasure would it give a modern electrician, were the thing possible, to entertain such a man as Sir Isaac for a few hours with his principal experiments!

To return from this excursion to the business of a preface. Besides relating the history of electrical discoveries, in the order in which they were made, I thought it necessary, in order to make the work more useful, especially to young electricians, to subjoin a methodical treatise on the subject, containing the substance of the history in another form, with observations and instructions of my own. The particular uses of these parts of the work are expressed at large in the introductions to them. And, in the last place, I have given an account of such original experiments as I have been so fortunate as to hit upon myself.

I entitle the work the *History and Present State of Electricity;* and whether there be any new editions of the whole work or not, care will be taken to preserve the propriety of the title, by occasionally printing additions, in the same size, as new discoveries are made; which will always be sold at a reasonable price to the purchasers of the book; or given gratis, if the bulk be inconsiderable.

Considering what respectable persons have already honored this work with their valuable communications, I hope it will not be deemed arrogance in me, if I here advertise, that if any person shall make discoveries in electricity, which he would choose to see recorded in this history, he will oblige me by a communication of them; and if they be really original, a proper place shall certainly be assigned to them in the next edition, or paper of additions. And I hope that, if electricians in general would fall into this method, and make either a periodical, or occasional, but joint communication of their discoveries to the public, the greatest advantage would thence accrue to the science.

The business of philosophy is so multiplied, that all the books of general philosophical transactions cannot be purchased by private persons, or read by any person. It is high time to subdivide the business, that every man may have an opportunity of seeing everything that relates to his own favorite pursuit; and all the various branches of philosophy would find their account in this amicable separation. Thus the numerous branches of a large overgrown family, in the patriarchal ages, found it necessary to separate; and the convenience of the whole, and the strength, and increase of each branch were promoted by the separation. Let the youngest daughter of the sciences set the example to the rest, and show that she thinks herself considerable enough to make her appearance in the world without the company of her sisters.

But before this general separation, let each collect together everything that belongs to her, and march off with her whole stock. To drop the allusion, let histories be written of all that has been done in every particular branch of science, and let the whole be seen at one view. And when once the entire progress, and present state of every science shall be fully and fairly exhibited, I doubt not but we shall see a new and capital era commence in the history of all the sciences. Such an easy, full, and comprehensive view of what has been done hitherto could not fail to give new life to philosophical inquiries. It would suggest an infinity of new experiments, and would undoubtedly greatly accelerate the progress of knowledge; which is at present retarded, as it were, by its own weight, and the mutual entanglement of its several parts.

I will just throw out a further hint, of what, I think, might be favorable to the increase of philosophical knowledge. At present there are, in different countries in Europe, large incorporated societies, with funds for promoting philosophical knowledge in general. Let philosophers now begin to subdivide themselves, and enter into smaller combinations. Let the several companies make small funds, and appoint a director of experiments. Let every member have a right to appoint the trial of experiments in some proportion to the sum he subscribes, and let a periodical account be published of the result of them all, successful or unsuccessful. In this manner, the powers of all the members would be united, and increased. Nothing would be left untried which could be compassed at a moderate expense, and it being one person's business to attend to these experiments, they would be made, and reported without loss of time. Moreover, as all incorporations in these smaller societies should be avoided, they would be encouraged only in proportion as they were found to be useful; and success in smaller things would excite them to attempt greater.

I by no means disapprove of large, general and incorporated societies. They have their peculiar uses too; but we see by experience that they are apt to grow too large, and their forms are too slow for the dispatch of the minutiae of business, in the present multifarious state of philosophy. Let recourse be had to rich incorporated societies to defray the expenses of experiments to which the funds of smaller societies shall be unequal. Let their transactions contain a summary of the more important discoveries, collected from the smaller periodical publications. Let them, by rewards, and other methods, encourage those who distinguish themselves in the inferior societies; and thus give a general attention to the whole business of philosophy.

I wish all the incorporated philosophical societies in Europe would join their funds (and I wish they were sufficient for the purpose) to fit out ships for the complete discovery of the face of the earth, and for many capital experiments which can only be made in such extensive voyages.

Princes will never do this great business to any purpose. The spirit of adventure seems to be totally extinct in the present race of merchants. This discovery is a grand desideratum in science; and where may this pure and noble enthusiasm for such discoveries be expected but among philosophers, men uninfluenced by motives either of policy or gain? Let us think ourselves happy if princes give no obstruction to such designs. Let them fight for the countries when they are discovered, and let merchants scramble for the advantage that may be made of them. It will be an acquisition to philosophers if the seat of war be removed so far from the seat of science; and fresh room will be given to the exertion of genius in trade, when the old beaten track is deserted, when the old system of traffic is unhinged, and when new and more extensive plans of commerce take place. I congratulate the present race of philosophers on what is doing by the English court in this way; for with whatever view expeditions into the South Seas are made, they cannot but be favorable to philosophy.

Natural philosophy is a science which more especially requires the aid of wealth. Many others require nothing but what a man's own reflection may furnish him with. They who cultivate them find within themselves everything they want. But experimental philosophy is not so independent. Nature will not be put out of her way, and suffer her materials to be put into all that variety of situations which philosophy requires, in order to discover her wonderful powers, without trouble and expense. Hence the patronage of the great is essential to the flourishing state of this science. Others may project great improvements, but they only have the power of carrying them into execution.

Besides, they are the higher classes of men which are most interested in the extension of all kinds of natural knowledge; as they are most able to avail themselves of any discoveries which lead to the felicity and embellishment of human life. Almost all the elegancies of life are the produce of those polite arts which could have had no existence without natural science, and which receive daily improvements from the same source. From the great and the opulent, therefore, these sciences have a natural claim for protection; and it is evidently their interest not to suffer promising inquiries to be suspended, for want of the means of prosecuting them.

But other motives, besides this selfish one, may reasonably be supposed to attach persons in the higher ranks of life to the sciences; motives more exalted, and flowing from the most extensive benevolence. From natural philosophy have flowed all those great inventions, by means of which mankind in general are able to subsist with more ease, and in greater numbers upon the face of the earth. Hence arise the capital advantages of men above brutes, and of civilization above barbarity. And by these sciences also it is, that the views of the human mind itself are enlarged, and our common nature improved and ennobled. It is for the honor of the species, therefore, that these sciences should be cultivated with the utmost attention.

And of whom may these enlarged views, comprehensive of such great objects, be expected, but of those whom Divine Providence has raised above the rest of mankind. Being free from most of the cares peculiar to individuals, they may embrace the interests of the whole species, feel for the wants of mankind, and be concerned to support the dignity of human nature.

Gladly would I indulge the hope that we shall soon see these motives operating in a more extensive manner than they have hitherto done; that by the illustrious example of a few, a taste for natural science will be excited in many, in whom it will operate the most effectually to the advantage of science and of the world; and that all kinds of philosophical inquiries will, henceforward, be conducted with more spirit, and with more success than ever.

Were I to pursue this subject, it would carry me far beyond the reasonable bounds of a preface. I shall therefore conclude with mentioning that sentiment, which ought to be uppermost in the mind of every philosopher, whatever be the immediate object of his pursuit: that speculation is only of use as it leads to practice; that the immediate use of natural science is the power it gives us over nature, by means of the knowledge we acquire of its laws, whereby human life is, in its present state, made more comfortable and happy; but that the greatest, and noblest use of philosophical speculation is the discipline of the heart, and the opportunity it affords of inculcating benevolent and pious sentiments upon the mind.

A philosopher ought to be something greater, and better than another man. The contemplation of the works of God should give a sublimity to his virtue, should expand his benevolence, extinguish everything mean, base, and selfish in his nature, give a dignity to all his sentiments, and teach him to aspire to the moral perfections of the great author of all things. What great and exalted beings would philosophers be, would they but let the objects about which they are conversant have their proper moral effect upon their minds! A life spent in the contemplation of the productions of divine power, wisdom, and goodness, would be a life of devotion. The more we see of the wonderful structure of the world, and of the laws of nature, the more clearly do we comprehend their admirable uses, to make all the percipient creation happy, a sentiment which cannot but fill the heart with unbounded love, gratitude, and joy.

Even everything painful and disagreeable in the world appears to a philosopher, upon a more attentive examination, to be excellently provided, as a remedy of some greater inconvenience, or a necessary means of a much greater happiness; so that, from this elevated point of view, he sees all temporary evils and inconveniences to vanish, in the glorious prospect of the greater good to which they are subservient. Hence he is able to venerate and rejoice in God, not only in the bright sunshine, but also in the darkest shades of nature, whereas vulgar minds are apt to be disconcerted with the appearance of evil.

Nor is the cultivation of piety useful to us only as men, it is even useful to us as philosophers; and as true philosophy tends to promote piety, so a generous and manly piety is, reciprocally, subservient to the purposes of philosophy; and this both in a direct, and an indirect manner. While we keep in view the great final cause of all the parts and the laws of nature, we have some clue, by which to trace the efficient cause. This is most of all obvious in that part of philosophy which respects the animal creation. As the great and excellent Dr. Hartley observes: "Since this world is a system of benevolence, and consequently its author the object of unbounded love and adoration, benevolence and piety are our only true guides in our inquiries into it; the only keys which will unlock the mysteries of nature, and clues which lead through her labyrinths. Of this all branches of natural history, and natural philosophy afford abundant instances. In all these inquiries, let the inquirer take it for granted previously, that everything is right, and the best that can be *ceteris manentibus;* that is, let him, with a pious confidence, seek for benevolent purposes, and he will be always directed to the right road; and after a due continuance in it, attain to some new and valuable truth; whereas every other principle and motive of examination, being foreign to the great plan on which the universe is constructed, must lead into endless mazes, errors, and perplexities."[6]

[6] David Hartley, *Observations on Man* (2 vols., London, 1749), II, 245-246.

With respect to the indirect use of piety, it must be observed that the tranquility, and cheerfulness of mind, which results from devotion forms an excellent temper for conducting philosophical inquiries; tending to make them both more pleasant, and more successful. The sentiments of religion and piety tend to cure the mind of envy, jealousy, conceit, and every other mean passion, which both disgrace the lovers of science, and retard the progress of it, by laying an undue bias upon the mind, and diverting it from the calm pursuit of truth.

Lastly, let it be remembered, that a taste for science, pleasing, and even honorable as it is, is not one of the highest passions of our nature, and the pleasures it furnishes are even but one degree above those of sense; and therefore that temperance is requisite in all scientifical pursuits. Besides the duties of every man's proper station in life, which ought ever to be held sacred and inviolate, the calls of piety, common friendship, and many other avocations ought generally to be heard before that of study. It is therefore only a small share of their leisure that most men can be justified in giving to the pursuit of science; though this share is more or less in proportion to a man's situation in life, his natural abilities, and the opportunity he has for conducting his inquiries.

I shall conclude with another passage from Dr. Hartley to this purpose. "Though the pursuit of truth be an entertainment and employment suitable to our rational natures, and a duty to him who is the fountain of all knowledge and truth, yet we must make frequent intervals and interruptions; else the study of science, without a view to God and our duty, and from a vain desire of applause, will get possession of our hearts, engross them wholly, and by taking deeper root than the pursuit of vain amusements, become, in the end, a much more dangerous, and obstinate evil than that. Nothing can easily exceed the vainglory, self-conceit, arrogance, emulation, and envy, that are found in the eminent professors of the sciences, mathematics, natural philosophy, and even divinity itself. Temperance in these studies is, therefore, evidently required, both in order to check the rise of such ill passions, and to give room for the cultivation of other essential parts of our natures. It is with these pleasures as with the sensible ones; our appetites must not be made the measure of our indulgence, but we ought to refer all to a higher rule.

"But when the pursuit of truth is directed by this higher rule, and entered upon with a view to the glory of God, and the good of mankind, there is no employment more worthy of our natures, or more conducive to their purification and perfection."[7]

THE EXPERIMENTS AND DISCOVERIES
OF DR. FRANKLIN

We have hitherto seen what had been done in electricity by the English philosophers, and those on the continent of Europe, till about the year 1750; but our attention is now strongly called to what was doing on the continent of America, where Dr. Franklin and his friends were as assiduous in trying experiments, and as successful in making discoveries, as any of their brethren in Europe. For this purpose, we must look back a few years. As Dr. Franklin's discoveries were made entirely independent of any in Europe, I was unwilling to interrupt the former general account, by introducing them in their proper year. For the same reason, I imagine it will be generally more agreeable to see, at one view, what was done in America for some considerable space of time, without interrupting this account with what was doing, in the meantime, in Europe. I shall, therefore, digest, in the best manner I can, the three first publications

[7] *Ibid.*, pp. 255-256. This footnote and the one above are included in the original edition. They are a reminder of Hartley's special importance in Priestley's development. See *Memoirs*, above, p. 13, and introduction to Chapter V, below, p. 262.

of Dr. Franklin, entitled *New Experiments and Observations on Electricity, Made at Philadelphia in America,* communicated in several letters to Peter Collinson, Esq., of London, Fellow of the Royal Society; the first of which is dated July 28th 1747, and the last April 18th 1754.[8]

Nothing was ever written upon the subject of electricity which was more generally read and admired in all parts of Europe than these letters. There is hardly any European language into which they have not been translated; and, as if this were not sufficient to make them properly known, a translation of them has lately been made into Latin.[9] It is not easy to say whether we are most pleased with the simplicity and perspicuity with which these letters are written, the modesty with which the author proposes every hypothesis of his own, or the noble frankness with which he relates his mistakes, when they were corrected by subsequent experiments.

Though the English have not been backward in acknowledging the great merit of this philosopher, he has had the singular good fortune to be, perhaps, even more celebrated abroad than at home; so that to form a just idea of the great and deserved reputation of Dr. Franklin, we must read the foreign publications on the subject of electricity; in many of which the terms *Franklinism, Franklinist,* and the *Franklinian system* occur in almost every page. In consequence of this, Dr. Franklin's principles bid fair to be handed down to posterity, as equally expressive of the true principles of electricity, as the Newtonian philosophy is of the true system of nature in general.

---

[8] Peter Collinson (1694-1768) was an English mercer who became much interested in American affairs as a result of his trade with the colonies. He corresponded extensively with Franklin in regard to electrical experiments and with John Bartram on the subject of botany. See Stephen and Lee, eds., *Dictionary of National Biography,* XI, 382-383.

[9] This appears to be an error. See Cohen, ed., *Franklin's Experiments,* p. 140.

The greatest discovery which Dr. Franklin made concerning electricity, and which has been of the greatest practical use to mankind, was that of the perfect similarity between electricity and lightning. The analogy between these two powers had not been wholly unobserved by philosophers, and especially by electricians, before the publication of Dr. Franklin's discovery. It was so obvious, that it had struck several persons, but I shall give only one instance, in the sagacious Abbé Nollet.[10]

The Abbé says: "If any one should take upon him to prove, from a well connected comparison of phenomena, that thunder is, in the hands of nature, what electricity is in ours, that the wonders which we now exhibit at our pleasure are little imitations of those great effects which frighten us, and that the whole depends upon the same mechanism; if it is to be demonstrated, that a cloud, prepared by the action of the winds, by heat, by a mixture of exhalations, etc., is opposite to a terrestrial object; that this is the electrized body, and, at a certain proximity from that which is not; I avow that this idea, if it was well supported, would give me a great deal of pleasure; and in support of it, how many specious reasons present themselves to a man who is well acquainted with electricity. The universality of the electric matter, the readiness of its action, its inflammability, and its activity in giving fire to other bodies; its property of striking bodies externally and internally, even to their smallest parts, the remarkable example we have of this effect in the experiment of Leyden, the idea which we might truly adopt in supporting a greater degree of electric power, etc., all these points of analogy, which I have been some time meditating, begin to make me believe, that one might, by taking electricity for the model, form to one's self, in

[10] Jean Antoine Nollet (1700-1770) was a French cleric and physicist, in his later years preceptor to the royal family in France. He was the author of several books on electricity and carried on a scientific feud with Franklin. See Cohen, ed., *Franklin's Experiments*, pp. 98-99, 113-117.

relation to thunder and lightning, more perfect and more probable ideas than what have been offered hitherto, etc."[11]

But though the Abbé, and others, had been struck with the obvious analogy between lightning and electricity, they went no farther than these arguments *a priori*. It was Dr. Franklin who first proposed a method of verifying this hypothesis, entertaining the bold thought, as the Abbé Nollet expresses it, of bringing lightning from the heavens, of thinking that pointed iron rods, fixed in the air, when the atmosphere was loaded with lightning, might draw from it the matter of the thunderbolt, and discharge it without noise or danger into the immense body of the earth, where it would remain as it were absorbed.

Moreover, though Dr. Franklin's directions were first begun to be put in execution in France, he himself completed the demonstration of his own problem, before he heard of what had been done elsewhere; and he extended his experiments so far as actually to imitate all the known effects of lightning by electricity, and to perform every electrical experiment by lightning.

But before I relate any of Dr. Franklin's experiments concerning lightning, I must take notice of what he observed concerning the power of pointed bodies, by means of which he was enabled to carry his great designs into execution. He was properly the first who observed the entire and wonderful effect of pointed bodies, both in drawing, and throwing off the electric fire.

Mr. Jallabert was perhaps the first who observed that a body, pointed at one end, and round at another, produced different appearances upon the same body, according as the pointed, or round end was presented to it.[12] But as Mr. Nollet, in whose presence he made the experiment, says,

[11] Jean Antoine Nollet, *Leçons de Physique Experimentale* (5 vols., Amsterdam and Leipzig, 1754), IV, 34. This footnote was included in the original edition.

[12] Jean Jallabert (1712-1768) was a Swiss minister, physicist, and political leader who wrote on electricity. He was for some years professor at Geneva and later became president of the Swiss Republic.

the effect was not constant, and nothing was inferred from it. And the Abbé acknowledges that Dr. Franklin was the first who showed the property of pointed bodies in drawing off electricity more effectually and at greater distances than other bodies could do it.

He electrified an iron shot, three or four inches in diameter, and observed that it would not attract a thread, when the point of a needle was presented to it; but that this was not the case unless the pointed body had a communication with the earth; for, presenting the same pointed body, stuck on a piece of sealing wax, it had not that effect; though the moment the pointed body was touched with his finger, the electricity of the ball to which it was suspended was discharged. The converse of this he proved, by finding it impossible to electrify the iron shot when a sharp needle lay upon it.

By observing points of different degrees of acuteness, Dr. Franklin corrected the observation of Mr. Ellicott,[13] and other English electricians, that a pointed body, as a piece of leaf gold, would always be suspended nearer to the plate which was unelectrified than that which was electrified, if it were put between them. For the Doctor observed that it always removed farthest from that plate to which its sharpest point was presented, whether it was electrified or not; and if one of the points was very blunt, and the other very sharp, it would be suspended in the air by its blunt end, near the electrified body, without any unelectrified plate being held below it at all.

Dr. Franklin endeavored to account for this effect of pointed bodies by supposing that the base on which the electric fluid at the point of an electrified body rested, being small, the attraction by which the fluid was held to the body

See André Berthelot, ed., *La Grande Encyclopédie* (31 vols., Paris, 1886-1902), XX, 1189.

[13] John Ellicott (1706?-1772) was a London clockmaker and man of science. See Stephen and Lee, eds., *Dictionary of National Biography,* XVII, 249-250.

was slight; and that, for the same reason, the resistance to the entrance of the fluid was proportionably weaker in that place than where the surface was flat. But he himself candidly owns that he was not quite satisfied with this hypothesis. Whatever we think of Dr. Franklin's theory of the influence of pointed conductors in drawing and throwing off the electric fluid, the world is greatly indebted to him for the practical use he made of this doctrine.

Dr. Franklin begins his account of the similarity of the electric fluid and lightning by cautioning his readers not to be staggered at the great difference of the effects in point of degree, since that was no argument of any disparity in their nature. It is no wonder, says he, if the effects of the one should be so much greater than those of the other. For if two gun barrels electrified will strike at two inches distance, and make a loud report, at how great a distance will 10,000 acres of electrified cloud strike, and give its fire, and how loud must be that crack!

I shall digest all Dr. Franklin's observations concerning lightning under the several points of resemblance which he observed between it and electricity, mentioning these points of similarity in the order in which he himself remarked them; only bringing into one place the observations which may happen to lie in different parts of his letters, when they relate to the same subject.

1. Flashes of lightning, he begins with observing, are generally seen crooked, and waving in the air. The same, says he, is the electric spark always, when it is drawn from an irregular body at some distance. He might have added, when it is drawn by an irregular body, or through a space in which the best conductors are disposed in an irregular manner, which is always the case in the heterogeneous atmosphere of our globe.

2. Lightning strikes the highest and most pointed objects in its way preferably to others, as high hills, and trees, towers, spires, masts of ships, points of spears, etc. In like manner, all pointed conductors receive or throw off the

electric fluid more readily than those which are terminated
by flat surfaces.

3. Lightning is observed to take the readiest and best
conductor. So does electricity in the discharge of the Leyden phial. For this reason, the Doctor supposes that it
would be safer, during a thunderstorm, to have one's clothes
wet than dry, as the lightning might then, in a great measure, be transmitted to the ground, by the water, on the outside of the body. It is found, says he, that a wet rat cannot
be killed by the explosion of the electrical bottle, but that
a dry rat may.

4. Lightning burns. So does electricity. Dr. Franklin
says that he could kindle with it hard dry rosin, spirits un-
warmed, and even wood. He says that he fired gunpowder
by only ramming it hard in a cartridge, into each end of
which pointed wires were introduced, and brought within
half an inch of one another, and discharging a shock through
them.

5. Lightning sometimes dissolves metals. So does electricity, though the Doctor was mistaken when he imagined
it was a cold fusion, as will appear in its proper place. The
method in which Dr. Franklin made electricity melt metals
was by putting thin pieces of them between two panes of
glass bound fast together, and sending an electric shock
through them. Sometimes the pieces of glass, by which they
were confined, would be shattered to pieces by the discharge, and be broken into a kind of coarse sand, which
once happened with pieces of thick looking glass; but if
they remained whole, the piece of metal would be missing
in several places where it had lain between them, and instead of it, a metallic stain would be seen on both the
glasses, the stains on the under and upper glass being exactly similar in the minutest stroke.

A piece of leaf gold used in this manner appeared not
only to have been melted, but, as the Doctor thought, even
vitrified, or otherwise so driven into the pores of the glass,
as to be protected by it from the action of the strongest

aqua regis. Sometimes he observed that the metallic stains would spread a little wider than the breadth of the thin pieces of metal. True gold, he observed, made a darker stain, somewhat reddish, and silver a greenish stain.

Mr. Wilson[14] supposes that, in this experiment, the gold was not driven into the pores of the glass, but only into so near a contact with the surface of the glass, as to be held there by an exceeding great force; such a one, he says, as is exerted at the surface of all bodies whatever.

6. Lightning rends some bodies. The same does electricity. The Doctor observes that the electric spark would strike a hole through a quire of paper. When wood, bricks, stone, etc., are rent by lightning, he takes notice that the splinters will fly off on that side where there is the least resistance. In like manner, he says, when a hole is struck through a piece of pasteboard by an electrified jar, if the surfaces of the pasteboard are not confined and compressed, there will be a bur raised all round the hole on both sides of the pasteboard; but that if one side be confined, so that the bur cannot be raised on that side, it will all be raised on the other side, which way soever the fluid was directed. For the bur round the outside of the hole is the effect of the explosion, which is made every way from the center of the electric stream, and not an effect of its direction.

7. Lightning has often been known to strike people blind. And a pigeon, after a violent shock of electricity, by which the Doctor intended to have killed it, was observed to have been struck blind likewise.

8. In a thunderstorm at Stretham, described by Dr. Miles,[15] the lightning stripped off some paint which had covered a gilded molding of a panel of wainscot, without

[14] Benjamin Wilson (1721-1788) was a painter and scientist who took great interest in the problems of electricity. He carried on a controversy with Franklin over the question of whether lightning rods should be round or pointed at the top. See Van Doren, *Franklin*, p. 430.

[15] Henry Miles (1698-1763) was a dissenting minister and scientific writer, who contributed to the Royal Society papers on natural

hurting the rest of the paint. Dr. Franklin imitated this, by pasting a slip of paper over the filleting of gold, on the cover of a book, and sending an electric flash through it. The paper was torn off from end to end, with such force that it was broken in several places; and in others there was brought away part of the grain of the Turkey leather in which the book was bound. This convinced the Doctor that if it had been paint, it would have been stripped off in the same manner with that on the wainscot at Stretham.

9. Lightning destroys animal life. Animals have likewise been killed by the shock of electricity. The largest animals which Dr. Franklin and his friends had been able to kill were a hen, and a turkey which weighed about ten pounds.

10. Magnets have been observed to lose their virtue, or to have their poles reversed by lightning. The same did Dr. Franklin by electricity. By electricity he frequently gave polarity to needles, and reversed them at pleasure. A shock from four large jars, sent through a fine sewing needle, he says, gave it polarity, so that it would traverse when laid on water. What is most remarkable in these electrical experiments upon magnets is that if the needle, when it was struck, lay east and west, the end which was entered by the electric blast pointed north; but that if it lay north and south, the end which lay towards the north, would continue to point north, whether the fire entered at that end or the contrary; though he imagined that a stronger stroke would have reversed the poles even in that situation, an effect which had been known to have been produced by lightning. He also observed that the polarity was strongest when the needle was struck lying north and south, and weakest when it lay east and west. He takes notice that, in these experiments, the needle, in some cases, would be finely blued, like the spring of a watch, by the electric flame; in which case the color given by a flash from two jars only might be

---

history, meteorology, and electricity. See Stephen and Lee, eds., *Dictionary of National Biography*, XXXVII, 378.

wiped off, but that a flash from four jars fixed it, and frequently melted the needles. The jars the Doctor used held seven or eight gallons, and were coated and lined with tinfoil.

To demonstrate, in the completest manner possible, the sameness of the electric fluid with the matter of lightning, Dr. Franklin, astonishing as it must have appeared, contrived actually to bring lightning from the heavens, by means of an electrical kite, which he raised when a storm of thunder was perceived to be coming on. This kite had a pointed wire fixed upon it, by which it drew the lightning from the clouds. This lightning descended by the hempen string, and was received by a key tied to the extremity of it; that part of the string which was held in the hand being of silk, that the electric virtue might stop when it came to the key. He found that the string would conduct electricity even when nearly dry, but that when it was wet, it would conduct it quite freely; so that it would stream out plentifully from the key, at the approach of a person's finger.

At this key he charged phials, and from electric fire thus obtained, he kindled spirits, and performed all other electrical experiments which are usually exhibited by an excited globe or tube.

As every circumstance relating to so capital a discovery as this (the greatest, perhaps, that has been made in the whole compass of philosophy, since the time of Sir Isaac Newton) cannot but give pleasure to all my readers, I shall endeavor to gratify them with the communication of a few particulars which I have from the best authority.[16]

The Doctor, after having published his method of verifying his hypothesis concerning the sameness of electricity with the matter of lightning, was waiting for the erection of a spire in Philadelphia to carry his views into execution; not imagining that a pointed rod, of a moderate height, could answer the purpose; when it occurred to him that, by means of a common kite, he could have a readier and

[16] I.e., presumably, Franklin himself.

better access to the regions of thunder than by any spire whatever. Preparing, therefore, a large silk handkerchief, and two cross sticks, of a proper length, on which to extend it; he took the opportunity of the first approaching thunderstorm to take a walk into a field, in which there was a shed convenient for his purpose. But dreading the ridicule which too commonly attends unsuccessful attempts in science, he communicated his intended experiment to nobody but his son, who assisted him in raising the kite.

The kite being raised, a considerable time elapsed before there was any appearance of its being electrified. One very promising cloud had passed over it without any effect; when, at length, just as he was beginning to despair of his contrivance, he observed some loose threads of the hempen string to stand erect, and to avoid one another, just as if they had been suspended on a common conductor. Struck with this promising appearance, he immediately presented his knuckle to the key, and (let the reader judge of the exquisite pleasure he must have felt at that moment) the discovery was complete. He perceived a very evident electric spark. Others succeeded, even before the string was wet, so as to put the matter past all dispute, and when the rain had wet the string, he collected electric fire very copiously. This happened in June 1752, a month after the electricians in France had verified the same theory, but before he heard of anything they had done.

Besides this kite, Dr. Franklin had afterwards an insulated iron rod to draw the lightning into his house, in order to make experiments whenever there should be a considerable quantity of it in the atmosphere; and that he might not lose any opportunity of that nature, he connected two bells with this apparatus, which gave him notice, by their ringing, whenever his rod was electrified.

The Doctor being able, in this manner, to draw the lightning into his house, and make experiments with it at his leisure; and being certain that it was in all respects of the same nature with electricity, he was desirous to know if it was of the positive or negative kind. The first time he succeeded in making an experiment for this purpose was the 12th of April 1753, when it appeared that the lightning was negative. Having found that the clouds electrified negatively in eight successive thundergusts, he concluded they were always electrified negatively, and formed a theory to account for it. But he afterwards found he had concluded too soon. For, on the sixth of June following, he met with one cloud which was electrified positively; upon which he corrected his former theory, but did not seem able perfectly to satisfy himself with any other. The Doctor sometimes found the clouds would change from positive to negative electricity several times in the course of one thundergust, and he once observed the air to be strongly electrified during a fall of snow, when there was no thunder at all.

But the grand practical use which Dr. Franklin made of his discovery of the sameness of electricity and lightning was to secure buildings from being damaged by lightning, a thing of vast consequence in all parts of the world, but more especially in several parts of North America, where thunderstorms are more frequent, and their effects, in that dry air, more dreadful, than they are ever known to be with us.

This great end Dr. Franklin accomplished by so easy a method, and by so cheap, and seemingly trifling apparatus, as fixing a pointed metalline rod higher than any part of the building, and communicating with the ground, or rather the nearest water. This wire the lightning was sure to seize upon, preferable to any other part of the building; whereby this dangerous power would be safely conducted to the earth, and dissipated, without doing any harm to the building.

Dr. Franklin was of [the] opinion that a wire of a quarter of an inch of thickness would be sufficient to conduct a greater quantity of lightning than was ever actually discharged from the clouds in one stroke. He found that the gilding of a book was sufficient to conduct the charge of five large jars, and thought that it would probably have conducted the charge of many more. He also found by experiment that if a wire was destroyed by an explosion, it was yet sufficient to conduct that particular stroke, though it was thereby rendered incapable of conducting another.

The Doctor also supposed that pointed rods erected on edifices might likewise often prevent a stroke of lightning in the following manner. He says that an eye so situated as to view horizontally the underside of a thundercloud, will see it very ragged, with a number of separate fragments, or petty clouds, one under another, the lowest sometimes not far from the earth. These, as so many stepping stones, assist in conducting a stroke between a cloud and a building. To represent these by an experiment, he directs us to take two or three locks of fine loose cotton and connect one of them with the prime conductor, by a fine thread of two inches (which may be spun out of the same lock), another to that, and a third to the second, by like threads. He then bids us to turn the globe, and says we shall see these locks extending themselves towards the table (as the lower small clouds do towards the earth) but, that, on presenting a sharp point, erect under the lowest, it will shrink up to the second, the second to the first, and all together to the prime conductor, where they will continue as long as the point continues under them. A most ingenious and beautiful experiment! May not, he adds, in like manner, the small electrified clouds, whose equilibrium with the earth is soon restored by the point, rise up to the main body, and by that means occasion so large a vacancy, as that the grand cloud cannot strike in that place.

EXPERIMENTS ON MEPHITIC AIR AND CHARCOAL

I have related several instances of self-deception in other persons; to show that I do not mean to spare myself, I shall now relate one of my own. However, it is a mistake that

I should not have troubled the reader with, had it not terminated in a real discovery.

Having read, and finding by my own experiments, that a candle would not burn in air that had passed through a charcoal fire, or through the lungs of animals, or in any of that air which the chemists call *mephitic*,[17] I was considering what kind of change it underwent, by passing through the fire, or through the lungs, etc., and whether it was not possible to restore it to its original state, by some operation or mixture. For this purpose, I gave a great degree of intestine motion to it; I threw a quantity of electric matter from the point of a conductor into it, and performed various other operations upon it, but without any effect.

Among other random experiments, I dipped a charged phial into it; but, though I could not perceive that it produced any effect upon the air, I was surprised to find, upon taking out the phial, that it was wholly discharged. I imagined, however, at that time, that the discharge was owing to some imperfection in the manner of making the experiment, which I could not easily remedy.

Afterwards, concluding from some experiments of my own and others of Dr. Macbride[18] that this mephitic air was not anything that had ever been common air, but a fluid *sui generis,* that had several properties very different from those of common air; I thought of resuming my experiments, to ascertain whether it was not different from common air with respect to electricity; mephitic air being perhaps a conductor, as common air was a nonconductor.

Accordingly, some time in the month of January 1766, I filled a receiver, which was open at the top, and which held about three pints, with air from my lungs; and, with every precaution I could think of, dipped a small charged

[17] I.e., air filled with carbon dioxide.
[18] David Macbride (1726-1778) was a medical writer and chemist who was secretary of the Medico-Philosophical Society in Dublin. His *Experimental Essays* (1764) brought him into notice. See Stephen and Lee, eds., *Dictionary of National Biography*, XXXIV, 424-425.

phial into it; and, upon taking it out after continuing there about two seconds, found it quite discharged, just as might have been expected from dipping it into water. I repeated the experiment several times, and always with the same success. Lest I should have discharged the phial, some way or other, in passing the neck of the receiver, I changed the air, and then introduced the charged phial as before, several times, but never found it in the least discharged. Hence I concluded that, in the former case, it must have been discharged by the quality of the air in the receiver.

As there still remained some suspicion that the phial might have been discharged by the moisture which was mixed with the air as expired from my lungs (though I did not doubt but that what moisture there was in it was quickly attracted by the sides of the glass vessel, so as to leave the center free from it, and imagined that no quantity of moisture which the air could be supposed to contain could be able to discharge the phial so quickly) I immediately repeated the experiment, with air which I thought could not be supposed to contain any moisture.

I filled the same receiver with air from the center of a charcoal fire, and dipping the charged phial into it, as I had done before, found it as effectually discharged as in the former case. I repeated this experiment also a great number of times, and always with the same success. Upon changing the air also, and then introducing the phial, I found it not discharged. There seemed, therefore, to be no doubt, but that air in which flame would not subsist was a conductor of electricity.

I was confirmed in this opinion by placing a coated phial in a receiver filled with mephitic air, and finding that it was absolutely impossible to charge it in the smallest degree, in that situation; though it was charged very well, the moment I took it out of that air, without any wiping; which seemed to show that the incapacity of charging had not been owing to any moist vapors that adhered to the glass.

I was also confirmed in my opinion of the conducting power of mephitic air, by considering that all metallic bodies, which are the most perfect conductors we know, consist of a vitrifiable earth, and what the chemists call *phlogiston*, or probably nothing more than this same mephitic air in a fixed state.

In this confidence of having made a complete discovery, and one of some importance, after having repeated the above-mentioned experiments, and many others to the same purpose, a great number of times; I once happened to change the mephitic for common air in my receiver, without wiping the inside of the glass, which had been my usual method, though I had done it with no other view than more effectually to change the air; but now, though the air was sufficiently changed, by moving the receiver several times up and down, I had no sooner dipped the charged phial into it, than I found it discharged, in the same manner as it had been done in the mephitic air. The discharge had, after all, been made by the moisture on the inside. To ascertain this, I moistened the inside of the receiver with a sponge, and found that no phial could remain charged in it for the least space of time. This showed that the experiments above recited were ambiguous.

Dr. Franklin, to whom I had communicated these experiments, recollected them when he was this last summer at Pyrmont, where a large body of mephitic air always lies upon the surface of the medicinal spring (for this air is evidently specifically heavier than common air, and does not easily mix with it) but not having a proper apparatus, and the company there making experiments inconvenient, he did nothing that was decisive; though, from the little that he had an opportunity of doing, he imagined it was not a conductor.

These experiments on mephitic air, deceitful or, at least, ambiguous as they were, led, however, to a discovery, which may possibly throw some new light upon some of the most fundamental principles of electricity; and which certainly strengthen the suspicion that mephitic air may still be a conductor, at least in its fixed state.

Finding that I could make nothing of mephitic air itself (for I had endeavored to procure it in a variety of ways, but without success) I considered that it was from charcoal that I procured it in the greatest quantity, and thought I would try charcoal itself in substance. Accordingly, on May the 4th 1766, I tried the charcoal, in a variety of ways and states; and found it to be, what I had suspected, an excellent conductor of electricity.

Presenting a piece of charcoal to the prime conductor, together with my finger, or a piece of brass wire, I constantly observed that the electric spark struck the charcoal before either of the other conductors, if it happened to be advanced ever so little before them. Having a very rough surface, the charcoal did not take a dense spark from the conductor, till it was made a little smooth, and brought within about half an inch; when, to all appearance, it did quite as well as any piece of metal, there being a constant stream of dense and white electric fire between the conductor and it. I tried the charcoal in every state of heat or cold, and found no alteration of its conducting power.

I placed a great number of pieces of charcoal, not less than twelve or twenty, of various sizes, in a circuit, and discharged a common jar through them; when, to all appearance, the discharge was as perfect, as if so many pieces of metal had been placed in the same manner. Two of the pieces, about the middle of the circuit, I placed about an inch and a half from one another; but, upon the discharge, the spark passed the interval very full and strong. A piece of charcoal also made the discharge at the wire with one spark, but the report was not so loud as when the discharge was made with a piece of metal. It was observable that a black gross smoke rose from between each of the pieces of charcoal, at the moment of the discharge; but the ignition was momentary, and the fire could not be perceived on the charcoal.

To make the experiment of the conducting power of charcoal in the most indisputable manner, I took a piece of baked wood, which I had often used for the purpose of insulation, being an excellent nonconductor, and putting it into a long glass tube, I thrust it into the fire, and converted it into charcoal. In this operation, a very great quantity of gross smoke rose from it, so that, seeming to part with more of its moisture, one would have expected it would have come out a better nonconductor; but, upon trial, its electric property was quite gone, and it was become a very good conductor.

The experiments above-mentioned were first made with wood charcoal, of which I found pieces of very different degrees of conducting power; but the most perfect conductors I have found of this kind are some pieces of pit charcoal. These seem to be, in all respects, as perfect conductors as metals. They receive a strong bright spark from the prime conductor, though seldom at above an inch distance, on account of the roughness on their surface, which cannot be taken off; and in discharging a jar through them, or with them, no person can imagine any difference between them and metal, either in the color of the electric spark, or the sound made by the explosion. When they are broken, they exhibit an appearance which very much resembles that of broken steel. There is, however, a great variety in the electrical properties of different pieces of this kind of charcoal; and for want of proper opportunity I have not yet succeeded in ascertaining, with sufficient certainty, the circumstances, in the preparation, etc., on which this variety depends.

I would have preferred the examination of wood charcoal on many accounts; particularly, as the same substance is, in this case, converted from a perfect electric to a perfect conductor; and all the degrees of conducting power may be found in different specimens of it; whereas pit coal is itself a conductor, though an imperfect one; but not having any opportunity, I procured specimens of all the varieties I could imagine in the same heap of pit charcoal, with respect to their nearness or distance from the surface, etc.; but though I examined them with all the care and attention that I could apply, and in every method that I could think of, the differences were so exceedingly small, if any, that I could not fix upon any circumstance that I could depend upon for the cause of them.

Even common cinders from an open fire, of the kind of coals which we generally burn, I find to be very little inferior to charcoal, which is suffered to flame, but covered very close as soon as it is well burnt, and before any ashes are formed. Coals and cinders from a common fire being a very commodious subject for experiments, I did not fail to make as many upon them as I could imagine would be of any use; except that I had no opportunity of trying a sufficient variety of coals. I took several out of the fire after they had done blazing, some of which I covered with ashes, some I quenched in water, and some I left to cool in the open air. I also reduced some of the coals to cinders in a glass vessel, without suffering them to flame; and I treated in the very same manner various pieces of oak, cut from the same plank; but when I examined them, I found their differences, with respect to their power of conducting electricity, very inconsiderable, if any. I thought the cinder of a coal which we call cannel, and which is remarkable for flaming much while it burns, to be a better conductor than a cinder from a common coal; but the difference might be owing to its more uniform texture, and smoother surface. Charcoal made of coals which yield a strong sulphurous smell when they are burnt, and of which the charcoal itself is not quite divested, was, to all appearance, as good a conductor as that of the other kind, which is more esteemed.

In this course of experiments I have found myself much at a loss for a sufficiently accurate method of ascertaining the difference of conducting substances, and I wish that electricians would endeavor to find such a measure. One of the best that I am acquainted with, and which I applied among others on this occasion, is by the residuum of discharges, measured by Mr. Lane's electrometer.[19] It is well known that the worse the conductors are that form the circuit, the greater residuum will be left in a jar after a discharge; and Mr. Lane's electrometer, which measures an explosion, will likewise measure the residuum. To apply this method with accuracy, I put pieces of charcoal, etc., of the same length into the circuit, I used the very same chain in every experiment, and the same disposition of every part of the apparatus; I also made the explosions exactly equal, and after every discharge completed the circuit by the chain before I took the residuum; and lastly, I was careful to take up the same time in each operation, which I repeated very often. This method of measuring the conducting power of substances I learned of Mr. Lane, to whom, if what I have said be not quite intelligible, I must refer my reader. On the other hand, if I have said too much of it, that ingenious electrician must blame his own backwardness to publish an account of his electrometer and its various uses.

In the prosecution of these experiments on charcoal, I burned a piece which I had found to be a most excellent conductor, first between two crucibles, and then in the open fire, and tried it at different times till it was almost burned away; but, contrary to my expectations, I found its property very little diminished. I was, likewise, surprised to find that soot whether of wood coal, or pit coal hardly conducted at all. I made five or six inches of the soot of pit coal part of the electric circuit, which completed the communication between the inside and outside of a charged jar for several seconds; and yet found the charge not much diminished. A piece of wood soot, which is a firm shining substance, which does not soil the fingers, and which seems to break

19 Timothy Lane (1734-1807) was a London apothecary who invented a machine for ascertaining the quality and quantity of electricity in an electrified body, described in the *Philosophical Transactions of the Royal Society*, LVII (1767), 451-460.

in a polish in several places, would hardly conduct any part of a charge in the least sensible degree. When rubbed against my hand, or my waistcoat in frosty weather (though it was difficult to find any part of it that was large and smooth enough for the purpose) I more than once thought it attracted the thread of trial. The snuff of a candle would not conduct a shock, though it was placed in the middle of the circuit, and it was easily set on fire by the explosion of a small jar.

But notwithstanding my want of success, I make no doubt but that any person of tolerable sagacity, who has an opportunity of making experiments in a laboratory, where he could reduce to a coal all kinds of substances, in every variety of method, might very soon ascertain what it is that makes charcoal a conductor of electricity. In all the methods in which I could make charcoal, the fume of the bodies was suffered to escape; but let trials be made of substances reduced to a char without any communication with the open air, or where the vapors emitted from them shall meet with different degrees of resistance to their escape, ascertained by actual pressure.

Charcoal, besides its property of conducting electricity, is, on many other accounts, a very remarkable substance; being indestructible by any method besides burning in the open air; and yet it seems not to have been sufficiently studied by any chemist. A proper examination of it promises very fair, not only to ascertain the cause of its conducting, and, perhaps, of all conducting powers; but to be an opening to various other important discoveries in chemistry and natural philosophy; and the subject seems to be fairly within our reach.

Pit coal, and probably all other substances, at the same time that they lose much of their weight, increase considerably in their bulk in the operation of charring. Does it not seem to follow from hence, that its conducting power may possibly be owing to the largeness of its pores, agreeable to the hypothesis of Dr. Franklin, that electric substances have exceeding small pores, which disposes them to break with a polish?

Or, since the calces of metals, which are electric bodies, become metals, and conductors, by being fused in contact with charcoal; are not metals themselves conductors of electricity, in consequence of something they get from the charcoal? Is not this the mephitic air; as the modern chemists suppose, that this is all that the metallic calces require to their revivification?

This course of experiments, however, evidently overturns one of the earliest, and, hitherto, universally received maxims in electricity, viz. that water and metals are conductors, and all other bodies nonconductors; for we have here a substance, which is clearly neither water, nor a metal, and yet a good conductor.

Experiments and Observations
on Different Kinds of Air

Joseph Priestley is best remembered today for his early experiments with the chemistry of gases. These are described in his three-volume Experiments and Observations on Different Kinds of Air *(1774-1777). His first important achievement in this field was an effective method for the preparation of carbonated water, which is discussed in the next selection, "Of Fixed Air," from Volume One.*[20] *The extracts from Volume Two of this work include one of Priestley's typically moralistic prefaces and his own account of the discovery of "dephlogisticated air" — to which Antoine Lavoisier gave the name oxygen.*[21] *Priestley clung to the old phlogiston theory of combustion until the end of his life. Three additional volumes of* Observations on Air *were published in later years.*[22]

OF FIXED AIR

It was in consequence of living for some time in the neighborhood of a public brewery, that I was induced to make experiments on fixed air, of which there is always a large body, ready formed, upon the surface of the fermenting liquor, generally about nine inches, or a foot in depth, within which any kind of substance may be very conveniently placed; and though, in these circumstances, the fixed air

[20] Text from third edition (London, 1781), pp. 25-43.

[21] Text from second edition (London, 1784), pp. v-x, 29-49.

[22] On Priestley's contribution to chemistry, consult T. E. Thorpe, *Joseph Priestley* (London and New York, 1906), pp. 167-223, now somewhat outdated, and Sir Philip J. Hartog, "The Newer Views of Priestley and Lavoisier," *Annals of Science,* V (1941), 1-56.

must be continually mixing with the common air, and is therefore far from being perfectly pure, yet there is a constant fresh supply from the fermenting liquor, and it is pure enough for many purposes.[23]

A person, who is quite a stranger to the properties of this kind of air, would be agreeably amused with extinguishing lighted candles, or chips of wood in it, as it lies upon the surface of the fermenting liquor; for the smoke readily unites with this kind of air, probably by means of the water which it contains; so that very little or none of the smoke will escape into the open air, which is incumbent upon it. It is remarkable that the upper surface of this smoke, floating in the fixed air, is smooth, and well defined; whereas the lower surface is exceedingly ragged, several parts hanging down to a considerable distance within the body of the fixed air, and sometimes in the form of balls, connected to the upper stratum by slender threads, as if they were suspended. The smoke is also apt to form itself into broad flakes, parallel to the surface of the liquor, and at different distances from it, exactly like clouds. These appearances will sometimes continue above an hour, with very little variation. When this fixed air is very strong, the smoke of a small quantity of gunpowder fired in it will be wholly retained by it, no part escaping into the common air.[24]

Making an agitation in this air, the surface of it (which still continues to be exactly defined) is thrown into the form of waves, which it is very amusing to look upon; and if, by this agitation, any of the fixed air be thrown over the side of the vessel, the smoke, which is mixed with it, will fall to the ground, as if it was so much water, the fixed air being heavier than common air.

The red part of burning wood was extinguished in this air, but I could not perceive that a red-hot poker was sooner cooled in it.

[23] In modern terminology, fixed air is carbon dioxide.
[24] Common air is the atmosphere.

Fixed air does not instantly mix with common air. Indeed if it did, it could not be caught upon the surface of the fermenting liquor. A candle put under a large receiver, and immediately plunged very deep below the surface of the fixed air, will burn some time. But vessels with the smallest orifices, hanging with their mouths downwards in the fixed air, will in time have the common air, which they contain, perfectly mixed with it. When the fermenting liquor is contained in vessels close covered up, the fixed air, on removing the cover, readily affects the common air which is contiguous to it, so that candles held at a considerable distance above the surface will instantly go out. I have been told by the workmen that this will sometimes be the case when the candles are held two feet above the mouth of the vessel.

Fixed air unites with the smoke of rosin, sulphur, and other electrical substances, as well as with the vapor of water; and yet, by holding the wire of a charged phial among these fumes, I could not make any electrical atmosphere, which surprised me a good deal, as there was a large body of this smoke, and it was so confined, that it could not escape me.

I also held some oil of vitriol[25] in a glass vessel within the fixed air, and by plunging a piece of red-hot glass into it, raised a copious and thick fume. This floated upon the surface of the fixed air like other fumes, and continued as long.

Considering the near affinity between water and fixed air, I concluded that if a quantity of water was placed near the yeast of the fermenting liquor, it could not fail to imbibe that air, and thereby acquire the principal properties of Pyrmont, and some other medicinal mineral waters. Accordingly, I found, that when the surface of the water was considerable, it always acquired the pleasant acidulous taste that Pyrmont water has.[26] The readiest way of impreg-

[25] Oil of vitriol is concentrated sulphuric acid.
[26] From Bad Pyrmont, a noted German spa with mineral springs.

nating water with this virtue, in these circumstances, is to take two vessels, and to keep pouring the water from one into the other, when they are both of them held as near the yeast as possible; for by this means a great quantity of surface is exposed to the air, and the surface is also continually changing. In this manner, I have sometimes, in the space of two or three minutes, made a glass of exceedingly pleasant sparkling water, which could hardly be distinguished from very good Pyrmont, or rather Seltzer water.[27]

But the most effectual way of impregnating water with fixed air is to put the vessels which contain the water into glass jars, filled with the purest fixed air, made by the solution of chalk in diluted oil of vitriol, standing in quicksilver. In this manner I have, in about two days, made a quantity of water to imbibe more than an equal bulk of fixed air, so that, according to Dr. Brownrigg's[28] experiments, it must have been much stronger than the best imported Pyrmont; for though he made his experiments at the springhead, he never found that it contained quite so much as half its bulk of this air. If a sufficient quantity of quicksilver cannot be procured, oil may be used with sufficient advantage, for this purpose, as it imbibes the fixed air very slowly. Fixed air may be kept in vessels standing in water for a long time, if they be separated by a partition of oil, about half an inch thick. Pyrmont water made in these circumstances is little or nothing inferior to that which has stood in quicksilver.

The readiest method of preparing this water for use is to agitate it strongly with a large surface exposed to the fixed air. By this means more than an equal bulk of air may be communicated to a large quantity of water in the space of a few minutes. But since agitation promotes the dissipation

[27] Originally obtained from Niederselters, a village in Hessen, West Germany.
[28] William Brownrigg (1711-1800) was a physician and chemist, who did important work on gases from coal mines and who pioneered in analyzing mineral waters. Priestley benefited from his prior work on carbonated water. See Stephen and Lee, eds., *Dictionary of National Biography*, VII, 85-86.

of fixed air from water, it cannot be made to imbibe so great a quantity in this method as in the former, where more time is taken.

Easy directions for impregnating water with fixed air I have published in a small pamphlet,[29] designed originally for the use of seamen in long voyages, on the presumption that it might be of use for preventing or curing the sea scurvy, equally with wort, which was recommended by Dr. Macbride for this purpose, on no other account than its property of generating fixed air, by its fermentation in the stomach.

Water thus impregnated with fixed air readily dissolves iron, as Mr. Lane has discovered; so that if a quantity of iron filings be put to it, it presently becomes a strong chalybeate, and of the mildest and most agreeable kind.[30]

I have recommended the use of chalk and oil of vitriol as the cheapest, and, upon the whole, the best materials for this purpose. But some persons prefer pearl ashes, pounded marble, or other calcareous or alkaline substances, and perhaps with reason. My own experience has not been sufficient to enable me to decide in this case.

Whereas some persons had suspected that a quantity of the oil of vitriol was rendered volatile by this process, I examined it, by all the chemical methods that are in use; but could not find that water thus impregnated contained the least perceivable quantity of that acid.

Mr. Hey,[31] indeed, who assisted me in this examination, found that distilled water, impregnated with fixed air, did not mix so readily with soap as the distilled water itself;

[29] Joseph Priestley, *Directions for Impregnating Water with Fixed Air* (London, 1772). This pamphlet has been reprinted by the American Bottlers of Carbonated Waters (Washington, D.C., 1945) with a useful preface by John J. Riley on "Priestley and Carbonated Waters."

[30] Chalybeate is water impregnated or flavored with iron, as mineral water.

[31] William Hey, a surgeon, took an interest in Priestley's experiments at Leeds. See Priestley's *Memoirs*, above, pp. 38-39.

but this was also the case when the fixed air had passed through a long glass tube filled with alkaline salts, which, it may be supposed, would have imbibed any of the oil of vitriol that might have been contained in that air.

Fixed air itself may be said to be of the nature of an acid, though of a weak and peculiar sort. Mr. Bergman of Upsala,[32] who honored me with a letter upon the subject, calls it *the aërial acid*, and, among other experiments to prove it to be an acid, he says that it changes the blue juice of turnsole into red.[33] This Mr. Hey found to be true, and he moreover discovered that when water tinged blue with the juice of turnsole, and then red with fixed air, has been exposed to the open air, it recovers its blue color again.

The heat of boiling water will expel all the fixed air, if a phial containing the impregnated water be held in it; but it will often require above half an hour to do it completely.

Dr. Percival, who is particularly attentive to every improvement in the medical art, and who has thought so well of this impregnation as to prescribe it in several cases, informs me that it seems to be much stronger, and sparkles more, like the true Pyrmont water, after it has been kept some time.[34] This circumstance, however, shows that, in time, the fixed air is more easily disengaged from the water; and though, in this state, it may affect the taste more sensibly, it cannot be of so much use in the stomach and bowels, as when the air is more firmly retained by the water.

[32] Torbern Bergman (1735-1784), Swedish analytical chemist and physicist, was professor at the University of Upsala and the author of many scientific papers. See Uno Bokland, "Torbern Bergman as Pioneer in the Domain of Mineral Waters," in Torbern Bergman, *On Acid of Air* (Stockholm, 1956), pp. 105-128.

[33] Turnsole refers to the plant *chrozophora tinctoria*, which yields a violet-blue coloring matter. Litmus, also a plant extract, is chemically related and is used today for the same purpose.

[34] Thomas Percival (1740-1804), a physician, was author of various medical and scientific papers published in the *Philosophical Transactions of the Royal Society* which attracted wide attention. He was a student of Priestley's at Warrington Academy. See Stephen and Lee, eds., *Dictionary of National Biography*, XLIV, 383-384.

By the process described in my pamphlet, fixed air may be readily incorporated with wine, beer, and almost any other liquor whatever; and when beer, wine, or cider, is become flat or dead (which is the consequence of the escape of the fixed air they contained) they may be revived by this means; but the delicate and agreeable flavor, or acidulous taste, communicated by fixed air, and which is very manifest in water, can hardly be perceived in wine, or any liquors which have much taste of their own.

I should think that there can be no doubt, but that water thus impregnated with fixed air must have all the medicinal virtues of genuine Pyrmont or Seltzer water; since these depend upon the fixed air they contain. If the genuine Pyrmont water derives any advantage from its being a natural chalybeate, this may also be obtained by providing a common chalybeate water, and using it in these processes, instead of common air.

Having succeeded so well with this artificial Pyrmont water, I imagined that it might be possible to give ice the same virtue, especially as cold is known to promote the absorption of fixed air by water; but in this I found myself quite mistaken. I put several pieces of ice into a quantity of fixed air, confined by quicksilver, but no part of the air was absorbed in two days and two nights; but upon bringing it into a place where the ice melted, the air was absorbed as usual.

I then took a quantity of strong artificial Pyrmont water, and putting it into a thin glass phial, I set it in a pot that was filled with snow and salt. This mixture instantly freezing the water that was contiguous to the sides of the glass, the air was discharged plentifully, so that I caught a considerable quantity in a bladder tied to the mouth of the phial.

I also took two quantities of the same Pyrmont water, and placed one of them where it might freeze, keeping the other in a cold place, but where it would not freeze. This retained its acidulous taste, though the phial which contained it was not corked; whereas the other being brought into the same place, where the ice melted very slowly, had at the same time the taste of common water only. That quantity of water which had been frozen by the mixture of snow and salt was almost as much like snow as ice, such a quantity of air bubbles were contained in it, by which it was prodigiously increased in bulk.

The pressure of the atmosphere assists very considerably in keeping fixed air confined in water; for in an exhausted receiver, Pyrmont water will absolutely boil, by the copious discharge of its air. This is also the reason why beer and ale froth so much *in vacuo*. I do not doubt, therefore, but that, by the help of a condensing engine, water might be much more highly impregnated with the virtues of the Pyrmont spring; and it would not be difficult to contrive a method of doing it.

The manner in which I made several experiments to ascertain the absorption of fixed air by different fluid substances was to put the liquid into a dish, and holding it within the body of the fixed air at the brewery, to set a glass vessel into it, with its mouth inverted. This glass being necessarily filled with the fixed air, the liquor would rise into it when they were both taken into the common air, if the fixed air was absorbed at all.

Making use of ether in this manner, there was a constant bubbling from under the glass, occasioned by this fluid easily rising in vapor, so that I could not, in this method, determine whether it imbibed the air or not. I concluded, however, that they did incorporate, from a very disagreeable circumstance, which made me desist from making any more experiments of the kind. For all the beer, over which this experiment was made, contracted a peculiar taste; the fixed air impregnated with the ether being, I suppose, again absorbed by the beer. I have also observed that water which remained a long time within this air has sometimes acquired a very disagreeable taste. At one time it was like tar-water. How this was acquired, I was very desirous of making some experiments to ascertain, but I was discouraged by the fear of injuring the fermenting liquor. It could not come from the fixed air only.

Insects and animals which breathe very little are stifled in fixed air, but are not soon quite killed in it. Butterflies and flies of other kinds, will generally become torpid, and seemingly dead, after being held a few minutes over the fermenting liquor; but they revive again after being brought into the fresh air. But there are very great varieties with respect to the time in which different kinds of flies will either become torpid in the fixed air, or die in it. A large strong frog was much swelled, and seemed to be nearly dead, after being held about six minutes over the fermenting liquor; but it recovered upon being brought into the common air. A snail treated in the same manner died presently.

Fixed air is presently fatal to vegetable life. At least sprigs of mint growing in water, and placed over the fermenting liquor, will often become quite dead in one day, or even in a less space of time; nor do they recover when they are afterwards brought into the common air. I am told, however, that some other plants are much more hardy in this respect.

A red rose, fresh gathered, lost its redness, and became of a purple color, after being held over the fermenting liquor about twenty-four hours; but the tips of each leaf were much more affected than the rest of it. Another red rose turned perfectly white in this situation; but various other flowers, of different colors, were very little affected. These experiments were not repeated, as I wish they might be done, in pure fixed air, extracted from chalk by means of oil of vitriol.

For every purpose in which it was necessary that the fixed air should be as unmixed as possible, I generally made it by pouring oil of vitriol upon chalk and water, catching it in a bladder, fastened to the neck of the phial in which they were contained, taking care to press out all the common air, and also the first, and sometimes the second, produce of fixed air; and also, by agitation, making it as quickly as I possibly could. At other times, I made it pass from the phial in which it was generated through a glass tube, without the intervention of any bladder, which, as I found by experience, will not long make a sufficient separation between several kinds of air and common air.

I had once thought that the readiest method of procuring fixed air, and in sufficient purity, would be by the simple process of burning chalk, or pounded limestone in a gun-barrel, making it pass through the stem of a tobacco pipe, or a glass tube carefully luted to the orifice of it. In this manner I found that air is produced in great plenty; but, upon examining it, I found, to my very great surprise, that little more than one-half of it was fixed air, capable of being absorbed by water; and that the rest was inflammable, sometimes very weakly, but sometimes pretty highly so.

Whence this inflammability proceeds, I am not able to determine, the lime or chalk not being supposed to contain any other than fixed air. I conjecture, however, that it must proceed from the iron, and the separation of it from the calx[35] may be promoted by that small quantity of oil of vitriol, which I am informed is contained in chalk, if not in limestone also.

But it is an objection to this hypothesis that the inflammable air produced in this manner burns blue, and not at all like that which is produced from iron, or any other metal, by means of an acid. It also has not the smell of that kind of inflammable air which is produced from mineral substances. Besides, oil of vitriol without water will not dissolve iron; nor can inflammable air be got from it, unless the acid be considerably diluted; and when I mixed brim-

[35] In modern terminology, a calx is an oxide. In this case, iron oxide.

stone with the chalk, neither the quality nor the quantity of
the air was changed by it. Indeed no air, or permanently
elastic vapor, can be got from brimstone, or any oil.

Perhaps this inflammable principle may come from some
remains of the animals, from which it is thought that all
calcareous matter proceeds.

In the method in which I generally made the fixed air
(and indeed always, unless the contrary be particularly
mentioned, viz. by diluted oil of vitriol and chalk) I found
by experiment that it was as pure as Mr. Cavendish made
it.[36] For after it had passed through a large body of water
in small bubbles, still $\frac{1}{50}$ or $\frac{1}{60}$ part only was not absorbed
by water. In order to try this as expeditiously as possible,
I kept pouring the air from one glass vessel into another, im-
mersed in a quantity of cold water, in which manner I found
by experience that almost any quantity may be reduced as
far as possible in a very short time. But the most expedi-
tious method of making water imbibe any kind of air is to
confine it in a jar, and agitate it strongly, in the manner
described in my pamphlet on the impregnation of water
with fixed air. . . .

At the same time that I was trying the purity of my fixed
air, I had the curiosity to endeavor to ascertain whether that
part of it which is not miscible in water be equally diffused
through the whole mass; and, for this purpose, I divided a
quantity of about a gallon into three parts, the first consisting of that which was uppermost, and the last of that
which was the lowest, contiguous to the water; but all these
parts were reduced in about an equal proportion, by passing
through the water, so that the whole mass had been of an
uniform composition. This I have also found to be the case
with several kinds of air, which will not properly incorporate.

[36] Henry Cavendish (1731-1810), the distinguished chemist, was
also working with carbon dioxide at this time. See A. Wolf, *A History of Science, Technology, and Philosophy in the Eighteenth Century,* 2nd edition (London, 1952), p. 362.

A mouse will live very well, though a candle will not burn, in the residuum of the purest fixed air that I can make; and I once made a very large quantity for the sole purpose of this experiment. This, therefore, seems to be one instance of the generation of genuine common air, though vitiated in some degree. It is also another proof of the residuum of fixed air being, in part at least, common air, that it becomes turbid, and is diminished by the mixture of nitrous air, as will be explained hereafter.

That fixed air only wants some addition to make it permanent, and immiscible with water, if not, in all respects, common air, I have been led to conclude, from several attempts which I once made to mix it with air in which a quantity of iron filings and brimstone, made into a paste with water, had stood; for, in several mixtures of this kind, I imagined that not much more than half of the fixed air could be imbibed by water; but, not being able to repeat the experiment, I conclude that I either deceived myself in it, or that I overlooked some circumstance on which the success of it depended.

These experiments, however, whether they were fallacious or otherwise, induced me to try whether any alteration would be made in the constitution of fixed air, by this mixture of iron filings and brimstone. I therefore put a mixture of this kind into a quantity of as pure fixed air as I could make, and confined the whole in quicksilver, lest the water should absorb it before the effects of the mixture could take place. The consequence was that the fixed air was diminished, and the quicksilver rose in the vessel, till about the fifth part was occupied by it; and, as near as I could judge, the process went on, in all respects, as if the air in the inside had been common air.

What is most remarkable, in the result of this experiment, is that the fixed air, into which this mixture had been put, and which had been in part diminished by it, was in part also rendered insoluble in water by this means. I made this experiment four times, with the greatest care, and observed, that in two of them about one-sixth, and in the other two about one-fourteenth, of the original quantity, was such as could not be absorbed by water, but continued permanently elastic. Lest I should have made any mistake with respect to the purity of the fixed air, the last time that I made the experiment, I set part of the fixed air, which I made use of, in a separate vessel, and found it to be exceedingly pure, so as to be almost wholly absorbed by water; whereas the other part, to which I had put the mixture, was far from being so.

In one of these cases, in which fixed air was made immiscible with water, it appeared to be not very noxious to animals; but in another case, a mouse died in it pretty soon. This difference probably arose from my having inadvertently agitated the air in water rather more in one case than in the other.

As the iron is reduced to a calx by this process, I once concluded that it is phlogiston[37] that fixed air wants, to make it common air; and, for anything I yet know, this may be the case, though I am ignorant of the method of combining them; and when I calcined a quantity of lead in fixed air, in the manner which will be described hereafter, it did not seem to have been less soluble in water than it was before.

PREFACE

I have seen abundant reason, since the publication of my former volume of *Observations on Different Kinds of Air,* to applaud myself for the little delay I made in putting it to the press; the consequence having been that, instead of the experiments being prosecuted by myself only, or a few

[37] In premodern chemistry "phlogiston" was the quintessence or "principle" which was believed thrown off from substances during the process of combustion, leaving a "dephlogisticated" residue. Thus a metal heated in air lost its phlogiston and became a "calx." Under this theory a metal was held to be more complex than the corresponding "calx" (oxide).

others, the subject has now gained almost universal attention among philosophers, in every part of Europe. In consequence of this, considerable discoveries have been made by people of distant nations; and this branch of science, of which nothing, in a manner, was known till very lately indeed, now bids fair to be farther advanced than any other in the whole compass of natural philosophy. The attention which my former volume excited has been a motive with me to continue my own researches, till I have been led to discoveries of more importance than any that I had made before, and of which I had not at that time the most distant idea. It has, likewise, been the means of extending my acquaintance among philosophers, of whose lights I have availed myself, as my narrative will witness.

Sig. Felice Fontana of Florence, Sig. Landriani of Milan, and Mr. Lavoisier of Paris, have already announced, in their late publications on this subject, that they have much more to follow with respect to it, and that they are at present intent upon the investigation of it. Mr. Montigny (when I had the pleasure of meeting him at Mr. Trudaine's, as mentioned in the course of the work) gave me an account of some very curious experiments which he had made on inflammable air, and which I expect he will soon communicate to the public.[38] That veteran in philosophy, Father Beccaria of Turin,[39] has also made some valuable experiments of this kind, and will, I doubt not, prosecute them with his usual address and success. Mr. Bergman of Upsala, who, as I have said, wrote to me formerly on this subject, has since published a paper on fixed air in the Swedish language, which I cannot read. Several ingenious persons, whose names are not yet known to the public, are,

[38] Priestley met a number of distinguished French scientists, including Lavoisier, on his visit to Paris with Shelburne in 1774. See his *Memoirs,* above, p. 44.

[39] Giovanni Battista Beccaria (1716-1781), who held the chair of physics at the University of Turin and worked especially with electricity, should not be confused with Cesare Bonesana Beccaria (c. 1738-1794), who wrote on crimes and punishments.

to my knowledge, engaged in these pursuits; and we are not without expectations from the oldest living fathers of this philosophy, Dr. Brownrigg and Dr. Black,[40] as well as other gentlemen in Scotland. Besides these, there must be, I doubt not, at least twice as many persons at work upon this subject as I can have had any opportunity of hearing of.

Upon the whole, there is not perhaps an example, in all the history of philosophy, of so much zeal and emulation being excited by any object. I even question whether the subject of electricity, under the auspices of Dr. Franklin, ever engaged more general attention; and now these two pursuits are happily united, and admirably promote each other.

In reality, this is not now a business of air only, as it was at the first; but appears to be of much greater magnitude and extent, so as to diffuse light upon the most general principles of natural knowledge, and especially those about which chemistry is particularly conversant. And it will not now be thought very assuming to say, that, by working in a tub of water, or a basin of quicksilver, we may perhaps discover principles of more extensive influence than even that of gravity itself, the discovery of which, in its full extent, contributed so much to immortalize the name of Newton.

Having been the means of bringing so many champions into the field, I shall with peculiar pleasure attend to all their achievements, in order to prepare myself, as I promised in the preface to my last volume, for writing the history of the campaign; and I trust that all my brethren in the science will have confidence in my justice to their respective merits.

I flatter myself that the very frank and candid manner in which I have related what I have done myself will procure me sufficient credit for my impartiality with respect to

[40] Joseph Black (1728-1799) was a distinguished Scottish physician and chemist, who conducted pioneer experiments with carbon dioxide. An authoritative review of his life and work, "Joseph Black and Fixed Air," by Henry Guerlac, may be found in *Isis*, XLVIII (June 1957), 124-151, and (December 1957), 433-456.

others. It will be very evident that I have left myself hardly any other merit than that of patient industry and attention, and that of keeping my mind so far detached from the influence of prejudice as to be able to pursue fairly such casual observations as presented themselves to me.

There is nothing capital in this volume from which I can hope to derive any other kind of honor, than that of being the instrument in the hands of Divine Providence, which makes use of human industry to strike out, and diffuse, that knowledge of the system of nature, which seems, for some great purpose that we cannot as yet fully comprehend, to have been reserved for this age of the world; concerning which I threw out some farther hints in my former preface, which the excellent French translator was not permitted to insert in his version.

I even think that I may flatter myself so much, if it be any flattery, as to say that there is no history of experiments more truly ingenuous than mine, and especially the section on the discovery of dephlogisticated air, which is the most important in the volume. I am not conscious to myself of having concealed the least hint that was suggested to me by any person whatever, any kind of assistance that has been given me, or any views or hypotheses by which the experiments were directed, whether they were verified by the result, or not.

In this volume the reader will find much light thrown upon many things which were inexplicable to me when I published the former volume; but, on the other hand, there are many things in this as inexplicable to me now as the others were before; and for the elucidation of them we must wait for more experiments, and more discoveries.

OF DEPHLOGISTICATED AIR AND OF THE CONSTITUTION OF THE ATMOSPHERE

The contents of this section will furnish a very striking illustration of the truth of a remark, which I have more than once made in my philosophical writings, and which can hardly be too often repeated, as it tends greatly to encourage philosophical investigations; viz. that more is owing to what we call chance, that is, philosophically speaking, to the observation of events arising from unknown causes, than to any proper design, or preconceived theory in this business. This does not appear in the works of those who write synthetically upon these subjects; but would, I doubt not, appear very strikingly in those who are the most celebrated for their philosophical acumen, did they write analytically and ingenuously.

For my own part, I will frankly acknowledge that, at the commencement of the experiments recited in this section, I was so far from having formed any hypothesis that led to the discoveries I made in pursuing them, that they would have appeared very improbable to me had I been told of them; and when the decisive facts did at length obtrude themselves upon my notice, it was very slowly, and with great hesitation, that I yielded to the evidence of my senses. And yet, when I reconsider the matter, and compare my last discoveries relating to the constitution of the atmosphere with the first, I see the closest and the easiest connection in the world between them, so as to wonder that I should not have been led immediately from the one to the other. That this was not the case, I attributed to the force of prejudice, which, unknown to ourselves, biases not only our judgments, properly so called, but even the perceptions of our senses; for we may take a maxim so strongly for granted, that the plainest evidence of sense will not entirely change, and often hardly modify our persuasions; and the more ingenious a man is, the more effectually he is entangled in his errors; his ingenuity only helping him to deceive himself, by evading the force of truth.

There are, I believe, very few maxims in philosophy that have laid firmer hold upon the mind than that air, meaning atmospherical air (free from various foreign matters, which were always supposed to be dissolved, and intermixed with it), is a simple elementary substance, indestructible, and unalterable, at least as much so as water is supposed to be. In the course of my inquiries, I was, however, soon satisfied that atmospherical air is not an unalterable thing; for that the phlogiston with which it becomes loaded from bodies burning in it, and animals breathing it, and various other chemical processes, so far alters and depraves it, as to render it altogether unfit for inflammation, respiration, and other purposes to which it is subservient; and I had discovered that agitation in water, the process of vegetation, and probably other natural processes, by taking out the superfluous phlogiston, restore it to its original purity. But I own I had no idea of the possibility of going any farther in this way, and thereby procuring air purer than the best common air. I might, indeed, have naturally imagined that such would be air that should contain less phlogiston than the air of the atmosphere; but I had no idea that such a composition was possible.

It will be seen in my last publication, that from the experiments which I made on the marine acid air,[41] I was led to conclude that common air consisted of some acid (and I naturally inclined to the acid that I was then operating upon) and phlogiston; because the union of this acid vapor and phlogiston made inflammable air; and inflammable air, by agitation in water, ceases to be inflammable, and becomes respirable. And though I could never make it quite so good as common air, I thought it very probable that vegetation, in more favorable circumstances than any in which I could apply it, or some other natural process, might render it more pure.

Upon this, which no person can say was an improbable supposition, was founded my conjecture, of volcanoes having given birth to the atmosphere of this planet, supplying it with a permanent air, first inflammable, then deprived of its inflammability by agitation in water, and farther purified by vegetation.

[41] Marine acid air is hydrogen chloride.

Several of the known phenomena of the nitrous acid might have led me to think that this was more proper for the constitution of the atmosphere than the marine acid; but my thoughts had got into a different train, and nothing but a series of observations, which I shall now distinctly relate, compelled me to adopt another hypothesis, and brought me, in a way of which I had then no idea, to the solution of the great problem, which my reader will perceive I have had in view ever since my discovery that the atmospherical air is alterable, and therefore that it is not an elementary substance, but a composition, viz. what this composition is, or what is the thing that we breathe, and how is it to be made from its constituent principles.

At the time of my former publication, I was not possessed of a burning lens of any considerable force; and for want of one, I could not possibly make any of the experiments that I had projected, and which, in theory, appeared very promising. I had, indeed, a mirror of force sufficient for my purpose. But the nature of this instrument is such that it cannot be applied, with effect, except upon substances that are capable of being suspended, or resting on a very slender support. It cannot be directed at all upon any substance in the form of powder, nor hardly upon anything that requires to be put into a vessel of quicksilver; which appears to me to be the most accurate method of extracting air from a great variety of substances, as was explained in the introduction to this volume. But having afterwards procured a lens of twelve inches diameter, and twenty inches focal distance, I proceeded with great alacrity to examine, by the help of it, what kind of air a great variety of substances, natural and factitious, would yield, putting them into . . . vessels . . . which I filled with quicksilver, and kept inverted in a basin of the same. Mr. Warltire,[42] a good chemist, and lecturer in natural philosophy, happening to be at that time in Calne, I explained my views to him, and was furnished

[42] John Warltire (c. 1738-1810) was an itinerant scientific lecturer.

by him with many substances, which I could not otherwise have procured.

With this apparatus, after a variety of other experiments, an account of which will be found in its proper place, on the 1st of August, 1774, I endeavored to extract air from *mercurius calcinatus per se;*[43] and I presently found that, by means of this lens, air was expelled from it very readily. Having got about three or four times as much as the bulk of my materials, I admitted water to it, and found that it was not imbibed by it. But what surprised me more than I can well express was that a candle burned in this air with a remarkably vigorous flame, very much like that enlarged flame with which a candle burns in nitrous air, exposed to iron or liver of sulphur; but as I had got nothing like this remarkable appearance from any kind of air besides this particular modification of nitrous air, and I knew no nitrous acid was used in the preparation of *mercurius calcinatus,* I was utterly at a loss how to account for it.[44]

In this case, also, though I did not give sufficient attention to the circumstance at that time, the flame of the candle, besides being larger, burned with more splendor and heat than in that species of nitrous air; and a piece of red-hot wood sparkled in it, exactly like paper dipped in a solution of niter, and it consumed very fast; an experiment which I had never thought of trying with nitrous air.

At the same time that I made the above-mentioned experiment, I extracted a quantity of air, with the very same property, from the common red precipitate, which being produced by a solution of mercury in spirit of niter, made me conclude that this peculiar property, being similar to that of the modification of nitrous air above mentioned, depended upon something being communicated to it by the

[43] I.e., mercury calx or oxide of mercury, a red powder.
[44] He had isolated oxygen! It remained for Lavoisier to explain the significance of his achievement. See James B. Conant, ed., *The Overthrow of the Phlogiston Theory: The Chemical Revolution of 1775-1789* (Cambridge, Mass., 1950).

nitrous acid; and since the *mercurius calcinatus* is produced by exposing mercury to a certain degree of heat, where common air has access to it, I likewise concluded that this substance had collected something of niter, in that state of heat, from the atmosphere.

This, however, appearing to me much more extraordinary than it ought to have done, I entertained some suspicion that the *mercurius calcinatus*, on which I had made my experiments, being bought at a common apothecary's, might, in fact, be nothing more than red precipitate; though, had I been anything of a practical chemist, I could not have entertained any such suspicion. However, mentioning this suspicion to Mr. Warltire, he furnished me with some that he had kept for a specimen of the preparation, and which, he told me, he could warrant to be genuine. This being treated in the same manner as the former, only by a longer continuance of heat, I extracted much more air from it than from the other.

This experiment might have satisfied any moderate skeptic; but, however, being at Paris in the October following, and knowing that there were several very eminent chemists in that place, I did not omit the opportunity, by means of my friend Mr. Magellan,[45] to get an ounce of *mercurius calcinatus* prepared by Mr. Cadet,[46] of the genuineness of which there could not possibly be any suspicion; and at the same time, I frequently mentioned my surprise at the kind of air which I had got from this preparation to Mr. Lavoisier, Mr. LeRoy,[47] and several other philosophers, who honored me with their notice in that city; and who, I dare say, cannot fail to recollect the circumstance.

[45] Jean Hyacinthe de Magellan (1723-1790), originally from Portugal, became a cosmopolitan man of science who traveled widely and corresponded with leading scholars all over Europe. Cf. Priestley's *Memoirs*, above, p. 44.

[46] Louis Claude Cadet-de-Gassicourt (1731-1799) was a French pharmacist and chemist.

[47] Dr. Charles LeRoy (1726-1779) was a French physician and chemist who wrote about mineral waters.

At the same time, I had no suspicion that the air which I had got from the *mercurius calcinatus* was even wholesome, so far was I from knowing what it was that I had really found; taking it for granted that it was nothing more than such kind of air as I had brought nitrous air to be by the processes above mentioned; and in this air I have observed that a candle would burn sometimes quite naturally, and sometimes with a beautiful enlarged flame, and yet remain perfectly noxious.

At the same time that I had got the air above mentioned from *mercurius calcinatus* and the red precipitate, I had got the same kind from red lead or minium.[48] In this process, that part of the minium on which the focus of the lens had fallen, turned yellow. One third of the air, in this experiment, was readily absorbed by water, but in the remainder a candle burned very strongly and with a crackling noise.

That fixed air is contained in red lead I had observed before; for I had expelled it by the heat of a candle, and had found it to be very pure. I imagine it requires more heat than I then used to expel any of the other kind of air.

This experiment with red lead confirmed me more in my suspicion that the *mercurius calcinatus* must get the property of yielding this kind of air from the atmosphere, the process by which that preparation, and this of red lead is made, being similar. As I never make the least secret of anything that I observe, I mentioned this experiment also, as well as those with the *mercurius calcinatus,* and the red precipitate, to all my philosophical acquaintance at Paris, and elsewhere; having no idea at that time, to what these remarkable facts would lead.

Presently after my return from abroad, I went to work upon the *mercurius calcinatus,* which I had procured from Mr. Cadet; and, with a very moderate degree of heat, I got from about one-fourth of an ounce of it, an ounce-measure of air, which I observed to be not readily imbibed, either by the substance itself from which it had been expelled (for

[48] Red lead or minium is red oxide of lead.

I suffered them to continue a long time together before I transferred the air to any other place) or by water, in which I suffered this air to stand a considerable time before I made any experiment upon it.

In this air, as I had expected, a candle burned with a vivid flame; but what I observed new at this time (Nov. 19), and which surprised me no less than the fact I had discovered before, was that, whereas a few moments agitation in water will deprive the modified nitrous air of its property of admitting a candle to burn in it, yet, after more than ten times as much agitation as would be sufficient to produce this alteration in the nitrous air, no sensible change was produced in this. A candle still burned in it with a strong flame; and it did not, in the least, diminish common air, which I have observed that nitrous air, in this state, in some measure, does.

But I was much more surprised, when, after two days, in which this air had continued in contact with water (by which it was diminished about one-twentieth of its bulk) I agitated it violently in water about five minutes, and found that a candle still burned in it as well as in common air. The same degree of agitation would have made phlogisticated nitrous air fit for respiration indeed, but it would certainly have extinguished a candle.

These facts fully convinced me that there must be a very material difference between the constitution of the air from *mercurius calcinatus,* and that of phlogisticated nitrous air, notwithstanding their resemblance in some particulars. But though I did not doubt that the air from *mercurius calcinatus* was fit for respiration, after being agitated in water, as every kind of air without exception, on which I had tried the experiment, had been, I still did not suspect that it was respirable in the first instance; so far was I from having any idea of this air being what it really was, much superior, in this respect, to the air of the atmosphere.

In this ignorance of the real nature of this kind of air, I continued from this time (November) to the 1st of March following; having, in the meantime, been intent upon my experiments on the vitriolic acid air above recited, and the various modifications of air produced by spirit of niter, an account of which will follow. But in the course of this month, I not only ascertained the nature of this kind of air, though very gradually, but was led by it to the complete discovery of the constitution of the air we breathe.

Till the 1st of March, 1775, I had so little suspicion of the air from *mercurius calcinatus,* etc., being wholesome, that I had not even thought of applying to it the test of nitrous air; but thinking (as my reader must imagine I frequently must have done) on the candle burning in it after long agitation in water, it occurred to me at last to make the experiment; and putting one measure of nitrous air to two measures of this air, I found, not only that it was diminished, but that it was diminished quite as much as common air, and that the redness of the mixture was likewise equal to that of a similar mixture of nitrous and common air.

After this I had no doubt that the air from *mercurius calcinatus* was fit for respiration, and that it had all the other properties of genuine common air. But I did not take notice of what I might have observed, if I had not been so fully possessed by the notion of there being no air better than common air that the redness was really deeper, and the diminution something greater than common air would have admitted.

Moreover, this advance in the way of truth, in reality, threw me back into error, making me give up the hypothesis I had first formed, viz. that the *mercurius calcinatus* had extracted spirit of niter from the air; for I now concluded that all the constituent parts of the air were equally, and in their proper proportion, imbibed in the preparation of this substance, and also in the process of making red lead. For at the same time that I made the above-mentioned experiment on the air from *mercurius calcinatus,* I likewise observed that the air which I had extracted from red lead, after the fixed air was washed out of it, was of the same nature, being diminished by nitrous air like common air; but, at the same time, I was puzzled to find that air from the red precipitate was diminished in the same manner, though the process for making this substance is quite different from that of making the two others. But to this circumstance I happened not to give much attention.

I wish my reader be not quite tired with the frequent repetition of the word surprise, and others of similar import; but I must go on in that style a little longer. For the next day I was more surprised than ever I had been before, with finding that, after the above-mentioned mixture of nitrous air and the air from *mercurius calcinatus* had stood all night (in which time the whole diminution must have taken place; and, consequently, had it been common air, it must have been made perfectly noxious, and entirely unfit for respiration or inflammation), a candle burned in it, and even better than in common air.

I cannot, at this distance of time, recollect what it was that I had in view in making this experiment; but I know I had no expectation of the real issue of it. Having acquired a considerable degree of readiness in making experiments of this kind, a very slight and evanescent motive would be sufficient to induce me to do it. If, however, I had not happened, for some other purpose, to have had a lighted candle before me, I should probably never have made the trial; and the whole train of my future experiments relating to this kind of air might have been prevented.

Still, however, having no conception of the real cause of this phenomenon, I considered it as something very extraordinary; but as a property that was peculiar to air extracted from these substances, and adventitious; and I always spoke of the air to my acquaintance as being substantially the same thing with common air. I particularly remember my telling Dr. Price that I was myself perfectly satisfied of its being common air, as it appeared to be so by the test of nitrous air; though, for the satisfaction of others, I wanted a mouse to make the proof quite complete.

On the 8th of this month I procured a mouse, and put it into a glass vessel, containing two ounce-measures of the air from *mercurius calcinatus*. Had it been common air, a full-grown mouse, as this was, would have lived in it about a quarter of an hour. In this air, however, my mouse lived a full half-hour; and though it was taken out seemingly dead, it appeared to have been only exceedingly chilled; for, upon being held to the fire, it presently revived, and appeared not to have received any harm from the experiment.

By this I was confirmed in my conclusion that the air extracted from *mercurius calcinatus,* etc., was at least as good as common air; but I did not certainly conclude that it was any better; because, though one mouse would live only a quarter of an hour in a given quantity of air, I knew it was not impossible but that another mouse might have lived in it half an hour, so little accuracy is there in this method of ascertaining the goodness of air; and indeed I have never had recourse to it for my own satisfaction, since the discovery of that most ready, accurate, and elegant test that nitrous air furnishes. But in this case I had a view to publishing the most generally satisfactory account of my experiments that the nature of the thing would admit of.

This experiment with the mouse, when I had reflected upon it some time, gave me so much suspicion that the air into which I had put it was better than common air, that I was induced, the day after, to apply the test of nitrous air to a small part of that very quantity of air which the mouse had breathed so long; so that, had it been common air, I was satisfied it must have been very nearly, if not altogether, as noxious as possible, so as not to be affected by nitrous air; when, to my surprise again, I found that though it had been breathed so long, it was still better than common air. For after mixing it with nitrous air, in the usual proportion of two to one, it was diminished in the proportion of $4\frac{1}{2}$ to $3\frac{1}{2}$; that is, the nitrous air had made it two-ninths less than before, and this in a very short space of time;

whereas I had never found that, in the longest time, any common air was reduced more than one-fifth of its bulk by any proportion of nitrous air, nor more than one-fourth by any phlogistic process whatever. Thinking of this extraordinary fact upon my pillow, the next morning I put another measure of nitrous air to the same mixture, and, to my utter astonishment, found that it was farther diminished to almost one-half of its original quantity. I then put a third measure to it, but this did not diminish it any farther; but, however, left it one measure less than it was even after the mouse had been taken out of it.

Being now fully satisfied that this air, even after the mouse had breathed it half an hour, was much better than common air; and having a quantity of it still left, sufficient for the experiment, viz. an ounce-measure and a half, I put the mouse into it; when I observed that it seemed to feel no shock upon being put into it, evident signs of which would have been visible if the air had not been very wholesome; but that it remained perfectly at its ease another full half-hour, when I took it out quite lively and vigorous. Measuring the air the next day, I found it to be reduced from 1½ to ⅔ of an ounce-measure. And after this, if I remember well (for in my register of the day I only find it noted that it was considerably diminished by nitrous air) it was nearly as good as common air. It was evident, indeed, from the mouse having been taken out quite vigorous, that the air could not have been rendered very noxious.

For my farther satisfaction I procured another mouse, and putting it into less than two ounce-measures of air extracted from *mercurius calcinatus* and air from red precipitate (which, having found them to be of the same quality, I had mixed together) it lived three-quarters of an hour. But not having had the precaution to set the vessel in a warm place, I suspect that the mouse died of cold. However, as it had lived three times as long as it could probably have lived in the same quantity of common air, and I did not expect much accuracy from this kind of test, I did not think it necessary to make any more experiments with mice.

Being now fully satisfied of the superior goodness of this kind of air, I proceeded to measure that degree of purity, with as much accuracy as I could, by the test of nitrous air; and I began with putting one measure of nitrous air to two measures of this air; as if I had been examining common air; and now I observed that the diminution was evidently greater than common air would have suffered by the same treatment. A second measure of nitrous air reduced it to two-thirds of its original quantity, and a third measure to one-half. Suspecting that the diminution could not proceed much farther, I then added only half a measure of nitrous air, by which it was diminished still more, but not much, and another half measure made it more than half of its original quantity; so that, in this case, two measures of this air took more than two measures of nitrous air, and yet remained less than half of what it was. Five measures brought it pretty exactly to its original dimensions.

At that same time, air from the red precipitate was diminished in the same proportion as that from *mercurius calcinatus,* five measures of nitrous air being received by two measures of this without any increase of dimensions. Now as common air takes about one-half of its bulk of nitrous air, before it begins to receive any addition to its dimensions from more nitrous air, and this air took more than four half-measures before it ceased to be diminished by more nitrous air, and even five half-measures made no addition to its original dimensions, I conclude that it was between four and five times as good as common air. It will be seen that I have since procured air better than this, even between five and six times as good as the best common air that I have ever met with.

Being now fully satisfied with respect to the nature of this new species of air, viz. that, being capable of taking more phlogiston from nitrous air, it therefore originally contains less of this principle; my next inquiry was by what means it comes to be so pure, or philosophically speaking, to be so much dephlogisticated; and since the red lead yields the same kind of air with *mercurius calcinatus,* though mixed with fixed air, and is a much cheaper material, I proceeded to examine all the preparations of lead, made by heat in the open air, to see what kind of air they would yield, beginning with the grey calx, and ending with litharge.[49]

The red lead which I used for this purpose yielded a considerable quantity of dephlogisticated air, and very little fixed air; but to what circumstance in the preparation of this lead, or in the keeping of it, this difference is owing, I cannot tell. I have frequently found a very remarkable difference between different specimens of red lead in this respect, as well as in the purity of the air which they contain. This difference, however, may arise in a great measure, from the care that is taken to extract the fixed air from it. In this experiment two measures of nitrous air being put to one measure of this air, reduced it to one-third of what it was at first, and nearly three times its bulk of nitrous air made very little addition to its original dimensions; so that this air was exceedingly pure, and better than any that I had procured before.

[49] Grey calx is grey oxide of lead. Litharge is lead monoxide.

Like the great Newton before him and like other distinguished scientists after him, Priestley saw no incompatibility between religion and science. There was a natural partnership, he insisted, between the "word" and the "works" of God. This significant idea is particularly well illustrated in his Disquisitions Relating to Matter and Spirit *(1777),*[1] *which set forth the metaphysical system underlying his later theology. Without any sense of contradiction, Priestley combined a vigorous assertion of scientific materialism with a strong justification of the Christian doctrine of resurrection of the body. Appended to this work was a treatise called* The Doctrine of Philosophical Necessity Illustrated, *setting forth Priestley's theory of "Necessarianism." Both his materialism and his determinism were probably based in the last analysis on Newtonian physics, but more directly Priestley borrowed from David Hartley's* Observations on Man.[2]

[1] Text of selections from John T. Rutt, ed., *The Theological and Miscellaneous Works of Joseph Priestley* (25 vols., London, 1817-1832), III, 218-221, 226-229, 244, 276, 332, 453, 464, and 532-535.

[2] George S. Brett, *A History of Psychology* (3 vols., London and New York, 1912-1921), II, 286. See also Basil Willey, *The Eighteenth Century Background* (New York and London, 1941), pp. 136-154 (on Hartley), and pp. 168-204 (on Priestley).

Disquisitions Relating to Matter and Spirit

THE INTRODUCTION

Lest any person should hastily misapprehend the nature, or importance, of the questions discussed in this treatise, or the manner in which I have decided for myself with respect to them, I shall here state the several subjects of inquiry as concisely, and with as much distinctness, as I can, and also inform the reader what my opinions concerning them really are.

It has generally been supposed that there are two distinct kinds of substance in human nature, and they have been distinguished by the terms matter and spirit. The former of these has been said to be possessed of the property of extension, viz. of length, breadth and thickness, and also of solidity or impenetrability, but it is said to be naturally destitute of all powers whatever. The latter has of late been defined to be a substance entirely destitute of all extension, or relation to space, so as to have no property in common with matter; and therefore to be properly immaterial, but to be possessed of the powers of perception, intelligence and self-motion.

Matter is that kind of substance of which our bodies are composed, whereas the principle of perception and thought belonging to us is said to reside in a spirit, or immaterial principle, intimately united to the body; while the higher orders of intelligent beings, and especially the Divine Being, are said to be purely immaterial.

It is maintained, in this treatise, that neither matter nor spirit (meaning by the latter the subject of sense and thought) correspond to the definitions above-mentioned. For, that matter is not that inert substance that it has been supposed to be; that powers of attraction or repulsion are necessary to its very being, and that no part of it appears to be impenetrable to other parts. I therefore define it to be a substance possessed of the property of extension, and of powers of attraction or repulsion. And since it has never yet been asserted that the powers of sensation and thought are incompatible with these (solidity, or impenetrability only, having been thought to be repugnant to them), I therefore maintain that we have no reason to suppose that there are in man two substances so distinct from each other as have been represented.

It is likewise maintained, in this treatise, that the notion of two substances that have no common property, and yet are capable of intimate connection and mutual action, is both absurd and modern; a substance without extension or relation to place being unknown both in the Scriptures, and to all antiquity; the human mind, for example, having till lately been thought to have a proper presence in the body, and a proper motion together with it; and the Divine Mind having always been represented as being, truly and properly, omnipresent.

It is maintained, however, in the sequel of this treatise, that such a distinction as the ancient philosophers did make between matter and spirit, though it was by no means such a distinction as was defined above (which does not admit of their having any common property), but a distinction which made the Supreme Mind the author of all good, and matter the source of all evil; that all inferior intelligences are emanations from the Supreme Mind, or made out of its substance, and that matter was reduced to its present form not by the Supreme Mind itself, but by another intelligence, a peculiar emanation from it, has been the real source of the greatest corruptions of true religion in all ages, many of which remain to this very day. It is here maintained that this system of philosophy, and the true system of revelation, have always been diametrically opposite, and hostile to each other; and that the latter can never be firmly established but upon the ruins of the former.

To promote this firm establishment of the system of pure revelation, in opposition to that of a vain and absurd philosophy, here shown to be so, is the true object of this work; in the perusal of which I beg the candor and patient attention of the judicious and philosophical reader.

It may not be unuseful to observe that a distinction ought to be made with respect to the relative importance and mutual subordination of the different positions contended for in this treatise. The principal object is to prove the uniform composition of man, or that what we call mind, or the principle of perception and thought, is not a substance distinct from the body, but the result of corporeal organization; and what I have advanced preliminary to this, concerning the nature of matter, though subservient to this argument, is by no means essential to it; for, whatever matter be, I think I have sufficiently proved that the human mind is nothing more than a modification of it.

Again, that man is wholly material is eminently subservient to the doctrine of the proper, or mere humanity of Christ. For, if no man has a soul distinct from his body, Christ, who, in all other respects, appeared as a man, could not have had a soul which had existed before his body; and the whole doctrine of the pre-existence of souls (of which the opinion of the pre-existence of Christ was a branch) will be effectually overturned. But I apprehend that, should I have failed in the proof of the materiality of man, arguments enough remain, independent of this, to prove the nonpre-existence of Christ, and of this doctrine having been introduced into Christianity from the system of Oriental philosophy.

Lastly, the doctrine of necessity, maintained in the appendix, is the immediate result of the doctrine of the materiality of man; for mechanism is the undoubted consequence of materialism. But, whether man be wholly material or not, I apprehend that proof enough is advanced that every human volition is subject to certain fixed laws, and that the pretended self-determining power is altogether imaginary and impossible.

In short, it is my firm persuasion that the three doctrines of materialism, of that which is commonly called Socinianism, and of philosophical necessity, are equally parts of one system, being equally founded on just observations of nature, and fair deductions from the Scriptures; and that whoever shall duly consider their connection, and dependence on one another, will find no sufficient consistency in any general scheme of principles that does not comprehend them all. At the same time, each of these doctrines stands on its own independent foundation, and is capable of such separate demonstration, as subjects of a moral nature require or admit.

I have advanced what has occurred to me in support of all the three parts of this system; confident that, in due time, the truth will bear down before it every opposing prejudice, how inveterate soever, and gain a firm establishment in the minds of all men.

OF IMPENETRABILITY AS ASCRIBED TO MATTER

As philosophers have given too little to matter, in divesting it of all powers, without which I presume it has been proved that no such substance can exist, so it equally follows, from the plain rules of philosophizing above laid down, that they have ascribed too much to it, when they have advanced that impenetrability is one of its properties. Because, if there be any truth in late discoveries in philosophy, resistance is in most cases caused by something of a quite different nature from anything material, or solid, viz. by a power of repulsion acting at a distance from the body to which it has been supposed to belong, and in no case whatever can it be proved that resistance is occasioned by anything else.

Now if resistance, from which alone is derived the idea of impenetrability, is in most cases certainly caused by powers, and in no case certainly by anything else, the rules of philosophizing oblige us to suppose that the cause of all resistance is repulsive power, and in no case whatever the thing that we have hitherto improperly termed solid, or impenetrable matter.

As all resistance can differ only in degree, this circumstance can only lead us to the supposition of a greater or less repulsive power, but never to the supposition of a cause of resistance entirely different from such a power. This would be exceedingly unphilosophical. To judge in this manner is to judge altogether without, nay, really contrary to evidence. But I come to the facts themselves, which no philosopher will pretend to controvert.

When I press my hand against the table, as was mentioned above, I naturally imagine that the obstacle to its going through the table is the solid matter of which it consists; but a variety of philosophical considerations demonstrate that it generally requires a much greater power of pressure than I can exert to bring my fingers into actual contact with the table. Philosophers know that, notwithstanding their seeming contact, they are actually kept at a real distance from each other, by powers of repulsion common to them both. Also, electrical appearances show that a considerable weight is requisite to bring into contact even links of a chain hanging freely in the air; they being kept asunder by a repulsive power belonging to a very small surface, so that they do not actually touch, though they are supported by each other.

I have myself, as will be seen in the account of my electrical experiments, endeavored to ascertain the weight requisite to bring a number of pieces of money, lying upon one another, into seeming contact, or so near to one another only as the particles that compose the same continued piece of metal, and I found it to be very considerable. These, however, are supposed by philosophers not to be in actual contact, but to be kept at certain distances from each other by powers of resistance within the substance itself.

Indeed, that the component particles of the hardest bodies do not actually touch one another is demonstrable from their being brought nearer together by cold, and by their being removed farther from each other by heat. The power, sufficient to overcome these internal forces of repulsion, by which the ultimate particles of bodies are prevented from coming into actual contact, is what no person can pretend to compute. The power, requisite to break their cohesion, or to remove them from the sphere of each other's attractions, may, in some measure, be estimated; but this affords no data for ascertaining the force that would be necessary to bring them into actual contact, which may exceed the other almost infinitely.

Mr. Melville[3] has shown, from optical considerations, that a drop of water rolls upon a cabbage leaf without ever coming into actual contact with it; and indeed all the phenomena of light are most remarkably unfavorable to the hypothesis of the solidity or impenetrability of matter.

When light is reflected back from a body on which it seems to strike, it was natural to suppose that this was occasioned by its impinging against the solid parts of the body; but it has been demonstrated by Sir Isaac Newton that the rays of light are always reflected by a power of repulsion, acting at some distance from the body. Again, when part of a beam of light has overcome this power of repulsion, and has entered any transparent substance, it goes on in a right line, provided the medium be of an uniform density, without the least interruption, and without a single particle being reflected, till it comes to the opposite side; having met with no solid particles in its way, not even in the densest transparent substances, as glass, crystal, or diamond, and

[3] Thomas Melville (1726-1753) was a young Scottish scientist who worked particularly in the field of optics. He is referred to a number of times in Priestley's *History and Present State of Discoveries Relating to Vision, Light, and Colors* (London, 1772).

when it is arrived at the opposite side, it is solely affected by the laws of attraction and repulsion. For, with a certain angle of incidence, the greatest part, or the whole of it, will be drawn back into the solid body, without going on into the air, where it should seem that there would have been less obstruction to its passage.

Now these facts seem to prove that such dense bodies as glass, crystal and diamonds have no solid parts, or so very few, that the particles of light are never found to impinge upon them, or to be obstructed by them. And certainly till some portion of light can be shown to be reflected within the substance of a homogeneous transparent body, there can be no reason from fact and appearances to conclude that they have any such solid parts; but, on the contrary, there must be all the reason in the world to believe that no such solid resisting particles exist. All the phenomena may be explained without them, and indeed cannot be explained with them.

Since then it is demonstrable that no common pressure is sufficient to bring bodies even into seeming contact, or that near approach which the component parts of the same body make to each other (though these are by no means in absolute contact, as the phenomena of heat and cold fully prove), but the resistance to a nearer approach is in all cases caused by powers of repulsion, there can be no sufficient reason to ascribe resistance in any case to anything besides similar powers. Nay, the established rules of philosophizing above recited, absolutely require that we ascribe all resistance to such powers; and consequently the supposition of the solidity or impenetrability of matter, derived solely from the consideration of the resistance of the solid parts of bodies (which, exclusive of a power operating at a distance from them, cannot be proved to have any resistance), appears to be destitute of all support whatever. The hypothesis was suggested by a mere fallacy, and therefore ought to be discarded now that the fallacy is discovered.

It will be said that if matter be not a solid, or impenetrable substance, what is it? I answer, with respect to this, as I should with respect to any other substance, that it is possessed of such properties, and such only, as the actual well-examined appearances prove it to be possessed of. That it is possessed of powers of attraction and repulsion, and of several spheres of them, one within another, I know, because appearances cannot be explained without supposing them; but that there is anything in, or belonging to matter, capable of resistance, besides those powers of repulsion, does not appear from any phenomena that we are yet acquainted with, and, therefore, as a philosopher, I am not authorized to conclude that any such thing exists. On the contrary, I am obliged to deny that matter has such a property.

———

Had we formed a judgment concerning the necessary seat of thought, by the circumstances that universally accompany it, which is our rule in all other cases, we could not but have concluded, that in man it is a property of the nervous system, or rather of the brain; because, as far as we can judge, the faculty of thinking, and a certain state of the brain, always accompany and correspond to one another; which is the very reason why we believe that any property is inherent in any substance whatever. There is no instance of any man retaining the faculty of thinking when his brain was destroyed; and whenever that faculty is impeded, or injured, there is sufficient reason to believe that the brain is disordered in proportion, and therefore we are necessarily led to consider the latter as the seat of the former.

Moreover, as the faculty of thinking in general ripens and comes to maturity with the body, it is also observed to decay with it; and if, in some cases, the mental faculties continue vigorous when the body in general is enfeebled, it is evidently because, in those particular cases, the brain is not much affected by the general cause of weakness. But, on the other hand, if the brain alone be affected, as by a blow on the head, by actual pressure within the skull, by sleep, or by inflammation, the mental faculties are universally affected in proportion.

Likewise, as the mind is affected in consequence of the affections of the body and brain, so the body is liable to be reciprocally affected by the affections of the mind, as is evident in the visible effects of all strong passions, hope or fear, love or anger, joy or sorrow, exultation or despair. These are certainly irrefragable arguments, that it is properly no other than one and the same thing that is subject to these affections, and that they are necessarily dependent upon one another.

———

How easy is it to get rid of all the embarrassment attending the doctrine of a soul, in every view of it, by admitting, agreeably to all the phenomena, that the power of thinking belongs to the brain of a man, as that of walking to his feet, or that of speaking to his tongue; that, therefore, man, who is one being, is composed of one kind of substance, made of the dust of the earth; that when he dies, he, of course, ceases to think; but when his sleeping dust shall be reanimated at the resurrection, his power of thinking, and his consciousness, will be restored to him?

This system gives a real value to the doctrine of a resurrection from the dead, which is peculiar to revelation, on which alone the sacred writers build all our hope of a future life, and it explains the uniform language of the Scriptures, which speak of one day of judgment for all mankind, and represent all the rewards of virtue, and all the punishments of vice, as taking place at that awful day, and not before. This doctrine of a resurrection was laughed at by the conceited Athenians, and will always be the subject of ridicule to persons of a similar turn of mind; but it is abundantly confirmed to us by the well-attested resurrection of

Jesus Christ, and the promises of the gospel, established on all the miraculous events by which the promulgation of Christianity was attended.

Death, with its concomitant putrefaction, and dispersion of parts, is only a decomposition; and whatever is decomposed may be recomposed by the Being who first composed it; and I doubt not but that, in the proper sense of the word, the same body that dies shall rise again, not with everything that is adventitious and extraneous (as all that we receive by nutrition), but with the same stamina, or those particles that really belonged to the germ of the organical body. And there can be no proof that these particles are ever properly destroyed, or interchanged.

This idea of the doctrine of the resurrection is perfectly agreeable to the light in which St. Paul represents it (though I should not condemn his comparison, if it should be found not to be so complete), when he compares it to the revival of a seed that has been sown in the earth, and become seemingly dead. For the germ does not die, and in our future transformation we may be as different from what we are in our present state, as the plant is from the seed, or the butterfly from the egg, and yet be essentially the same.

The Doctrine of
Philosophical Necessity Illustrated

THE PREFACE

I did not originally intend to write a separate treatise on
the subject of philosophical necessity, but only to consider
the objection made to it from the sentiments of praise and
blame, and the use of rewards and punishments, which is
generally reckoned to be the greatest difficulty on the subject, in an appendix to my *Disquisitions Relating to Matter
and Spirit.* There would have been a sufficient propriety in
this; because, if man, as is maintained in that treatise, be
wholly material, it will not be denied but that he must be
a mechanical being. As, therefore, everything belonging to
the doctrine of materialism is, in fact, an argument for the
doctrine of necessity, and, consequently, the doctrine of
necessity is a direct inference from materialism, the defense
of that inference would naturally accompany the proof of
the proposition from which it was deduced.

———

In every determination of mind, or in cases where volition or choice is concerned, all the previous circumstances
to be considered are the state of mind (including everything
belonging to the will itself) and the views of things presented to it; the latter of which is generally called the
motive, though under this term some writers comprehend
them both. To distinguish the manner in which events depending upon will and choice are produced, from those in
which no volition is concerned, the former are said to be
produced voluntarily, and the latter mechanically. But the
same general maxims apply to them both. We may not be
able to determine *a priori* how a man will act in any particular case, but it is because we are not particularly ac-

quainted with his disposition of mind, precise situation and views of things. But neither can we tell which way the wind will blow tomorrow, though the air is certainly subject to no other than necessary laws of motion.

A particular determination of mind could not have been otherwise than it was, if the laws of nature respecting the mind be such, as that the same determination shall constantly follow the same state of mind, and the same views of things. And it could not be possible for any determination to have been otherwise than it has been, is, or is to be, unless the laws of nature had been such, as that, though both the state of mind and the views of things were the same, the determination might or might not have taken place. But, in this case, the determination must have been an effect without a cause, because in this case, as in that of the balance, there would have been a change of situation without any previous change of circumstances; and there cannot be any other definition of an effect without a cause. The application of the term *voluntary* to mental determinations cannot possibly make the least difference in this case.

THE CALVINISTIC DOCTRINE OF PREDESTINATION COMPARED WITH THE PHILOSOPHICAL DOCTRINE OF NECESSITY

The philosophical doctrine of necessity so much resembles the Calvinistic doctrine of predestination, in some views of it, that it may be worthwhile to point out distinctly in what they agree and in what they differ. I shall therefore do it, with as much fairness as I possibly can.

The scheme of philosophical necessity has been shown to imply a chain of causes and effects, established by infinite wisdom, and terminating in the greatest good of the whole universe; evils of all kinds natural and moral being admitted, as far as they contribute to that end, or may be in the nature of things inseparable from it. No Necessarian, however, supposes that any of the human race will suffer eternally, but that future punishments will answer the same purpose as temporal ones are found to do, all of which tend to good and are evidently admitted for that purpose; so that God, the author of all, is as much to be adored and loved for what we suffer as for what we enjoy; his intention being equally kind in both, since both are equally parts, and equally necessary parts of the same plan. Upon the doctrine of necessity also, the most indifferent actions of men are equally necessary with the most important; since every volition, like any other effect, must have an adequate cause, depending upon the previous state of the mind and the influence to which it is exposed.

On the other hand, the consistent, the moderate, or sublapsarian Calvinist, supposes that God created the first man absolutely free to sin, or not to sin, capable of sinless obedience to all the commands of God; but that without being predestined to it, he fell from this state of innocence by eating the forbidden fruit; and from that time became and all his posterity with him (he being their federal head) liable to the eternal wrath of God, and that their whole natures were at the same time so vitiated that they are naturally incapable of thinking a good thought or doing a good action.

The whole race of mankind being thus liable to everlasting damnation, God was pleased for his own glory and sovereign good will, and without any reason of preference, to reserve a small number in comparison with the rest of mankind, and predestinate them to everlasting happiness, on condition that his Son, the second person in the Trinity, in power, glory, and all other respects equal to himself, should become man, submit in their stead to death, and bear that infinite punishment of divine wrath which every sin against an infinite Being had deserved, and which infinite justice could not remit; while all the rest of the corrupted mass of mankind, not being redeemed by the death of Christ, remained necessarily doomed to sin here and to misery forever hereafter.

The elect being like other persons born in original sin, have their natures equally depraved, and of course are as incapable of all good thoughts or good works as the reprobate, till God, by a miraculous interposition, produces a change in their disposition, and, by this immediate agency on their minds, enables them to think and act so as to please him. But after this miraculous change or new birth, though an elected person may sin, and always will do so when he is left to himself, he will not finally fall away and perish; but God will, some time before his death, renew him again by repentance, and he shall certainly be happy forever. Whereas, the reprobate (the grace of repentance and of the new birth not being vouchsafed to them) are under a necessity of sinning and of sinning only. Though their actions should to all appearance be ever so praiseworthy in the sight of men, they are in fact of the nature of sin, and only serve to aggravate their certain and final condemnation. Moreover, though many of them die in infancy, before they were capable of committing actual sin, they are nevertheless liable to the eternal wrath of God, on account of the sin of their forefather and federal head.

Now, in comparing these two schemes, I can see no sort of resemblance, except that the future happiness or misery of all men is certainly foreknown and appointed by God. In all other respects they are most essentially different; and even where they agree in the end, the difference in the manner by which that end is accomplished is so very great that the influence of the two systems on the minds of those that adopt and act upon them is the reverse of one another, exceedingly favorable to virtue in the Necessarian, and as unfavorable to it in the Calvinist.

For, the essential difference between the two schemes is this: the Necessarian believes that his own dispositions and actions are the necessary and sole means of his present and future happiness; so that in the most proper sense of the words, it depends entirely upon himself whether he be virtuous or vicious, happy or miserable, just as much as it depends upon the farmer himself sowing his fields and weeding them, whether he will have a good crop; except that in favor of the doctrine of necessity where morals are concerned, his endeavors in the former case are much more certain in their effect than in the latter; which view of things cannot but operate to make him exert himself to the utmost in proportion to his regard for his own happiness, his success being certain in proportion to his exertion of himself. With this exertion he cannot miscarry, but without it he must, unless the laws of nature should change, be inevitably miserable. As far as any system of faith can induce men to cultivate virtuous principles and habits, this doctrine of necessity must do it.

An History of the
Corruptions of Christianity

Priestley's most famous theological work was An History of
the Corruptions of Christianity *(Birmingham, 1782).*[4] *The
"corruptions" of Christianity for Priestley included most of
what orthodox leaders had considered fundamental doctrines: the Trinity, the Virgin Birth, original sin, predestination, the vicarious atonement, and plenary inspiration of
Scripture. Priestley undertook to trace the history of these
ideas back to their sources.*

THE DEDICATION

To the Reverend Theophilus Lindsey, A.M.[5]

Dear Friend,

Wishing, as I do, that my name may ever be connected as
closely with yours after death, as we have been connected
by friendship in life, it is with peculiar satisfaction that I
dedicate this work (which I am willing to hope will be
one of the most useful of my publications) to you.

To your example of a pure love of truth, and of the most
fearless integrity in asserting it, evidenced by the sacrifices
you have made to it, I owe much of my own wishes to
imbibe the same spirit; though a more favorable education
and situation in life, by not giving me an opportunity of
distinguishing myself as you have done, has, likewise, not
exposed me to the temptation of acting otherwise; and for
this I wish to be truly thankful. For, since so very few of

[4] Text of selections from Rutt, V, 3-6, 13-15, 29-30, 40, 91-92, 180,
194-196, 296-297, 480-481, 492-494, and 506-507.

[5] On Priestley's friendship with Lindsey see the *Memoirs*, above,
pp. 41-42.

those who profess the same sentiments with you have had the courage to act consistently with them, no person, whatever he may imagine he might have been equal to, can have a right to presume that he would have been one of so small a number.

No person can see in a stronger light than you do the mischievous consequences of the corruptions of that religion which you justly prize as the most valuable of the gifts of God to man; and, therefore, I flatter myself, it will give you some pleasure to accompany me in my researches into the origin and progress of them, as this will tend to give all the friends of pure Christianity the fullest satisfaction that they reflect no discredit on the revelation itself; since it will be seen that they all came in from a foreign and hostile quarter. It will likewise afford a pleasing presage, that our religion will, in due time, purge itself of everything that debases it, and that for the present prevents its reception by those who are ignorant of its nature, whether living in Christian countries, or among Mahometans and heathens.

The gross darkness of that night which has for many centuries obscured our holy religion, we may clearly see, is past; the morning is opening upon us; and we cannot doubt but that the light will increase, and extend itself more and more unto the perfect day. Happy are they who contribute to diffuse the pure light of this everlasting gospel. The time is coming when the detection of one error or prejudice, relating to this most important subject, and the success we have in opening and enlarging the minds of men with respect to it, will be far more honorable than any discovery we can make in other branches of knowledge, or our success in propagating them.

In looking back upon the dismal scene which the shocking corruptions of Christianity exhibit, we may well exclaim with the prophet, "How is the gold become dim! how is the most fine gold changed!" But the thorough examination of everything relating to Christianity, which has been produced by the corrupt state of it; and which nothing else would probably have led to, has been as the "refiner's fire" with respect to it; and when it shall have stood this test, it may be presumed that the truth and excellency of it will never more be called in question.

This corrupt state of Christianity has, no doubt, been permitted by the Supreme Governor of the world for the best of purposes, and it is the same great Being who is also now, in the course of his providence, employing these means to "purge his floor." The civil powers of this world, which were formerly the chief supports of the anti-Christian systems, who had given "their power and strength unto the beast," *Rev. xvii. 13,* now begin to hate her, and are ready to "make her desolate and naked," *ver. 16.* To answer their own political purposes, they are now promoting various reformations in the church; and it can hardly be doubted, but that the difficuties in which many of the European nations are now involving themselves will make other measures of reformation highly expedient and necessary.

Also, while the attention of men in power is engrossed by the difficulties that more immediately press upon them, the endeavors of the friends of reformation in points of doctrine pass with less notice, and operate without obstruction. Let us rejoice in the good that results from this evil, and omit no opportunity that is furnished us, voluntarily to co-operate with the gracious intention of Divine Providence; and let us make that our primary object, which others are doing to promote their own sinister ends. All those who labor in the discovery and communication of truth, if they be actuated by a pure love of it, and a sense of its importance to the happiness of mankind, may consider themselves as workers together with God, and may proceed with confidence, assured that their labor in this cause shall not be in vain, whether they themselves see the fruit of it or not.

The more opposition we meet with in these labors, the more honorable it will be to us, provided we meet that opposition with the true spirit of Christianity. And to assist us in this, we should frequently reflect that many of our opponents are probably men who wish as well to the gospel as we do ourselves, and really think they do God service by opposing us. Even prejudice and bigotry, arising from such a principle, are respectable things, and entitled to the greatest candor. If our religion teaches us to love our enemies, certainly we should love, and, from a principle of love, should endeavor to convince those who, if they were only better informed, would embrace us as friends.

The time will come when the cloud, which for the present prevents our distinguishing our friends and our foes, will be dispersed, even that day in which the secrets of all hearts will be disclosed to the view of all. In the meantime, let us think as favorably as possible of all men, our particular opponents not excepted; and therefore be careful to conduct all hostility, with the pleasing prospect that one day it will give place to the most perfect amity.

You, my friend, peculiarly happy in a most placid, as well as a most determined mind, have nothing to blame yourself for in this respect. If, on any occasion, I have indulged too much asperity, I hope I shall, by your example, learn to correct myself, and without abating my zeal in the common cause.

As we are now both of us past the meridian of life, I hope we shall be looking more and more beyond it, and be preparing for that world, where we shall have no errors to combat, and consequently, where a talent for disputation will be of no use; but where the spirit of love will find abundant exercise; where all our labors will be of the most friendly and benevolent nature, and where our employment will be its own reward.

Let these views brighten the evening of our lives, that evening which will be enjoyed with more satisfaction in proportion as the day shall have been laboriously and well spent. Let us, then, without reluctance, submit to that temporary rest in the grave, which our wise Creator has thought proper to appoint for all the human race, our Saviour himself not wholly excepted; anticipating with joy the glorious morning of the resurrection, when we shall meet that Saviour, whose precepts we have obeyed, whose spirit we have breathed, whose religion we have defended, whose cup also we may, in some measure, have drunk of, and whose honors we have asserted, without making them to interfere with those of his Father and our Father, of his God and our God, that supreme, that great and awful Being, to whose will he was always most perfectly submissive, and for whose unrivaled prerogative he always showed the most ardent zeal.

With the truest affection,

I am, dear friend, your brother,

In the faith and hope of the Gospel,

J. PRIESTLEY

Birmingham, Nov. 1782.

THE HISTORY OF OPINIONS
RELATING TO JESUS CHRIST

The unity of God is a doctrine on which the greatest stress is laid in the whole system of revelation. To guard this most important article was the principal object of the Jewish religion; and, notwithstanding the proneness of the Jews to idolatry, at length it fully answered its purpose in reclaiming them, and in impressing the minds of many persons of other nations in favor of the same fundamental truth.

The Jews were taught by their prophets to expect a Messiah, who was to be descended from the tribe of Judah, and the family of David, a person in whom themselves and all the nations of the earth should be blessed; but none of their prophets gave them an idea of any other than a man like themselves in that illustrious character, and no other did they ever expect, or do they expect to this day.

Jesus Christ, whose history answers to the description given of the Messiah by the prophets, made no other pretensions; referring all his extraordinary power to God, his Father, who, he expressly says, spoke and acted by him, and who raised him from the dead; and it is most evident that the apostles, and all those who conversed with our Lord before and after his resurrection, considered him in no other light than simply as "a man approved of God, by wonders and signs which God did by him." *Acts ii. 22.*

Not only do we find no trace of so prodigious a change in the ideas which the apostles entertained concerning Christ, as from that of a man like themselves (which it must be acknowledged were the first that they entertained), to that of the most high God, or one who was in any sense their maker or preserver, that when their minds were most fully enlightened, after the descent of the Holy Spirit, and to the latest period of their ministry, they continued to speak of him in the same style; even when it is evident they must have intended to speak of him in a manner suited to his state of greatest exaltation and glory. Peter uses the simple language above quoted, of a man approved of God, immediately after the descent of the Spirit; and the Apostle Paul, giving what may be called the Christian creed, says, *I Tim. ii. 5:* "There is one God, and one mediator between God and men, the man Christ Jesus." He does not say the God, the God-man, or the superangelic being, but simply the man Christ Jesus; and nothing can be alleged from the New Testament in favor of any higher nature of Christ, except a few passages interpreted without any regard to the context, or the modes of speech and opinions of the times in which the books were written, and in such a manner, in other respects, as would authorize our proving any doctrine whatever from them.

From this plain doctrine of the Scriptures, a doctrine so consonant to reason and the ancient prophecies, Christians have at length come to believe what they do not pretend to have any conception of, and than which it is not possible to frame a more express contradiction. For, while they consider Christ as the supreme, eternal God, the maker of heaven and earth, and of all things visible and invisible, they moreover acknowledge the Father and the Holy Spirit to be equally God in the same exalted sense, all three equal in power and glory, and yet all three constituting no more than one God.

To a person the least interested in the inquiry, it must appear an object of curiosity to trace by what means, and by what steps, so great a change has taken place, and what circumstances in the history of other opinions, and of the world, proved favorable to the successive changes. An opinion, and especially an opinion adopted by great numbers of mankind, is to be considered as any other fact in history, for it cannot be produced without an adequate cause, and is therefore a proper object of philosophical inquiry. In this case I think it not difficult to find causes abundantly adequate to the purpose, and it is happily in our power to trace almost every step by which the changes have been successively brought about.

If the interest that mankind have generally taken in anything, will at all contribute to interest us in the inquiry concerning it, this history cannot fail to be highly interesting. For, perhaps, in no business whatever have the minds of men been more agitated, and, speculative as the nature of the thing is, in few cases has the peace of society been so much disturbed. To this very day, of such importance is the subject considered by thousands and tens of thousands, that they cannot write or speak of it without the greatest zeal, and without treating their opponents with the greatest rancor. If good sense and humanity did not interpose to mitigate the rigor of law, thousands would be sacrificed to the cause of orthodoxy in this single article; and the greatest number of sufferers would probably be in this very country, on account of the greater freedom of inquiry which prevails here, in consequence of which we entertain and profess the greatest diversity of opinions.

The various steps in this interesting history it is now my business to point out, and I wish that all my readers may attend me with as much coolness and impartiality as I trust I shall myself preserve through the whole of this investigation.

———

The first who held, and discussed, the doctrine of the divinity of Christ acknowledged that their opinion was exceedingly unpopular with the unlearned Christians, and that these latter were pious persons, who dreaded the doctrine of the Trinity, as thinking that it infringed upon that of the supremacy of God the Father.

The divinity of Christ was first advanced and urged by those who had been heathen philosophers, and especially those who were admirers of the doctrine of Plato, who held the opinion of a second God. Austin [Augustine] says that he considered Christ as no other than a most excellent man, and had no suspicion of the word of God being incarnate in him, or how "the catholic faith differed from the error of Photinus" (the last of the proper Unitarians whose name has come down to us), till he read the books of Plato; and that he was afterwards confirmed in his opinion by reading the Scriptures.[6] Constantine, in his oration to the fathers of the Council of Nice, speaks with commendation of Plato, as having taught the doctrine of "a second God, derived from the supreme God, and subservient to his will."[7]

There is a pretty easy gradation in the progress of the

[6] Austin is St. Augustine (354-430 A.D.), the Bishop of Hippo. The quotation is from his *Confessions,* Book VII, Chapter 19. Photinus was a fourth-century bishop who emphasized the humanity of Jesus; he was condemned as a heretic in 344 A.D. See Philip Schaff, *History of the Christian Church* (7 vols., New York, 1916-1923), III, 653.

[7] This oration may be found in *A Select Library of Nicene and Post-Nicene Fathers of the Christian Church,* 2nd series, ed. by Philip Schaff and Henry Wace (14 vols., Oxford and New York, 1890-1916), I, 561-580, esp. p. 566.

doctrine of the divinity of Christ; as he was first thought to be a God in some qualified sense of the word, a distinguished emanation from the supreme mind, and then the *Logos* or wisdom of God personified; and it was not till near four hundred years after Christ that he was thought to be properly equal to the Father. Whereas, on the other hand, it is now pretended that the apostles taught the doctrine of the proper divinity of Christ; and yet it cannot be denied that, in the very times of the apostles, the Jewish church, and many of the Gentiles, held the opinion of his being a mere man. Here the transition is quite sudden, without any gradation at all. This must naturally have given the greatest alarm, such as is now given to those who are called orthodox by the present Socinians; and yet nothing of this kind can be perceived. Besides, it was certainly more probable that the Christians of those times, urged as they were with the meanness of their Master, should incline to add to, rather than take from, his natural rank and dignity.

We find nothing like divinity ascribed to Christ before Justin Martyr, who, from being a philosopher, became a Christian, but always retained the peculiar habit of his former profession. As to Clemens Romanus, who was contemporary with the apostles, when he is speaking in the highest terms concerning Christ, he only calls him "the sceptre of the majesty of God."[8] Whether Justin Martyr was the very first who started the notion of the pre-existence of Christ, and of his superangelic or divine nature, is not certain, but we are not able to trace it any higher. We find it, indeed, briefly mentioned in the *Shepherd of Hermas,* but though this is supposed by some to be the Hermas men-

[8] A reference to Clement I, Bishop of Rome around 100 A.D. and the author of an *Epistle to the Corinthians,* which may be found in *The Ante-Nicene Fathers: Translations of the Writings of the Fathers Down to A.D. 325,* ed. by Alexander Roberts and James Donaldson (10 vols., New York, 1926), I, 5-21, esp. p. 9.

tioned by Paul, and to have written towards the end of the first century, others suppose this to be the work of one Hermes, brother of Pius, Bishop of Rome, and to have been written about the year 141, or perhaps later; and as this work contains such a pretension to visions and revelations, as I cannot but think unworthy of the Hermas mentioned by Paul, I cannot help being of this opinion. He says, "Having seen an old rock and a new gate, they represent the son of God, who was more ancient than any creature, so as to be present with the Father at the creation, *ad condendam creaturam.*"[9] The book was written in Greek, but we have only a Latin version of it.

Justin Martyr being a philosopher, and writing an apology for Christianity to a philosophical Roman emperor, would naturally wish to represent it in what would appear to him and other philosophers the most favorable light; and this disposition appears by several circumstances. Thus he represents virtuous men, in all preceding ages, as being in a certain sense, Christians; and apologizing for calling Christ the son of God, he says that "this cannot be new to them who speak of Jupiter as having sons, and especially of Mercury, as his interpreter, and the instructor of all men. . . ." On the same subject he says, "If Christ be a mere man, yet he deserves to be called the Son of God, on account of his wisdom, and the heathens called God (i.e. Jupiter), the father of gods and men; and if, in an extraordinary manner, he be the *Logos* of God, this is common with those who call Mercury the *Logos* that declares the will of God. . . ."[10]

[9] *The Shepherd of Hermas,* Book III, Similitude IX, Chapter 12. For an English translation of this work and a commentary on the problem of its authorship (essentially confirming Priestley's view) see Roberts and Donaldson, eds., *The Ante-Nicene Fathers,* II, 3-58, esp. p. 47.

[10] Justin Martyr was born in Samaria of pagan parents around 100 A.D. After being well educated in Greek philosophy, he was converted to Christianity and wrote two famous *Apologies* in its behalf. He taught for many years in Rome but finally suffered a martyr's death around 165 A.D. See Roberts and Donaldson, eds., *The Ante-Nicene Fathers,* I, 159-306. The passage Priestley quotes from the *First Apology* may be found on p. 170.

With this disposition to make his religion appear in the most respectable light to the heathens, and having himself professed the doctrine of Plato, can it be thought extraordinary that he eagerly caught at the doctrine of the *Logos,* which he found ready formed to his hands in the works of Philo, and that he introduced it into the Christian system; that Irenaeus, who was also educated among the philosophers, about the same time, did the same thing; or that others, who were themselves sufficiently predisposed to act the same part, should follow their example?[11]

———

It also deserves to be noticed, that notwithstanding the supposed derivation of the Son from the Father, and therefore their being of the same substance, most of the early Christian writers thought the text "I and my Father are one" was to be understood of a unity or harmony of disposition only. Thus Tertullian observes that the expression is *unum,* one thing, not one person; and he explains it to mean unity, likeness, conjunction, and of the love that the Father bore to the Son. Origen says, "let him consider that text, 'all that believed were of one heart and of one soul,' and then he will understand this, "I and my Father are one.'" Novatian says one thing *(unum)* being in the neuter gender, signifies an agreement of society, not a unity of person, and he explains it by this passage in Paul: "He that planteth and he that watereth are both one." But the fathers of the Council of Sardica, held A.D. 347, reprobated the opinion that the

[11] The *Logos* doctrine came from the Greek term for "word" or "thought," which may be freely translated as "the divine Reason." It grew out of a long background of Greek speculation about the origins and operations of the universe. In the works of Philo of Alexandria, a Hellenistic Jewish philosopher who lived early in the first century, it was applied to Biblical interpretation. It found its classic expression in the first chapter of the Gospel of John, where the *Logos* was identified with Christ. It played a prominent part in the theology of Justin Martyr and of Irenaeus, who was Bishop of Lyons at the end of the second century and the author of *Against Heresies,* an early codification of Christian orthodoxy.

union of the Father and Son consists in consent and concord only, apprehending it to be a strict unity of substance; so much farther was the doctrine of the Trinity advanced at that time.[12]

As the doctrine of the divine unity was infringed by the introduction of that of the divinity of Christ, and of the Holy Spirit (as a person distinct from the Father), so the doctrine of the natural placability of the Divine Being, and our ideas of the equity of his government, have been greatly debased by the gradual introduction of the modern doctrine of atonement, which represents the Divine Being as withholding his mercy from the truly penitent, till a full satisfaction be made to his justice; and for that purpose, as substituting his own innocent Son in the place of sinful men.

This corruption of the genuine doctrine of revelation is connected with the doctrine of the divinity of Christ; because it is said that sin, as an offense against an infinite Being, requires an infinite satisfaction, which can only be made by an infinite person, that is, one who is no less than God himself. Christ, therefore, in order to make this infinite satisfaction for the sins of men, must himself be God, equal to the Father. The justice of God being now fully satisfied by the death of Christ, the sinner is acquitted. Moreover, as the sins of men have been thus imputed to Christ, his righteousness is, on the other hand, imputed to them; and thus they are accepted of God, not on account of what they have done themselves, but for what Christ had done for them.

As I conceive this doctrine to be a gross misrepresentation

12 One of the central issues in question among Christian leaders of the third and fourth century was whether Christ the Son was of the same essential being or substance with God the Father or simply of similar substance with Him. Tertullian, Origen, and Novatian were all third-century figures who wrote their works before the church councils settled the issue.

of the character and moral government of God, and to affect many other articles in the scheme of Christianity, greatly disfiguring and depraving it; I shall show, in a fuller manner than I mean to do with respect to any other corruption of Christianity, that it has no countenance whatever in reason, or the Scriptures; and, therefore, that the whole doctrine of atonement, with every modification of it, has been a departure from the primitive and genuine doctrine of Christianity.

THE HISTORY OF OPINIONS
RELATING TO SAINTS AND ANGELS

The idolatry of the Christian church began with the deification and proper worship of Jesus Christ, but it was far from ending with it. For, from similar causes, Christians were soon led to pay an undue respect to men of eminent worth and sanctity, which at length terminated in as proper a worship of them, as that which the heathens had paid to their heroes and demigods, addressing prayer to them, in the same manner as to the Supreme Being himself. The same undue veneration led them also to a superstitious respect for their relics, the places where they had lived, their pictures and images, and indeed everything that had borne a near relation to them; so that at length, not only were those persons whom they termed saints, the objects of their worship, but also their relics and images; and neither with respect to the external forms, nor, as far as we can perceive, their internal sentiments, were Christians to be at all distinguished from those who bowed down to wood and stone, in the times of paganism.

———

As our Saviour became the object of worship before any other man, so his mother soon began to be considered with a singular respect, and at length she engrossed so much of the devotion of the Christian world, that I shall make a separate article of it, in each period of this part of my work.

It is remarkable that, excepting what was said to Mary by the angel, "henceforth all generations shall call thee blessed," no particular compliment is paid to her in all the history of the evangelists. She is only mentioned as a pious woman, among several others, and was committed to the care of John by our Lord, as he hung upon the cross. Nay, several expressions of our Lord, though not really disrespectful, yet show that, in his character of a teacher sent from God, he considered her only as any other person or disciple.

When she applied to him about the failure of wine, at the marriage feast in Cana, he replied, "Woman, what hast thou to do with me?" and gave her no satisfaction with respect to what he intended to do. And again, when she and some others of his relations were endeavoring to make their way through a crowd, in order to speak to him, and he was told of it, he replied, "Who is my mother, and who are my brethren? He that does the will of God, the same is my brother, and sister, and mother." In the book of Acts her name is but once mentioned, as one of those who were assembled with the apostles after the ascension of Jesus, *Acts i. 14,* so that where, or how she lived, or died, we have no knowledge at all. On how narrow a foundation does the excessive veneration that was afterwards paid to the "blessed Virgin," as she is now called, rest!

The first mention that we find of any particular respect paid to the Virgin Mary, was in the time of Epiphanius,[13] when some women used to offer to her cakes called collyrides, from which they got the name of Collyridians; and as men had no concern in it, except by permitting their wives to do it, it is called by this writer a "heresy of the women." He himself greatly disapproved of it, and wrote against it.

[13] Epiphanius was a bishop in Cyprus during the latter part of the fourth century and the author of a treatise which described and refuted some eighty heresies. See Schaff, *History of the Christian Church,* III, 926-933 and 417-418.

This may be thought extraordinary, since oblations at the tombs of the dead were very common in this age. But as it was not known where the Virgin Mary was interred, the offering of cakes to her was a new step in the worship of the dead, and was therefore more particularly noticed. It is plain, however, from his account of this affair, that prayers were then offered to the Virgin Mary, and by some of the orthodox, as they were called, though he himself rejected the thought of it with indignation.

In a piece of Athanasius,[14] entitled *De Sanctissima Deipara,* we find a long address to the Virgin, but it seems to have been a piece of oratory, and we can hardly infer from it that it was his custom to address his devotions to her. In it he says, "Hear, O daughter of David, and of Abraham; incline thine ear to our prayers, and forget not thy people"; and again, "Intercede for us, lady, mistress, queen, and mother of God."

The first who was particularly noticed, as introducing this worship of the Virgin, is Peter Gnapheus, Bishop of Antioch, in the fifth century, who appointed her name to be called upon in the prayers of the church. This devotion, however, seems to have taken its rise towards the end of the fourth century, and in Arabia, where we read of a controversy respecting her; some maintaining that, after she was delivered of Jesus, she lived with her husband Joseph as his wife. This was violently opposed by others, who, running into the other extreme, worshipped her "as a goddess, and judged it necessary to appease her anger, and seek her favor, by libations, sacrifices, the oblations of cakes (collyridae), and such like services," as Epiphanius censured.

To persons much acquainted with ecclesiastical history, nothing of this kind will appear extraordinary. Otherwise we might be surprised how it should ever have been considered as a thing of any consequence, whether the mother of Christ had any commerce with her husband or not. The

---

14 Athanasius was Bishop of Alexandria in the middle years of the fourth century.

presumption is that, as they lived together, at least after the birth of Jesus, she had. However, the respect paid to virginity in that age was so great that it was thought to derogate from her virtue and honor, to suppose that she ever had any commerce with man; and therefore, without any proper evidence in the case, it was presumed that she must have continued a virgin; and to maintain the contrary was even deemed heretical. In the Council of Capua, in 389, Bonosus, a bishop in Macedonia, was condemned for maintaining that Mary, the mother of Jesus, was not always a virgin; following, it is said, the heresy of Paulinus.

When the doctrine of original sin was started, the veneration for the Virgin Mary was so great, that doubts were entertained whether she might not have been exempt from it, as well as her Son. Austin maintained that no person ever lived without sin except the Virgin Mary, concerning whom he, however, only says he will not hold any controversy, for the honor that we owe to our Saviour.

After the deification and worship of Christ, it was natural that the rank of his mother should rise in some proportion to it. Accordingly we find that after Christ was considered as God, it became customary to give Mary the title of mother of God. . . . This, however, was not done, at least generally, till after the Council of Chalcedon in 451. This title of mother of God happened to be a favorite term with Apollinaris and his followers, and in consequence of this, perhaps, it was, that Nestorius violently opposed this innovation, thinking it sufficient that Mary should be called the mother of Christ.[15]

This opposition, however, operated as in many other cases, viz. to increase the evil; and in the third Council of Ephesus [in 431], in which Nestorius was condemned, it was decreed that Mary should be called the mother of God. From this time she was honored more than ever; but still she had not the titles that were given her afterwards of queen of

[15] Both Apollinaris, who died about 390, and Nestorius, who died about 450, were condemned as heretics.

heaven, mistress of the world, goddess, mediatrix, gate of paradise, etc.

—————

In popish churches the first thing that we are struck with is a vessel of what is called holy water, into which those who enter dip their finger, and then mark their foreheads with the sign of the cross. This holy water, there can be no doubt, came from the lustral water of the pagans, as indeed learned Catholics allow. This water was also placed at the entrance of the heathen temples, and those who entered were sprinkled with it. The first express mention made of holy water among Christians is an epistle of Vigilius, bishop of Rome, written in 538, in speaking of the consecration of churches, as was mentioned above; though some have thought that to have been holy water which Synesius[16] mentions, as placed at the entrance of the churches, for the purpose of washing their hands before prayer. Middleton farther observes, that the composition of this holy water is the same with that of the heathens, viz. "a mixture of salt with common water; and the form of the sprinkling brush, called by the ancients *aspersorium* or *aspergillum,* is much the same with what the priests now make use of."[17]

A fondness for the sign of the cross was one of the first superstitions of Christians. It was probably first used by way of distinguishing themselves from the heathens, or to show the heathens that they were not ashamed of that with which they were most reproached, viz. the crucifixion of their Master. From this constant use of it they began to imagine that there was some peculiar virtue in the thing itself. They also imagined it to be alluded to in many pas-

[16] Synesius was Bishop of Ptolemais in the fifth century. See Schaff, *History of the Christian Church,* III, 604-605.

[17] Conyers Middleton (1683-1750) was a liberal Anglican clergyman, who attacked Roman Catholicism in his *Letter from Rome* (1729), from which this quotation is taken.

sages of the Old Testament, and various rites of the Jewish religion, and they were also pleased to find the traces of it everywhere else. Hence came the custom of marking themselves with it, which is said to have been first done by the Valentinians, and then by the Montanists, of whom was Tertullian, who makes great boast of it.[18] But it does not appear to have been used in the public offices of religion in the three first centuries, or that crosses, made of wood or metal, were ever used till it was imagined that Helena, the mother of Constantine, had discovered the true cross in 326.

Burning wax lights in the daytime were used in many heathen ceremonies, for which they are ridiculed by Lactantius.[19] "The heathens," says he, "light up candles to God, as if he lived in the dark; and do not they deserve to pass for madmen, who offer lamps to the author and giver of light?" But not long after this, these very wax lights were introduced into Christian worship.

Another thing that was noted by the early Christians, as peculiar to the pagans, was incense. But so early as the third century, we find this also made use of in Christian churches. And Middleton says, "We find not only the incense sellers, but the incense itself, and the *thuribulum,* taken into the service of the Christian altars, and mentioned by St. Ambrose and St. Chrysostom, as of common use, both in the Eastern and Western empire."[20] But both wax lights and incense were first introduced into the Eastern churches, and from them were adopted in the West.

Lastly, processions, which are conducted with great solemnity by the Papists, were also copied from the heathen worship.

[18] The Valentinians and the Montanists were sectarian groups of the second century.

[19] Lactantius, who lived around 300 A.D., was an associate of the Emperor Constantine and author of *The Divine Institutes.* See Roberts and Donaldson, eds., *The Ante-Nicene Fathers,* VII, 3-328, esp. p. 163.

[20] Quotation from Middleton's *Letter from Rome.* Ambrose and Chrysostom were Church Fathers of the fourth century A.D.

CONSIDERATIONS ADDRESSED TO UNBELIEVERS AND ESPECIALLY TO MR. GIBBON[21]

To consider the system (if it may be called a system) of Christianity *a priori,* one would think it very little liable to corruption, or abuse. The great outline of it is that the Universal Parent of mankind commissioned Jesus Christ to invite men to the practice of virtue, by the assurance of his mercy to the penitent, and of his purpose to raise to immortal life and happiness all the virtuous and the good, but to inflict an adequate punishment on the wicked. In proof of this he wrought many miracles, and after a public execution he rose again from the dead. He also directed that proselytes to his religion should be admitted by baptism, and that his disciples should eat bread and drink wine in commemoration of his death.

Here is nothing that any person could imagine would lead to much subtle speculation, at least such as could excite much animosity. The doctrine itself is so plain, that one would think the learned and the unlearned were upon a level with respect to it. And a person unacquainted with the state of things at the time of its promulgation would look in vain for any probable source of the monstrous corruptions and abuses which crept into the system afterwards. Our Lord, however, and his apostles, foretold that there would be a great departure from the truth, and that something would arise in the church altogether unlike the doctrine which they taught, and even subversive of it.

In reality, however, the causes of the succeeding corruptions did then exist; and accordingly, without anything more than their natural operation, all the abuses rose to their full height; and what is more wonderful still, by the operation of natural causes also, without any miraculous interposition of Providence, we see the abuses gradually corrected, and Christianity recovering its primitive beauty and glory.

[21] I.e., Edward Gibbon (1737-1794), author of *The Decline and Fall of the Roman Empire,* a work notorious for its hostile attitude toward Christianity.

The causes of the corruptions were almost wholly contained in the established opinions of the heathen world, and especially the philosophical part of it; so that when those heathens embraced Christianity, they mixed their former tenets and prejudices with it. Also, both Jews and heathens were so much scandalized at the idea of being the disciples of a man who had been crucified as a common malefactor that Christians in general were sufficiently disposed to adopt any opinion that would most effectually wipe away this reproach.

The opinion of the mental faculties of man belonging to a substance distinct from his body, or brain, and of this invisible spiritual part, or soul, being capable of subsisting before and after its union to the body, which had taken the deepest root in all the schools of philosophy, was wonderfully calculated to answer this purpose. For by this means Christians were enabled to give to the soul of Christ what rank they pleased in the heavenly regions before his incarnation. On this principle went the Gnostics, deriving their doctrine from the received Oriental philosophy.[22] Afterwards the philosophizing Christians went upon another principle, personifying the wisdom . . . of God the Father. But this was mere Platonism, and therefore cannot be said to have been unnatural in their circumstances, though at length they came, in the natural progress of things, to believe that Christ was, in power and glory, equal to God the Father himself.

I am sorry, however, to have occasion to admonish Mr. Gibbon, that he should have distinguished better than he has done between Christianity itself, and the corruptions of it. A serious Christian, strongly attached to some particular tenets, may be excused if, in reading ecclesiastical history,

[22] The Gnostics were heretics of the second century who postulated a numerous order of heavenly beings, of different ranks, and interpreted the significance of Christ in abstrusely symbolic, unhistorical terms. See Schaff, *History of the Christian Church*, II, 442-498.

he should not make the proper distinctions; but this allowance cannot be made for so cool and philosophical a spectator as Mr. Gibbon.

He should not have taken it for granted that the doctrine of three persons in one God, or the doctrine of atonement for the sins of all mankind, by the death of one man, were any parts of the Christian system; when, if he had read the New Testament for himself, he must have seen the doctrine of the proper unity of God, and also that of his free mercy to the penitent, in almost every page of it. As he does speak of the corruptions of Christianity, he should have examined farther, both as an historian and as a man. For as an individual, he is as much interested in the inquiry as any other person; and no inquiry whatever is so interesting to any man as this is.

As to what Mr. Gibbon, with a sneer of triumph, says of Plato having "360 years before Christ . . . ventured to explore the mysterious nature of the Deity," and of "the theology of Plato" having been "confirmed by the celestial pen of the last and most sublime of the evangelists," ninety-seven years after that era; like all his other sarcasms against Christianity, it is founded on ignorance. But he is more excusable in this than in other cases, as too many Christians have been chargeable with the same; confounding the *Logos* of Plato with that of John, and making of it a second person in the Trinity, than which no two things can be more different, as has been clearly explained by my excellent and judicious friend Mr. Lindsey, especially in his *Catechist*, in the preface to which he has very properly animadverted upon this passage of Mr. Gibbon.

Mr. Gibbon has much to learn concerning the gospel before he can be properly qualified to write against it. Hitherto he seems to have been acquainted with nothing but the corrupt establishments of what is very improperly called Christianity; whereas it is incumbent upon him to read and study the New Testament for himself. There he will find nothing like Platonism, but doctrines in every respect the reverse of that system of philosophy, which weak and un-distinguishing Christians afterwards incorporated with it.

Had Mr. Gibbon lived in France, Spain or Italy, he might, with the same reason, have ranked the doctrine of transub-stantiation, and the worship of saints and angels, among the essentials of Christianity, as the doctrines of the Trinity and of atonement.

The friends of genuine, and I will add of rational, Chris-tianity have not, however, on the whole, much reason to regret that their enemies have not made these distinctions; since, by this means, we have been taught to make them ourselves; so that Christianity is perhaps as much indebted to its enemies, as to its friends, for this important service. In their indiscriminate attacks, whatever has been found to be untenable has been gradually abandoned, and I hope the attack will be continued till nothing of the wretched out-works be left; and then, I doubt not, a safe and impregnable fortress will be found in the center, a fortress built upon a rock, against which the gates of death will not prevail.

When the present crisis is over (and I think we may see that the period is not far distant), that by means of the ob-jections of unbelievers, and the attention which, in conse-quence of it, will be given to the subject, by believers, Christianity shall be restored to its primitive purity, the cool and truly sensible part of mankind will, in this very circum-stance, perceive an argument for its truth; and thus even the corruptions of Christianity will have answered a very valu-able purpose; as having been the means of supplying such an evidence of its truth, as could not have been derived from any other circumstance. Let any other religion be named that ever was so much corrupted, and that recovered itself from such corruption, and continued to be professed with unquestionable zeal by men of reflection and understanding, and I shall look upon it with respect, and not reject it with-out a very particular examination. The revival of a zeal for the religion of Greece and Rome under Julian is not to be compared with the attachment to Christianity by inquisitive and learned men in the present age. Let literature and science flourish but one century in Asia, and what would be the state of Mahometanism, the religion of the Hindus, or that of the Tartars, subject to the Grand Lama? I should rejoice to hear of such a challenge as I give Mr. Gibbon, being sent from a Mahometan Mufti to the Christian world.

Should what I call pure Christianity (the most essential articles of which I consider to be the proper unity of God, and the proper humanity of Christ), continue to spread as it now does, and as, from the operation of the same causes, I have no doubt but that, in spite of all opposition, it will do, and literature revive among the Jews and Mahometans (who, it is remarkable, were never learned and inquisitive, but in an age in which all the Christianity they could see must have struck them with horror, as a system of abominable and gross idolatry, to which their own systems are totally repugnant); should learning and inquiry, I say, once more revive among the Jews and Mahometans, at the same time that a great part of the Christian world should be free from that idolatry which has given them such just offense, they would be much more favorably impressed with the idea of Christianity than they were in former times.

It, also, can hardly be supposed, but that the general conversion of the Jews, after a state of such long and violent opposition (which will in all future time exclude the idea of their having acted in concert with the Christians), will be followed by the conversion of all the thinking part of the world. And if, before or after this time, the Jews should return to their own country, the whole will be such a manifest fulfilment of the prophecies of Scripture, as will leave no reasonable color for infidelity.

In the prospect of this great and glorious event I rejoice; and I wish to contribute a little towards hastening its approach, both by unfolding the history of Christianity, with all the corruptions of it, and submitting to the most rigid examination whatever I think to be really a part of it. To this, all the friends of genuine Christianity will cheerfully say amen.

An History of Early Opinions Concerning Jesus Christ, Compiled from Original Writers, Proving that the Christian Church Was at First Unitarian

Priestley expanded his analysis of the Trinitarian "corruption" in An History of Early Opinions Concerning Jesus Christ, Compiled from Original Writers, Proving that the Christian Church Was at First Unitarian *(four vols., Birmingham, 1786).*[23] *An especially interesting aspect of this work is the discussion of the doctrine of the Virgin Birth, the truth of which Priestley had come to question. He suspected that it was not a part of the earliest gospel narratives. The Gospel of Mark did not contain it, and Priestley suggested that it was not included in the earliest versions of Matthew and Luke. He thought the introductions to these gospels were later interpolations. Here Priestley came close to anticipating modern higher criticism of the Bible.*

OF THE DOCTRINE OF
THE MIRACULOUS CONCEPTION[24]

Having considered the great principles on which all the Unitarians of antiquity were agreed, viz. the doctrines of the unity of God, and the simple humanity of Christ, with the arguments by which they supported them, I shall now consider an article with respect to which they held different opinions, viz. the miraculous conception of Christ, fairly

[23] Text from Rutt, VII, 57-69, 81-84, 100-103.
[24] I.e., the Virgin Birth of Christ, not to be confused with the doctrine of the Immaculate Conception of the Virgin Mary, proclaimed as Catholic dogma by Pius IX in 1854.

laying before my readers all that I could collect concerning it, that they may be able to form their own judgment. I had thought to have made some remarks on this subject in my *History of the Corruptions of Christianity,* but I did not do it there, because at that time I had not sufficiently considered it. But having now given to it all the attention of which I think I am capable, I shall with great frankness lay open the whole state of my mind with respect to it. From the same premises different persons will draw different conclusions.

Many, I doubt not, will be alarmed at so free a discussion of a doctrine which is held sacred by almost all the Christian world; the miraculous conception of Jesus appearing to them to rest upon the same authority with every other fact in the gospel history, and therefore involving in its consequences the truth of Christianity itself. I am fully apprised of the situation in which I write, and of the load of censure that I am sure to bring upon myself by it. Many of my best friends, those who think I have hitherto been a zealous and successful advocate of truth, will think that I am now going too far, and even risking what has been already gained. To these I would suggest the following considerations:

1. Calling in question the truth of the miraculous conception cannot appear more alarming to them, than the doctrine of the simple humanity of Christ now does to others, who are as sincere friends to the gospel as themselves; and, in this business, I cannot give greater offense than I did when I wrote against the doctrine of a soul and scrupled not to declare myself a materialist.

2. An alarm may be of use to excite attention to a subject; and when the first consternation is over, those who were the most startled will recover themselves, and consider the arguments dispassionately, and with a temper more proper for the discovery of truth. No man at this day can give more offense, or render himself more obnoxious, even to Christians, than the Apostle Paul did, by preaching

the gospel to the uncircumcised Gentiles. Neither himself, nor even his memory, ever survived the odium that he brought upon himself by this means, with the generality of the Jewish Christians. His principal object, in many of his epistles, is to justify himself in this respect. But though he was supported by reason, and an especial commission from God, he wrote in vain. Now, with respect to fortitude in bearing sufferings of this kind in the cause of truth, or, which is the same thing to me, what I seriously think to be so, I would not be behind St. Paul, or any man. I have been trained to it, and I hope the discipline has not been lost upon me.

3. I would farther observe that all those to whom it can be worth my while to make an apology, think as I do with respect to the Scriptures, viz. that they were written without any particular inspiration, by men who wrote according to the best of their knowledge, and who from their circumstances could not be mistaken with respect to the greater facts, of which they were proper witnesses, but (like other men, subject to prejudice) might be liable to adopt a hasty and ill-grounded opinion concerning things which did not fall within the compass of their own knowledge, and which had no connection with anything that did so; and such I hold the miraculous conception to be. We ought all of us, therefore, to consider ourselves as fully at liberty to examine with the greatest rigor, both the reasonings of the writers, and the facts of which we find any account in their writings; that, judging by the rules of just criticism, we may distinguish what may be depended upon from what may not. It may, perhaps, however, appear probable that neither Matthew nor Luke wrote anything about the miraculous conception, especially the former.

4. Lastly, I would observe that, though at present there are but few who disbelieve the miraculous conception, there have always, I believe, been some, and those men of learning and character among Christians, who have thought as I am now inclined to do with respect to it. I have seen a

small tract of Mr. Elwall's, written about sixty years ago, the design of which was to disprove it.[25] It made no impression upon me at the time, and I have not been able to procure it since. Dr. Eaton, a learned and respectable Dissenting minister, late of Nottingham, though he never wrote upon the subject, is well known by his acquaintance to have been decidedly of the same opinion with Mr. Elwall; and so have been, and are, several others, inferior to none that bear the Christian name for understanding, learning, or probity. To my certain knowledge, the number of such persons is increasing, and several of them think it to be a matter of great consequence that a doctrine which they regard as a discredit to the Christian scheme should be exploded. They also think it far better that this should be done by Christians themselves, than by unbelievers, who may say that we never give up any idle notion, till we can maintain it no longer.

Having premised thus much, I proceed to the consideration of the subject before me, and I shall do it with the greatest freedom, and, as far as I can judge concerning myself, with perfect impartiality. Observing that, though I frankly acknowledge the arguments against the miraculous conception considerably preponderate in my mind at present, I shall not form an absolutely decided opinion, till I shall have had an opportunity of seeing what weight may be thrown into the opposite scale, by any persons who shall candidly examine what they will find advanced in this chapter.

In the first place I would observe that the importance of this doctrine has been unreasonably magnified in modern times. It is one on which the ancient Unitarians held opposite opinions, without, as far as appears, having ever

[25] Edward Elwall (1676-1744) was the author of *A True Testimony for God . . . Against All the Trinitarians under Heaven* (1724), a Unitarian tract which led to his being tried for blasphemy. See Leslie Stephen and Sidney Lee, eds., *Dictionary of National Biography* (63 vols., London, 1885-1901), XVII, 341.

thought the worse of one another on that account; and, therefore, there can be no reason why we should not exercise the same mutual candor at this day. The value of the gospel depends not at all upon any idea that we may have concerning the person of Christ. All that we ought to regard is the object of his mission, and the authority with which his doctrine was promulgated. The doctrine of immortality, which is the great object of the whole revealed will of God, is just as acceptable to me from the mouth of the son of Joseph and Mary, as from the mouth of any man created for the purpose, from that of an angel, or from the voice of God himself speaking from heaven.

When the doctrine of the miraculous conception is not particularly attended to, we all readily say that it is the belief of the doctrines, the miracles, the death, and the resurrection of Christ, that makes the Christian; and also that the fewer things of an extraneous nature that we connect with these, and maintain to be inseparable from them, the better; especially if we thereby make the defense of Christianity the easier. And certainly no circumstance relating to the birth of Christ has any more connection with the articles above-mentioned, than the opinion of his having been a tall or short man, of a fair or a dark complexion. It does not at all concern us to know how Christ came into the world, but what he taught when he was in it, and what he did and suffered, as a proof of the authority by which he taught it. Every man, therefore, who believes that Christ had a divine commission to teach the great doctrines of a resurrection and of a life to come, is as much a Christian, and has as strong motives to govern his life by the precepts of Christianity, as he who likewise believes that he was without father, or without mother, that he was the maker of the world, or the eternal God himself. Such articles of faith as these can only serve to puzzle, to amaze, and confound men; but they have no tendency to mend the heart or the life.

I would farther observe that the doctrine of the miracu-

lous conception itself is not, in fact, of any more consequence to the Socinian, than it is to the Arian, or even the
Athanasian hypothesis.[26] For it is no impediment to the
union of the Arian or Athanasian *Logos* to the human nature
of Christ, that his body was derived from Joseph. For anything that we can judge, a body produced in the natural
way was just as proper for the residence of this heavenly
inhabitant, as one made on purpose. And if, on any scheme,
it was fit that Christ should have human nature at all, it
may be supposed to have been equally fit that he should
have a proper human nature, differing as little as possible
from that of his brethren. There is, therefore, no more
reason why the Arian or the Athanasian should be more attached to the belief of the miraculous conception than
the Socinian. The doctrine itself connects equally well, or
equally ill, with any particular hypothesis concerning the
nature of Christ.

It may be imagined to be more honorable to Christ to
have come into the world without the help of a man than
with it; but this is an affair of imagination only. And, for
the very same reason, it might have been imagined to be
still more honorable to him, to have come into the world
without the instrumentality of either woman or man, and
that the second Adam should have come from the hands of
God as immediately as the first. Ideas no better than these
gave rise to the doctrine of the Gnostics. For they meant to
do honor to Christ; and therefore we should be on our guard
against them. But even admitting ideas of this kind to have
some weight, is it not, in fact, just as humiliating to have a
mother, as it is to have a father; for it is nothing more than
the body that is concerned in the question?

We should likewise attend a little to the ideas of the Jews,
as well as to our own, on this subject. Now the doctrine of
the Messiah being the proper son of Joseph, a lineal de-
scendant from David, will certainly be more acceptable to

[26] Socinianism emphasized the humanity of Jesus, Arianism his similarity to God, Athanasianism his identity with God.

them, than that of his having had a miraculous conception. For, though we may fancy that this circumstance reflects more honor upon him; yet, in the eye of a Jew, he must, on that very account, appear to be less accurately described by their ancient prophets; though any doctrine which makes Christ to have been properly and simply a man, in whatever manner he was made so, must be infinitely more acceptable to them than the opinion of his having had a nature entirely different from that of man. I own, however, that the expectations of the Jews (any farther than they have a real foundation in the prophecies) ought not by any means to determine our judgment in the case, so as to weigh against any proper argument that may be alleged on the other side.

Should I have any controversy with a Jew, I should not feel myself at all embarrassed with this circumstance of the miraculous conception; as I should not hesitate to follow the example of the candid Justin Martyr with respect to it; telling him, that he was at full liberty to think as he should see reason to do on that subject; and that he might be as good a Christian as the Ebionites were before him, though he should believe no more of the miraculous conception than they had done.[27]

Indeed, with respect to the importance of the question in itself, there are few, I imagine, but would be ready enough to agree with me, if they did not imagine that a disbelief of this article would affect the credibility of the rest of the gospel history. But there is an argument of fact (which is the strongest of all arguments) directly against them. For the Ebionites, who did disbelieve the miraculous conception, were as firm believers in the rest of the gospel history as

[27] The Ebionites were a sect of early Jewish Christians who regarded Jesus as "the promised Messiah, the Son of David, and the supreme lawgiver, yet a mere man, sprung by natural generation from Joseph and Mary." (Schaff, *History of the Christian Church*, II, 433.) They used a Hebrew Gospel, now lost, which was rather similar to Matthew. See below, p. 320.

other Christians. And, besides, if we consider the nature of this apprehension, it will appear to be founded on a mistake; because the evidence for the miraculous conception, and that for the public life, miracles, death, and resurrection of Christ are exceedingly different; so that a total failure in the evidence for the one, will not affect the credibility of the other.

With the miraculous conception a few persons only could be acquainted; and we have not the testimony of any of those few, much less is it in our power to compare the evidence of one with that of others of them. Who were the persons that informed Matthew and Luke concerning it we cannot tell, nor through how many hands the story was transmitted before it came to them; admitting, for the present, that the introductions to their Gospels were written by themselves. Whereas the great events, subsequent to the preaching of John the Baptist, have not only the testimony of the writers themselves, but that of all the inhabitants of Judea, and of the strangers residing in it. For, as Paul says, "These things were not done in a corner."[28] And to give the gospel history its just degree of credibility, we must simply consider the writers as credible witnesses of what came to their knowledge, without any regard to their supposed inspiration, which will never make any impression on unbelievers. On no other ground shall we ever produce a just and rational defense of this most important history.

Setting aside all notions of inspiration, we should judge of the gospel history as we do of any other. Now no person, I apprehend, lays the less stress on the history of Livy, with respect to events near to his own time, because his account of Romulus and Remus is thought to be fabulous. Making myself, therefore, perfectly easy as to all the possible consequences of this discussion, I shall, with perfect freedom, consider the evidence for the miraculous conception as an article of history, and shall, with as much care as I can, state the arguments for and against it.

[28] Acts 26:26.

It has been more particularly said that, supposing Luke to have been the author of the introduction to his Gospel, we may, with the same reason, withhold our assent to any circumstance in our Saviour's history, that has been recorded by him only; for instance, the account of the raising the widow's son at Nain, and the mission of the seventy disciples, as to this of the miraculous conception. But this goes both upon the supposition of his being a competent witness to them all alike; and also of there being nothing more extraordinary in the latter case than in the two former; whereas, in both these respects, there is a remarkable difference between them.

The raising of the widow's son and the mission of the seventy fell within the term of the public life of Christ, of the transactions of which there were thousands of witnesses; and Luke himself, being generally said to have been one of the seventy, and consequently to have attended upon Christ during his ministry, might have been an eyewitness of what he relates; whereas he cannot be said to have been in circumstances to bear testimony to the miraculous conception at all, and, as I have said, through what hands the story came to him we are not told. They might, therefore, be very well or very ill informed concerning it.

Both the raising of the widow's son and the mission of the seventy, besides falling within the public life of Christ, are events similar to those for which we have the testimony of the other evangelists; the widow's son not being the only person that Jesus raised to life, nor the seventy disciples the only mission that he sent out. Whereas the miraculous conception was a miracle absolutely singular in its nature, there being nothing like it in the history of the Old or New Testament. And what makes still more against the credibility of it is that it does not appear to be adapted to answer any good purpose whatever; but, on the contrary, a manifestly bad one, in making our Saviour's Messiahship too soon and too generally known, or exposing his mother to undeserved reproach.

On the whole, therefore, we may very readily admit the credibility of Luke's account of the raising of the widow's son, and of the mission of the seventy disciples, and reject that of the miraculous conception, though related by the same historian.

The presumptive evidence of any doctrine depends upon the nature of it; and this should be considered before the direct evidence. For it is universally acknowledged that the less reason there is to expect any particular event, the stronger evidence it requires. A slight evidence is sufficient to certify us of such facts as happen every day, or very frequently. Miracles require much stronger evidence; and, accordingly, such evidence has always been provided.

Again, in miracles there is a gradation, and some of them being more extraordinary, and less probable, *a priori*, than others, require evidence proportionably more circumstantial and less liable to exception. Thus the resurrection of our Saviour, the most extraordinary, and, *a priori*, being the most improbable of all events, approaching the nearest to an impossibility, the evidence of it is remarkably circumstantial; in consequence of which there is not, perhaps, any fact in all ancient history so perfectly credible, according to the most established rules of evidence, as it is. And the arguments *a priori*, in this case, are as striking as those which may be called the arguments *a posteriori*, or the proper historical proof; because we are able to see the importance of the fact, the evidence of which required to be so exceedingly clear. Christ, coming to give mankind the fullest assurance of an universal resurrection, it was obviously necessary, at least highly desirable, that, besides solemnly announcing the doctrine, and confirming it by miracles, he should himself actually die and rise again, as a proof of it. Accordingly, we find that Christ did rest the evidence of his divine mission in a particular manner on the event of his resurrection. We therefore, see clearly, why "it behoved Christ" both "to suffer and to rise from the dead." (*Luke xxiv. 46.*)

Now, are we able to discover any reason why Christ should be born of a virgin, rather than in the usual way? Can we conceive it to have been at all necessary, or advantageous to the great object of his mission, or to qualify him for fulfilling it? I think I may answer for all Unitarians, that, *a priori,* we should rather have thought otherwise, viz. that there would have been a greater propriety in his being, in this as well as in all other respects, what other men are. For then, having had no natural advantage over us, his resurrection would have been calculated to give us the greater assurance of our own. Whereas, his coming into the world in a manner so very different from that of other men, might create a suspicion that there was some other essential difference between him and other men; and, therefore, that his nature might be subject to other laws than those of ours.

On this account, I am confident, that had mankind been desired to name a proper representative of themselves, in whom they should see exhibited what was to befall themselves, they would have chosen a man born as themselves had been. A *priori,* therefore, it must have appeared less probable that Christ, being sent on such a mission as his was, should be born of a virgin, than that he should be born like other men; as it might have been suspected that he would not have been produced in this manner, if it had not been for the sake of giving him such advantages in point of constitution, as men born in the usual way cannot naturally have. His example, therefore, is in all respects less properly proposed to us, and his resurrection affords less ground for our expectation that we also shall be raised to immortal life; since any peculiar constitution of nature may have unknown peculiar privileges.

In the Scriptures, mankind are generally apprised of the reasons of all the great measures that God has been pleased to take with respect to them. Our Saviour informs his disciples very particularly why it was expedient that he should die, and leave them for a time; assuring them that it was for their own advantage, etc., and with respect to those reasons which they were not at that time qualified to enter into, he plainly told them that they were not; and that, for that reason, the communication of more knowledge to them was deferred.

Now, are any reasons given us in the Scriptures, to show us that it was more proper that Christ was to be born of a virgin, than in the usual way? Or, is it there said, that there was a reason for it, but that men were not qualified to understand it? Neither of these is the case; and what is particularly remarkable, a thing of this extraordinary kind is not so much as mentioned, or in the most distant manner alluded to, by Christ himself, or by any writer in the New Testament; so that, if the doctrine be true, it does not appear to have answered any end whatever. And it is by no means analogous to the usual conduct of Divine Providence, to take extraordinary measures without a proportionable object and use. It is nowhere said that God honored mankind so far as either to send a person of a higher rank than man, to be his messenger to them, or to make a man in an extraordinary way, for that purpose; that more dignity might be given to his character, and greater attention secured to him.

There is only one expression in the whole New Testament, that is capable of being laid hold of as, in the most distant manner, alluding to the miraculous conception, which is Paul speaking of Christ *(Gal. iv. 4)*, as "made of a woman," as well as "made under the law." But the slightest knowledge of the Scripture phraseology may satisfy us that this is only synonymous to the term *man*. Job says *(xiv. 1)*, "Man that is born of a woman is of few days," etc.; and again *(xxv. 4)*, "How can he be clean that is born of a woman?" Our Saviour also says *(Matt. xi. 11)*, "Among them that are born of women, there hath not risen a greater than John the Baptist." To be born of women, therefore, or made of a woman, and to be a man, or a human being, is the same thing.

According to all appearance, therefore, if the doctrine of the miraculous conception be true, God wrought a most extraordinary miracle without any proper object or use. Nay, as far as we can judge, such a pretension as that of a miraculous birth, unless it had been much more particularly authenticated than the gospel history represents this to have been, must have operated greatly to the prejudice of our Saviour's character, and consequently must have obstructed the end of his mission; for, without the most circumstantial evidence, for which no provision was made, the story of the miraculous conception would never have been believed by the Jews. And does not this circumstance render the wisdom of the scheme very questionable? For, though it must always be acknowledged that the ways of God, even with respect to men, may be inscrutable to men, yet, when nothing is said of such wisdom, and no such submission of our judgments is required of us, the facts from which such mysterious conduct is inferred ought not to be admitted without proportionably clear evidence.

It has been said that the use of the miraculous conception was to be a motive with the parents of Jesus, to give him a pious and proper education. But to this it may be replied, in the first place, that his parents, being of themselves pious persons, would, of course, give their child a religious education; and, therefore, could not stand in need of so extraordinary a measure as this to engage them to attend to it. Besides, no motive is naturally so strong as the love that a parent bears to his own child, to do for him everything that he believes will be for his advantage; which, on the part of Joseph, would be wanting on this hypothesis.

The task of the education of the Messiah would, in all probability, have quite overwhelmed the minds of such persons as Joseph and Mary, who were in a low condition in life, and had enjoyed no particular advantage with respect to education themselves. Without express instruction from heaven, it is most probable that they would have put him under the care of some of their rabbis, and certainly would never have brought him up to the trade of a carpenter. Or they might naturally presume that, being born in a supernatural manner, he would be instructed and prepared for his office in a supernatural manner.

It does not appear that any particular care of the education of Jesus was at all necessary. A learned education he evidently had not; for the Jews expressed astonishment at his doctrine, on the account of his not knowing letters, meaning that he had not had the education of one of their rabbis. As far as appears, Jesus had not been taught anything more than to read and write his own language; and all the use that he had made of this learning was in his private study of the Scriptures; and that, before his baptism, he had given more attention to these than other pious Jews usually did, may be supposed, but cannot be proved.

We see no reason to think that Jesus's appearing as the Messiah at thirty years of age required any particular previous knowledge. He, like other Jews, would, of course, be brought up in the expectation of the Messiah; and, till his baptism, he might be under the same mistake, with respect to his character and kingdom, that other pious Jews were. But at that time (for we cannot be sure that it was before) he would be informed that he was the person, and would be instructed what he must teach and do, and also be apprised of what he must suffer in that character. And his supernatural illumination, and his private meditations, during the forty days which he passed in absolute retirement, will sufficiently account for the part that he acted, and the temper of mind that he discovered afterwards.

His first preaching was nothing more than John had taught before him. *Matt. iv. 17:* "From that time Jesus began to preach and to say, 'Repent; for the kingdom of heaven is at hand.'" Nor do I perceive anything in his subsequent teaching, which any other good man may not be supposed to have been always ready to deliver, on receiving instructions from God on the subject. His miracles evidently required no particular education, preparation, or instruction, for they were not his. The Father within him did the works.

Why then should we suppose that the miraculous conception was provided as a means to a certain end; when neither the existence nor the propriety of that end can be proved from the Scriptures? We are nowhere told that any particular attention to the education of Jesus by his parents was requisite, nor do we find that such attention was given. This then is a case in which both the fact and the hypothesis to account for it are alike imaginary.

Having thus stated the nature of the fact, the credibility of which I propose to discuss, and shown the appearance that it has *a priori,* which is of considerable moment with respect to the evidence that is necessary to establish its authenticity; I shall proceed to state the evidence for and against it, with as much impartiality as I can. This is all that is of any consequence to the reader. He must then, and he certainly will, judge for himself.

The whole strength of the evidence in favor of the miraculous conception is expressed in a few words. The thing itself appears *a priori* to be highly improbable, and the report of it must have operated unfavorably with respect to the credit of Christianity, and it is never argued from, or so much as alluded to, as of any use in the scheme, or as a part of it, in all the New Testament. But the testimony of the evangelists Matthew and Luke is expressly in its favor. Their histories are likewise supposed to be the earliest accounts of our Saviour's life; and Luke says that he took particular pains to trace the history to its source, from those who were best qualified to give him information.

This positive testimony, very circumstantially related by persons of such respectable characters, to say nothing of their supposed inspiration, is certainly entitled to the greatest credit. It may be said, what evidence can be stronger in favor of any event, than its being recorded by contemporary historians, whose writings were published in their own lifetime? If this part of the gospel history be fabulous, why may not the whole be so, since it is all related by the same evangelists? Is it not, therefore, to undermine the credit of the whole gospel history, to endeavor to weaken that of so considerable a part of it?

This, I think, is all that can be advanced in favor of the miraculous conception, setting aside all idea of the inspiration of the writers, to which, I own, I should pay no attention. I consider Matthew and Luke as simply historians, whose credit must be determined by the circumstances in which they wrote, and the nature of the facts which they relate. And before I consider the evidence that may be alleged against the fact which they have recorded, or are supposed to have recorded, I shall make one observation, which is of the greatest importance with respect to historical evidence, and which is always allowed its full weight with regard to all other histories. And it appears to me that it is our backwardness to consider the gospel historians in the same light in which we do other historians (notwithstanding the doctrine of their inspiration is nominally given up) that prevents our forming a right estimate in this particular case. In any other similar case, I apprehend, we should decide much more readily than the boldest of us feel ourselves disposed to do here.

The observation which I would now make, and which I wish to impress upon my reader, is this: that fully to establish the credibility of any fact, it must not only be recorded by contemporary historians, but it must also appear not to have been contradicted by those who were contemporary with the historians, and who may be supposed to have been as good judges as the historians themselves. Still less will the single circumstance of an event being recorded by contemporary historians avail to establish the credit of it, if it appear not to have been believed by those who may be supposed to have been favorably inclined to the belief of it, and to have wished it to be true.

Let us suppose that we should now recover a copy of the history of Livy, containing an account of the transactions of his own time, or so near to it, that it could not be doubted but that it was in his power to have procured good information concerning what he wrote; and that we should find in this copy of his history that Cleopatra, instead of dying by the bite of an asp in Egypt, was brought by Augustus to Rome, and publicly married to him. The story would not, at this day, gain any credit. We might not be able to deny that Livy wrote the account, but we should immediately say, if it was true, why does it not appear to have been believed at the time?

Supposing, farther, that we should discover another Roman history, viz. that of Sallust, which should contain the same account; still, if we saw no reason to think that it was believed at Rome, where the scene of the transaction was laid, we certainly should not believe it now; nor would even ten or twelve historians, agreeing ever so well in their accounts, make us believe it, unless it should appear to us that it was generally believed at the time. We might not be able to account for the misapprehensions and mistakes of the historians; but, in fact, their evidence would only be considered as that of ten or twelve men, opposed to the evidence of more than ten or twelve millions.

However, if the credit of Livy and Sallust was so well established that we could not believe that they would assert as a fact what they might easily have known not to be so; we should say that, though we had no method of accounting for such a narration being found in the copies of their works which have come down to us, we were satisfied that it was not of their composition. Passages, we might say, like that in Josephus concerning Christ, may have got into the works of more respectable writers (as a comparison of circumstances sufficiently proves) without our being able to say when, or by whom, the books were corrupted. And if we had any evidence that there were, in early times, copies of the entire histories of Livy and Sallust, in which nothing was said of the marriage of Augustus to Cleopatra, nothing farther, I imagine, would be wanting to our entire satisfaction on the subject.

Now these very material observations, and several others, apply to the case before us. It is true that we do find the story of the miraculous conception in the received Gospels of Matthew and Luke; and it is almost certain that they were there in the time of Justin Martyr; but it is no less certain, that there were in early times Gospels of Matthew, and of Luke too, which did not contain that story; and there is sufficient reason to think that the great body of Jewish Christians, who were contemporary with the apostles, did not believe it. It was probably a long time before it gained any credit at all with any of their posterity, and it is probable that it never did so with the generality of them. It is certain that some very learned persons, and therefore, probably the most inquisitive among them, and who wrote expressly on the subject, never believed it; and yet no good reason can be given why a history which has the appearance of being greatly to the credit of the founder of their religion should not have been believed by them, as well as by other Christians.

A circumstance of greater weight than even this is that the Gnostics of that age, to whose peculiar systems the doctrine of the miraculous conception could not but have appeared exceedingly favorable, did likewise reject it as fabulous. If these particulars can be well supported, it must appear that something is wanting to the full credibility of this part of the gospel history; and it will be farther weakened, if any circumstances in the story itself can be pointed out that affect the authenticity of the introductions to the Gospels of Matthew and Luke. Such facts of this kind, and such observations as have occurred to me on the subject, I now proceed to lay before my readers.

In comparing the four Gospels, we cannot but be struck with the remarkable difference between those of Matthew and Luke, and those of Mark and John, in this respect; neither of the latter giving the least hint of a miraculous conception. And yet it might well be thought that, if any part of the history required to be particularly authenticated, by the testimony of different historians, it was this; and many things of far less consequence are recorded by them all, and very circumstantially. With respect to John, it may, indeed, be said that as he knew that Matthew and Luke had recorded the circumstances of the miraculous conception, he had no occasion to do it.

But what shall we say with respect to Mark? If he was an epitomizer of Matthew, as some have supposed, but of which I own I have seen no sufficient evidence, how came he to leave out the whole of the two first chapters? And if he was, as I think most probable, an original writer, how came he to give no account at all of the miraculous conception, on the supposition that he really knew of it?[29] He could not tell that any other person of equal credit would write the history; and, therefore, as he did undertake it, he would certainly insert in it whatever he thought to be of principal importance. Consequently, he must either have never heard of the story, or have thought it of no importance. But it is of such a nature, that no person, believing it to be true, ever did, or ever could, consider it as of no importance. It was a singular and most extraordinary measure in Divine Providence, and could not but be considered as having some great object and end, whether we should be able to discover it or not. It was, therefore, such a fact as no historian could overlook; and it may, therefore, be presumed that Mark had either never heard of it, or that he did not believe it.

If we only take away the two first chapters of the Gospels of Matthew and Luke, and change a very few words in the

---

[29] Modern scholarship supports Priestley's suspicion of the priority of Mark among the Gospel authors and holds that Mark in turn borrowed from earlier sources, now lost. See, for example, Frederick C. Grant, *The Gospels: Their Origin and Growth* (New York, 1957).

verses that follow them, we shall find very proper beginnings for them both, and exactly corresponding to that natural and simple one of Mark. For they will then begin with an account of the preaching of John the Baptist; as, in fact, the Gospel of John likewise does, after a short introduction concerning the meaning of the word *Logos,* which was, probably, much talked of at that time.

Does not this circumstance give us some suspicion that both these Gospels of Matthew and Luke might originally have been published without these introductions; that the Hebrew copy of the Gospel of the Ebionites, which was that of Matthew without the two first chapters (and which they maintained to be the genuine Gospel of Matthew), might be all that Matthew himself ever wrote; that the copy of Luke's Gospel, which Marcion had, and which began, as Epiphanius says, at the third chapter, was all that Luke wrote; that the introductions were written afterwards by other persons; and that they were first annexed to the Gospels by those who admired them, and were afterwards copied, as proper parts of them? Supposing this to have been done, though it should not have been before the ancient versions were made, they would naturally be translated afterwards, and be annexed to the versions, as they had been to the originals.

The Gnostics in general seem to have selected what they thought proper of the different books of the New Testament, without regard to their authenticity. But it appears, from Tertullian, to have been the real opinion of Marcion (who was unquestionably a man of learning and ability), that Luke's original Gospel contained no account of the miraculous conception. For this writer, in his book against the Marcionites, says, concerning the two copies of Luke's Gospel, his own and Marcion's, "I say that mine is the true copy; Marcion, that his is so. I affirm that Marcion's copy is adulterated; he, that mine is so." He adds that his own copy was the more ancient, because Marcion himself did, for some time, receive it. But this he might do, till, on examination, he thought he saw sufficient reason to reject it. It must be acknowledged, however, that, according to the account we have of Marcion's Gospel of Luke, it contained many things which we cannot but think must have been different from the original. If, therefore, he would have maintained the genuineness of it in all respects, it would lessen the weight of his testimony in this case. Having nothing of Marcion's own writing, we cannot form any certain judgment in the case.[30]

How improbable soever this hypothesis may appear at first sight, no person can well doubt of something of the same nature having taken place with respect to several passages in the books of Scripture, even where we have no evidence whatever from history, from manuscripts, or from ancient versions, of the passages having ever been what we now take it for granted they originally were. This I think to have been the case with respect to the word ωασχα ["Passover"] *John vi. 4.* Bishop Pearce[31] supposes the whole verse, and many others, to have been interpolations; and the famous verse, *I John v. 7*, concerning the "three that bear record in heaven," has been sufficiently proved to have come into the epistle in this unauthorized manner; and had it been done in an early period, there would have appeared no more reason to have suspected the genuineness of it, than there now does that of the introductions to the Gospels of Matthew and Luke.

This was indisputably the case with the Gospel of the Ebionites itself; for, according to the most unsuspected evidence, it was the Gospel of Matthew, beginning at the

[30] Marcion was the leader of an heretical sect of the second century. He formed a canon of his own, consisting only of a modified version of Luke and ten of Paul's epistles. Our knowledge of the movement comes chiefly from Tertullian's *Five Books Against Marcion.* Priestley's quotation is taken from Book IV, chapter 4. See Roberts and Donaldson, eds., *The Ante-Nicene Fathers,* III, 349.

[31] Zachary Pearce (1690-1774) was Bishop of Rochester and the author of a two-volume commentary on the New Testament published in 1777. See Stephen and Lee, eds., *Dictionary of National Biography,* XLIV, 151-152.

third chapter; but that copy of the Ebionites' Gospel which Jerome saw, had, at least, the second chapter; for he quotes a passage from it.[32] It is very possible, therefore, that there might have been copies of the Greek Gospel of Matthew, without the two first chapters, as well as some of the Hebrew copies, with them.

As the Ebionites were not wanting in their respect for Matthew, or his Gospel, it is not to be supposed that they would have rejected the introduction, if they had really thought it to be his, even if they had not thought the history contained in it entitled to full credit. I therefore see no reason why they should leave it out entirely, but that they did not admit its authenticity; and, certainly, as I have said before, they for whose use the Gospel was particularly written, and in whose language it was probably first published, must be allowed to have been the best judges of it.

It favors the idea of the two first chapters of Matthew's Gospel not properly belonging to the rest, that they have a kind of separate title, viz. "the book of the generation of Jesus Christ," to which the history of the miraculous conception, and the circumstances connected with it, are an appendage, and, together with it, make a kind of preamble to the proper history of the Gospel, which begins with the account of the baptism of John.

As to the Gospel of Luke, though it should not be supposed that the copy which Marcion made use of (which wanted the two first chapters) affords any presumption that the original was without them, yet the authority of this writer is certainly less than that of an apostle; and, careful as he was to collect the particulars of the history from the very beginning, he might possibly have been misinformed with respect to the early part of it, and have taken up that splendid part of his narrative too hastily. Had the work of Symmachus been extant, we should, no doubt, have known

[32] St. Jerome (*c.* 347-420) prepared a fresh translation of the Bible into Latin from the original tongues. His work became the basis for the famous Vulgate.

much more concerning the subject.[33] Between the time of the publication of the Gospels, and that of Justin Martyr, who is the first writer that mentions the miraculous conception, there was an interval of about eighty years; and in this space of time it is possible that additions to the gospel history of this kind (which did not affect the great and public transactions) might have been made and have been annexed to some of the copies, though not to them all.

---

[33] Symmachus was an Ebionite writer of the second century.

A General History of the Christian Church
from the Fall of the Western Empire
to the Present Time

In the last decade of his life, after his removal to Pennsylvania, Joseph Priestley managed to complete his six-volume General History of the Christian Church, *which he had begun at Birmingham many years before. This work covered much the same ground as the* History of Corruptions *and the* Early Opinions *but continued the story of Christianity down to modern times. The last four volumes (1802-1803) were printed in Northumberland, Pennsylvania, and were dedicated to Thomas Jefferson. The dedication, written eighteen months before his death on February 6, 1804, at the age of seventy, is a fine testimony to the religious and political ideals to which Priestley devoted so much of his life. The conclusion provides an interesting assessment of the problems and prospects of Unitarianism.*[34]

THE DEDICATION

To Thomas Jefferson, President of the United States

Sir:

My high respect for your character, as a politician and a man, makes me desirous to connect my name in some measure with yours, while it is in my power, by means of some publication, to do it.

The first part of this work, which brought the history to

[34] Text from Rutt, IX, 3-6 and X, 532-543. A convenient summary of Priestley's theological development may be found in Ira V. Brown, "The Religion of Joseph Priestley," *Pennsylvania History,* XXIV (April, 1957), 85-100.

the fall of the Western empire, was dedicated to a zealous friend of civil and religious liberty, but in a private station. What he, or any other friend of liberty in Europe, could only do by their good wishes, by their writings, or by patient suffering, you, Sir, are actually accomplishing, and upon a theater of great and growing extent.

It is the boast of this country that it has a constitution the most favorable to political liberty and private happiness of any in the world; and all say that, besides your great merit with respect to several articles of the first importance to public liberty in the instrument itself, you have ever been one of the steadiest friends to the genuine principles and spirit of it; and to this opinion your conduct in various public offices, and now in the highest, in this free state, gives the clearest attestation.

Many have appeared the friends of liberty while they were subject to the power of others, and especially when they were suffering by it; but I do not recollect one besides yourself who retained the same principles, and acted upon them, in a situation of actual power. You, Sir, have done more than this; having voluntarily proposed to relinquish part of the power which the Constitution gave you; and instead of adding to the burdens of the people, you have endeavored to lighten them, though with the necessary consequence of a proportionable diminution of your influence. May this great example, which I doubt not will demonstrate the practicability of truly republican principles on the equal rights of all the members of a state, by the actual existence of a form of government calculated to answer all the useful purposes of government (giving equal protection to all, and leaving every man in the possession of every power that he can exercise to his own advantage without infringing the equal liberty of others), be followed in other countries, and at length become universal. The eyes of all the civilized, at least of all the Christianized, part of the world are now upon this country; as being evidently in a state of more rapid improvement than any other was ever known to be;

and I trust that, eventually, your administration will be a blessing not to the United States of America only, but to all mankind.

Another reason why I wish to prefix your name to this work, and more appropriate to the subject of it, is that you have been the strenuous and uniform advocate of religious as well as of civil liberty, both in your own state of Virginia, and through the United States in general; seeing in the clearest light the various and great mischiefs that have arisen from any particular form of religion being favored by the state more than any other. In consequence of this, the profession and practice of religion is here as free as that of philosophy or medicine; and now the experience of more than twenty years leaves little room to doubt, but that it is a state of things the most favorable to mutual candor (which is of great importance to domestic peace and good neighborhood), and to the cause of all truth, that of religion least of all excepted. When everything is thus left to free discussion, there can be no doubt but that truth will finally prevail, and establish itself by its own evidence; and he must know little of history, or of human nature, who can imagine that truth of any kind will be ultimately unfavorable to general happiness. A man must entertain a secret suspicion of his own principles, who wishes for any exclusive advantage in the defense or profession of them.

Having fled from a state of persecution in England, and having been not without some cause of apprehension in the late administration here,[35] I feel the greater satisfaction in the prospect of passing the remainder of an active life, when I naturally wish for repose, under your protection. Though I am arrived at the usual term of human life, it is now only that I can say I see nothing to fear from the hand of power,

[35] Under John Adams' administration, at the time of the naval war with France, there was talk of applying the Alien Acts to Priestley, who had accepted French citizenship in the early days of the Revolution. See James M. Smith, "The Enforcement of the Alien Friends Act of 1798," *Mississippi Valley Historical Review*, XLI (June, 1954), 101-102.

the government under which I live being for the first time truly favorable to me. And though I think it has been evident that I have never been improperly swayed by the principle of fear, it is certainly a happiness to be out of the possibility of its influence, especially towards the close of life; enjoying a degree of peace and rest, previous to the state of more perfect rest from labor in the grave; with the hope of rising to a state of greater activity, security and happiness beyond it. This is all that any man can wish, or have, in this world; and this, Sir, under your administration, I enjoy.

With the most perfect attachment and every good wish, I subscribe myself, not your subject, or your humble servant, but

Your sincere admirer,

JOSEPH PRIESTLEY

Northumberland, July, 1802.

THE CONCLUSION

I cannot conclude this history without a few observations, which I hope the perusal of it, and also that of the *History of the Corruptions of Christianity,* will naturally suggest.

1. It appears at first view truly wonderful that the most simple of all religions, consisting of few doctrines, and those perfectly rational and intelligible, and of few rites, and those as simple as can well be imagined, should, with respect to both, have been so grossly perverted as it evidently has been; for nothing can well be conceived more absurd than the doctrines which were, in a course of time, received as articles of Christian faith by what was called the Catholic Church; nor were any rites more disfigured by superstition than those of Christian baptism and the Lord's Supper. This departure from simplicity and truth will ever be one of the most memorable things in the history of the

human mind. And yet, strange as it may appear (when the extremes, things so manifestly heterogeneous, are contrasted) that the one should have arisen from the other, the history of the gradual deviation makes every step in the process perfectly intelligible.

This enables us to fill up the great chasm between the creed of the apostles and that which has been ascribed to Athanasius;[36] the former containing the doctrine of one God, and the latter that of three supreme deities, and which was soon followed by hundreds of subordinate ones.

By this means we see how a just and merciful God, freely pardoning all sins that are repented of and forsaken, who expresses the most earnest desire that all would repent and live, came to be regarded as the most unreasonable of tyrants; not only requiring an infinite satisfaction for the slightest offenses, but dooming the greater part of his creatures to everlasting torments; a catastrophe foreseen, and intended by him before they were born.

History shows us by what steps the rite of baptism, originally expressive of nothing more than the adoption of a new religion, and a profession of that repentance and reformation which it required, came to be considered as actually of itself washing away sin, and a passport for a child to the happiness of heaven, which, without that ceremony, would have gone to hell; and how, on the partaking of bread and wine merely in remembrance of Christ, was grafted the doctrine of transubstantiation, and the complex ceremonies of the mass.

What an immense distance there is between a primitive Christian minister, the true servant of the servants of God, and him who, retaining that title, assumed all power in heaven and earth; making kings and emperors hold up his train when he walked in procession, and hold his stirrups and bridle when he mounted his horse! How great is the

[36] The so-called Athanasian Creed, actually composed a century or more after the time of Athanasius, provided a classic formulation of Trinitarianism.

difference between the condition and character of the most patient of the persecuted, and the most cruel of persecutors, and that not of heathens but of their fellow Christians! And yet, when we consider the several links of the long chain by which these extremes were joined, we see them all perfectly and naturally connected with each other. Philosophical speculation, as well as Christian charity, is exercised by the subject, and our astonishment ceases.

2. The recovery of genuine Christianity from this deplorably corrupted state to the rational views we now entertain of it is no less extraordinary; and the contemplation of it cannot but impress the thoughtful and pious mind with sentiments of wonder and gratitude. This restoration admits, however, of as easy an explanation as the various corruptions of it. The Scriptures, though long misunderstood, remained, and were open to all who wished to study and understand them. The ancient state and gradual progress of Christianity were always capable of being traced by the sagacious and unprejudiced, if they would attend to the existing monuments of past transactions. Good sense on other subjects that bear some relation to religion, gradually prevailed. On the revival of literature light sprang up from various quarters, some the most unexpected; and by laborious and painful investigation, this light was reflected upon Christian truth. Thus the treasure that had been long buried was by patient labor dug up again; and one discovery, as in the investigation of natural science, prepared the way for others; Divine Providence conducting the whole, but without any miracle.

3. Hence we may safely conclude, that this natural process, now happily commenced, will proceed till every remaining corruption of Christianity be removed, and nothing will be found in it that any unbeliever, any Jew, or Mahometan, can reasonably object to. And since whatever is true and right will finally prevail, that is, when sufficient time has been given to the exhibition of it, rational Christianity will, in due time, be the religion of the whole world.

In the prophetical language of our Saviour, he will draw all men unto him.

4. Whenever freedom of inquiry, and knowledge of other kinds, shall prevail in Mahometan countries, the delusion of that system will disappear, like a fog before the sun. Then, also, will the veil be removed from the minds of the most obstinate and incredulous Jews; though probably the personal appearance of Jesus himself may be necessary, as it was to Paul, to their complete satisfaction, and this after their restoration to their own country.

5. Let us not, in this interesting speculation, forget our obligation to skeptics and unbelievers, for exciting the attention of Christians to the manifold abuses and corruptions of our religion. Without this powerful stimulus we should probably have been little farther advanced at present than the Christian world was in the time of Luther. Their doubts, and even their censurable sarcasms, insults and ridicule, have been useful steps in this process. Let not their conduct, then, excite our surprise or indignation. Plain good sense could not but be shocked at the appearance which Christianity made to them; and nothing but the strongest prejudice of education, and the influence of authority, of some kind or other, could have rendered Christians themselves blind to such absurdities.

Much, therefore, may be alleged in excuse for unbelievers, who had no advantage of religious education to bias their minds in favor of Christianity; but none for those Christians, who, losing sight of that spirit of meekness and forbearance which becomes their character, can wish to silence objections by authority, or penal laws. Rather, let unbelievers be invited to propose all their objections with the most perfect freedom. If anything in our religion be really objectionable, let it not be retained because it is pointed out to us by an enemy, but let us follow truth wherever we can find it.

Let us consider that unbelievers, by giving us their assistance, whether willingly or unwillingly, to purge our religion from everything that is offensive to right reason, are, in fact, preparing the way for their own conversion. Hitherto all their objections have had the happy effect of strengthening the evidences of Christianity; so that in this progress they will have less and less to object to, every day, and consequently all of them that are truly reasonable and candid will become Christians. And those of them that are prejudiced against Christianity, because it condemns the vices to which they are addicted, who "love darkness rather than light because their deeds are evil" (which, no doubt, is the case of great numbers), will be reduced to silence. The assent of the wise and good will in time force theirs. Thus becoming at first merely speculative, they will at length become practical believers. When the understanding is well formed, the will and affections, though refractory for some time, will follow at length.

If to this meekness and candor towards unbelievers we add the habitual exercise of the other Christian virtues, we shall have done everything that was in our power, to recommend our religion, and may safely leave it to the power of truth, and the God of truth; confident, that, in due time, the effect of this evidence will not fail to appear. "If our light shine before men, they will glorify our Father who is in heaven."

The prospect of the improving state of Christianity in my own time, and from facts within my own knowledge, is very encouraging. In England, till about A.D. 1750, the great body of Dissenters, among whom I was educated, were, with very few exceptions, rigid Calvinists. A few of the ministers were of the Arminian persuasion, a small portion of them were Arians, and a much smaller still, Socinians. Even now the majority are Calvinists; but the more liberal bear a much greater proportion to them than formerly. There is not a considerable town in England in which there is not a respectable society of Unitarian Dissenters, and they are continually increasing. Many individual members of Trinitarian congregations become at first more candid, and then Unitarians; whereas it is hardly ever known that a Unitarian becomes a Trinitarian.

It is particularly remarkable that in academies in which young men are educated for the ministry among the Calvinists, where freedom of inquiry cannot be entirely excluded, the more ingenious and inquisitive of the students frequently become Unitarians, as the opulent supporters of those academies lament; so that their societies are obliged to content themselves with lay preachers, or with ministers who have no great share of learning.

Unitarianism has of late made considerable progress among the Methodists, and this without any communication with Unitarians of older standing, or the perusal of their writings, but wholly from the study of the Scriptures. There are also now many congregations of Unitarians in Wales, where much attention was always given to the subject of religion.

Notwithstanding the subscription to the thirty-nine articles, required of all who take orders in the Church of England, and every other barrier against heterodoxy, Unitarianism has not failed to find its way into their churches. Many young men of a serious and inquisitive turn decline entering into the church, though they were educated with a view to it, and some have renounced their livings. But many do, by some means or other, reconcile to themselves their continuance in the church with the holding of sentiments which it reprobates, and this number there is reason to think is increasing. The articles of the church are clearly Calvinistic, and yet from the time of Archbishop Laud a majority of the clergy have been Arminians, and from the time of Dr. Clarke great numbers were Arians.[37] Of this class, till of late at least, were the generality of the more learned and elderly of the clergy, as the younger among them are now more generally Unitarians.

[37] William Laud (1573-1645), Archbishop of Canterbury, was noted as an opponent of Calvinism. Samuel Clarke (1675-1729) was an Arian leader who questioned orthodox views in his book *The Scripture Doctrine of the Trinity* (1712).

That Unitarianism is gaining ground on the continent of Europe, there is abundant evidence. It was said long ago, and it has never been contradicted, that in Geneva, where Servetus was burned for professing Unitarianism, the ministers in general are of his opinion. A Lutheran minister from Denmark lately told a friend of mine at Paris that having traveled through a great part of Germany, and seen many ministers of his denomination, he did not meet with one that was not a Unitarian, as he himself was. This, however, might be true, though the majority were Trinitarians, as indeed is most probable.

Though I have not had any particular information concerning the state of opinions among the Protestants in France, it can hardly be doubted but that the same causes must have produced the same effects among them, in proportion to their means of inquiry, and the opportunity of indulging it. And where ministers, as in Scotland, are not confined to set forms of prayer, or where, on their entrance on the ministry, and not afterwards, they only engage not to impugn particular opinions in preaching or writing (as I have been informed is in fact the case at Geneva), they may with no great difficulty maintain in private sentiments which they do not avow in public; but this, being known to their friends, will have its influence. In all these cases, the friends of ecclesiastical establishments naturally say, "They that are not openly with us, are against us."

6. Though it may be allowed that no particular form of church government is of divine appointment, and that they all have particular advantages to recommend them, it sufficiently appears from the whole of this history that extensive establishments of any kind are exceedingly unfavorable to reformation; because the concurrence of great numbers must be necessary to its taking effect. Ideas of improvements of every kind, in science or art, first occur to thinking individuals, and their gaining the concurrence of the majority of the body of which they are members may be impossible, in whatever degree of esteem they may be held.

In these circumstances the reformer and his friends, supposing him to have gained some, are sure to be outvoted; and then nothing can be done without a separation or schism; and few persons have strength of mind to bear even the opprobrium attached to the idea of a schismatic, though no more serious inconvenience be sustained by reputed heresy or schism. And it has been seen that in general this crime, as it has ever been deemed by the majority, has been thought deserving of the severest civil punishment, and often that of death, and in the most dreadful forms.

This has always been the case, in a greater or less degree, when wealth or power must be abandoned by the reformers. Worldly-minded men will not fail to pretend a zeal for truth, in defense of what they prefer to any truth; and the *bona fide* approvers of the system are generally drawn in to concur in the persecuting measures of those who are no bigots.

If this be considered, we cannot wonder that the Church of Rome, the Lutheran Church in Germany, the Episcopalian Church of England, or the Presbyterian Church of Scotland, are at this day what they were at their establishment, no articles in their creed being changed; and that all considerable changes in the religion of whole countries have been effected by the civil power. The members of the ecclesiastical establishments have never reformed themselves. Many individuals may disapprove of the system, and wish for a change; but the majority, educated of course in the old way, and having acquired prejudices in its favor, will be averse to it. We see that the great mass of mankind, and of all nations, are averse to any material change either in government or religion, and bear many inconveniences rather than hazard a revolution, even far short of a general one. If the younger part of a community should wish for it, they are restrained by their seniors.

On this account the Independent form of church government has, in this respect at least, a great advantage over every other; since no particular society has to wait for the concurrence of any other for the purpose of making a change in any article of faith or practice; and with proper address of the minister, or any other intelligent and leading member of the society, the rest may be brought to approve and concur in it. At most, the inconvenience attending a division in a single congregation is inconsiderable.

In consequence of this state of things, Unitarianism has got established, as it may be said, in many congregations of Dissenters in England, all the members of which were not long ago Trinitarians; and by the same means it has prevailed in many of the Independent congregations of New England. What is of more consequence still, in this state of things, every person acts according to the dictates of his own mind, and is under no temptation to prevaricate in any form or degree.

The case is very different from this (which has a near connection with general morality) in large national establishments of religion. There are, no doubt, many Unitarians in the churches of England and Scotland, and some among the Presbyterians of North America; but they are under the necessity of concealing their sentiments, and of joining in forms of devotion which they must regard as nothing less than idolatrous, being the worship of a creature like themselves, destitute of that omnipotence and omniscience which alone can constitute any being a proper object of Christian worship. This they cannot do with perfect sincerity. If they silently refuse their concurrence in what they hear and disapprove, still their example operates to continue and enforce it.

This is the case even with the laity; but that of the clergy, who derive some advantage from their situation, is much more unfavorable. If they be confined to Trinitarian forms of devotion, they must every time they officiate not only profess, but in reality act upon the profession, of what they do not believe. If the forms and discipline of their churches do not require so much as this, but leave them at liberty to make use of their own forms of devotion, they must, if they were Unitarians when they became members of such churches, be guilty of prevarication at that time; or if not, equity seems to require that whatever emolument, or advantage of any kind, a man acquires by any profession to which he no longer adheres, he should not retain, but openly abandon it; so that a person strictly conscientious must be greatly distressed.

It is, however, remarkable, and shows in a striking light how ensnaring and dangerous such a situation is, that the concurrence of numbers in acts of manifest insincerity will reconcile the minds of many to things at which they would revolt in any other exactly similar cases. How many are there who, in the most solemn forms, subscribe to articles of faith which they do not believe, when they would not on any account make a false declaration in any other form? This conduct, however, is such as no person can justify; and all that can be said in excuse for it is that it is doing evil that good may come. It is doing one bad thing, in order to place a person in a situation in which it will be in his power to do many good things. It makes him an authorized teacher of virtue, and among others that of sincerity. But how can a man with any effect inculcate that virtue on others which he has not practiced himself? And would not more good be done eventually by forbearing to do that thing which is confessedly bad, than by any good that he will probably do by means of it?

A strict adherence to what is in itself right, without regard to any consequences, is the best rule for men. Nothing can justify the doing of any evil that good may come, but a certain knowledge that the good will come, and of its having no connection with any greater evil. The Supreme Being who is omniscient, as well as omnipotent, may safely act, and continually does act, upon this maxim, many evils being introduced into his government of the world. But he knows that they will certainly lead to good, and no doubt to greater good than would be brought about by any other means; and man must not pretend to omniscience, and adopt such a line of conduct as nothing but the consciousness of omnipotence will authorize.

7. Disgusting as the perusal of a great part of ecclesiastical history must be, to every person who feels for the honor of Christianity, on account of the unchristian spirit that was shown by too many of its professors, and the factions, animosities, and persecuting spirit that has been too prevalent among them, we cannot but be pleased to see, in the persecuted at least, much of the genuine, the amiable, and exalted spirit of Christianity; a spirit of humility, benevolence, and true piety; of patience under reproach, and injuries of every kind; an indifference to the things of this world, and the placing of the heart and affections on the things of another. Also, though the generality of the Christian persecutors were men of no real religion, but were actuated by the very worst of passions, hatred and ambition, and were altogether destitute of compassion, it may clearly be perceived that some of them entered into these measures with reluctance, being deceived by the false maxims that in their time were universally prevalent, and thinking that they did God and religion real service by exterminating their enemies. Like Paul, and many of his countrymen, they had "a zeal for God, though not according to knowledge."

For this, no doubt, due allowance will be made in the great day of discrimination; when some of the persecutors and persecuted may embrace as friends. This I hope will be the case with Calvin and Servetus, with Cranmer and Rogers, and those whom the good king Edward VI was by them persuaded to commit to the flames; and perhaps with the emperors Trajan and Marcus Antoninus, whose ignorance and general good character will plead for them. But I cannot have the same charity for such men as Bonner, Gardiner and Laud, though I doubt not there is a course of discipline prepared by the merciful Parent of us all, that will, in due time, bring all men to think and feel as they ought to do.

Some of the martyrs themselves did not always discover

a Christian temper; though it must be acknowledged even by unbelievers, if they be ingenuous, that, in general, human nature never appeared to so much advantage as in their behavior; in their sacrificing everything dear to them in life, bearing reproach, suffering tedious confinement in loathsome prisons, destitute of all the comforts of life, and meeting death in its most frightful forms, from an adherence to what they considered as the cause of truth, and yet without any ill will towards the authors of their sufferings.

If this be not true magnanimity, and everything that is great and dignified in the human character, what is so? Surely not the spirit that carries a man into the field of battle, or that which prompts him to risk his life, or that of his enemy, in single combat, for a point of honor. This is acting from the impulse of momentary passion, and implies no command of temper at all, though it is in the control of the appetites and passions that the power of reason, which distinguishes men from brutes, is alone conspicuous.

As these virtues of the highest class always appeared when they were called for, as in time of persecution, they must have existed when they were not called for. I doubt not they do so among Christians at this day, in which persecution, at least in its most prominent feature and form, is not known. Many Christians, we may be confident, are now ready to act the part of those of former times, with the same alacrity, and the same excellent disposition; and their attachment to the things of this life, which naturally gains upon all persons whose attention is not drawn from them by urgent circumstances, would gradually lessen, and wholly disappear, when it should be evident to them that the love of the world and the love of God were in opposition to one another; which, in the present state of things, is not so apparent; and therefore Christians too often deceive themselves, and engage in worldly pursuits more than they otherwise would do.

Many Christians, however, though not persecuted to death, are in situations in which they show, in trials of a different kind, an energy of mind that would carry them through any trial; and that mode of persecution in which life is concerned is not that which, with many, requires so much real fortitude as some others.

I have in my eye several persons whose Christian principles have led them to make sacrifices to which many of the martyrs would probably have been unequal. In this some may be apt to think that I refer to the case of some Dissenters in England; and certainly their situation has in it, especially of late years, something very humiliating and discouraging; and to bear it, and to behave properly under it, has required something superior to the influence of general esteem, worldly ambition, or pecuniary advantage. But this I consider as a trifle compared with the strength of principle which has led some to abandon respectable and lucrative situations, and what is more, to bear the alienation of former friends and connections, together with such privations of a personal nature as must have been sensibly felt by persons who, like them, had lived in affluence. To such persons the greatest homage is due from all who have a just conception of the difficulty of such exertions; and of the strength of mind, and the force of principle, that alone could make men capable of them; as may be inferred from the small number of those who, in the same circumstances, have acted the same part.

The surest method of deciding concerning the difficulty of any kind of conduct is not to consider it, in the first instance, abstractedly from what we should imagine to be its nature, but to examine the numbers that have actually adopted it. Now, since it is evident from history, compared with present observation, that there have been many more persons who have died martyrs rather than openly renounce their principles, than of those who, without being particularly called upon, have relinquished desirable situations in life, and have quietly sunk into obscurity, with the risk of poverty; it is evident that there must be more real difficulty in the latter case than in the former, and that it requires stronger and purer principles of action. And it only requires attention to some pretty obvious considerations respecting the two cases, to see the reason of this.

In the case of open persecution, there is generally no choice between death and infamy, which is always, in a greater or less degree, attached to everything that has the appearance of cowardice or dissimulation. And openly, in the face of the world, to renounce a man's principles, and to conform to what he is well known inwardly to condemn is what no person can justify, though, out of compassion to human infirmity, he may, in some measure, excuse it, as he would do any other instance of wrong conduct to which the temptation was peculiarly strong. In this situation many persons, from a sense of shame only, without any peculiar strength of religious principle, may be supposed to prefer death to life.

But when a man is not particularly called upon to act at all, when it is in his power to continue to act as all his acquaintance do, and of course to enjoy affluence together with sufficient reputation; in this situation, to obey the secret call of conscience only, and against the remonstrances of all his friends and relatives to withdraw into obscurity and poverty, is great indeed. Besides, by indirectly reproaching others, he is sure to draw reproach and calumny upon himself; and instead of being held in general admiration, as the martyrs were, he must expect to be ridiculed for his singularity, which precludes all sympathy and compassion. In these circumstances to persist in doing what himself only will do is an argument, if anything in human life can be, of pure principle, without any mixture of ostentation, or any other motive improper for a Christian to act upon. The more I think of this case, the more it excites my admiration, and the less do I wonder that so few are equal to the conduct proper for it. Let no person who has not himself acted this extraordinary part imagine that he should or could have done it. I am far from thinking so highly of myself, and I am truly thankful that my principles have not been exposed to so great a trial.

INDEX